Our Price
£16

CH00825693

The New Hess Catalog
of
Beethoven's Works

Beethoven and Nature by N. C. Wyeth

The

New Hess Catalog

of

Beethoven's Works

edited, updated and translated from the original German
with a new foreword by
JAMES F. GREEN

and a new introduction by
SIEGHARD BRANDENBURG

Vance Brook Publishing
West Newbury, Vermont
2003

This book includes a translation of:
Verzeichnis der nicht in der Gesamtausgabe veröffentlichte Werke Ludwig van Beethovens
by Willy Hess, originally published by Breitkopf & Härtel, Wiesbaden 1957.

Library of Congress Cataloging-in-Publication Data

Green, James F., 1949-
         The New Hess Catalog of Beethoven's Works / edited, updated and translated from the original German with a new forward by James F. Green and a new introduction by Sieghard Brandenburg. – 1ˢᵗ English ed.
         p. cm.
Rev. ed. of: Verzeichnis der nicht in der Gesamtausgabe veröffentlichte Werke Ludwig van Beethovens / Willy Hess. 1957.
Includes bibliographical references (p.) and index.
         ISBN: 09640570-3-4 (alk. paper)
1. Beethoven, Ludwig van, 1770-1827 – Bibliography.   I. Hess, Willy, 1906-1997 – Verzeichnis der nicht in der Gesamtausgabe veröffentlichte Werke Ludwig van Beethovens.   II. Title.
         ML134.B4 G74 2003
         016.78'092–dc22   2003021091

Notice to our readers:
Comments and emendations are welcome, please write to the publisher,
Vance Brook Publishing
PO Box 35
West Newbury, Vermont 05085

Frontispiece and jacket: oil painting, "Beethoven and Nature" by N. C. Wyeth commissioned by Steinway & Sons in 1919. Reproduced courtesy of Steinway & Sons, New York.

Printed and bound in the United States of America by Signature Book Printing, Gaithersburg, Maryland.

Dedicated to

Ira F. Brilliant

who shared my vision and made it a reality.
Countless generations will be forever in his debt.

TABLE OF CONTENTS

New Appendices by James F. Green

Hess 96, Symphony No. 7, Op. 92 in A major (beginning)
    in a Piano Transcription by Ludwig van Beethoven
    first edition prepared by Mark S. Zimmer

Illustrations

Introduction to the New Edition

by Sieghard Brandenburg

"Fifty Years under the Spell of Leonore-Fidelio" was the
title for a review of the writings of Swiss musicologist Willy
Hess (1906-1997). He could just as correctly have written:
"Fifty Years Searching for the Unknown Beethoven." Discarded versions of works later published, fragments, lost and
unfinished works magically attracted him throughout his life.
Still at the beginning of his career, in early 1931 he published
a list of "works" of Beethoven that were not in the renowned
old complete edition of Beethoven's works (the old *Beethoven-
Gesamtausgabe* published by Breitkopf & Härtel in Leipzig
between 1862 and 1865; an additional volume appeared in
1888). With this list, Hess showed in simple words how much
there was still to be discovered about Beethoven and thus
stirred the curiosity of many a music lover who hadn't been
interested in musicology before.

Willy Hess, a small gentleman wearing glasses, was unquestionably one of the most productive and famous Beethoven
researchers of the 20th century within the Germanic coun-
tries. Most of his essays – there are well over 400 of them –
concern themselves with the questions of ordinary people
rather than with strictly academic problems. He never cared
for sophisticated discourses or philological details; he was
mainly looking for practical results. Between 1926 and 1930
he had studied piano and musicology at the Conservatory and
University of Zurich and later Berlin. Afterwards, he worked
as music teacher, composer, music critic and musicologist.
However, between 1942 and 1971 he earned his living playing
bassoon in the orchestra of his hometown of Winterthur, Switzerland. That he never acquired a degree didn't reduce his
influence on the academic world.

Besides his essays on the various versions of *Fidelio*, the *Verzeichnis der nicht in der Gesamtausgabe veröffentlichten Werke Ludwig van Beethovens* (this very book) is his most important publication. Its final version appeared in 1957 through Breitkopf & Härtel in Wiesbaden. However, the preliminary work goes back to the aforementioned list from 1931. This was published in a considerably extended version in the *Neues Beethoven-Jahrbuch VII* in 1937 (Supplement in Vol. IX, 1939). Giovanni Biamonti published an Italian translation in 1953. An English version scheduled for 1956 didn't make it into print, but eventually triggered the new and final German version of the year after.

According to his introduction, Hess's intention for the catalog was modest: he wanted to collect the material that seemed necessary for an addendum to the old Gesamtausgabe. He certainly didn't want to rival the catalog of Beethoven's works by Georg Kinsky and Hans Halm (G. Henle, Munich-Duisburg 1955). Despite this, some duplications between the two publications were inevitable. The large Kinsky/Halm catalog intends to be a catalog of all "finished" works by Beethoven and thus mainly deals with the works included in the old Gesamtausgabe. Hess of course omits those works, as he considered them well known enough. The section WoO (Werke ohne Opuszahl: Works without Opus [number]), on the other hand, lists numerous works that hardly differ in the compositional state from those listed by Hess. They're neither considered to be "finished" nor are they in the old Gesamtausgabe. However, Kinsky/Halm is much more moderate in listing these unfinished works than Hess is.

Willy Hess was firmly convinced that the canon of works represented by the old Gesamtausgabe did not present the whole of Beethoven's œuvre. According to him, the picture of the composer Beethoven is only completed by all the small, supposedly unimportant, byproducts of his genius, the discarded versions, unfinished projects, studies and musical jokes that have been made available by biographical works and examination of the sketches since the appearance of the old Gesamtausgabe. This view of Hess's eventually was to dominate research: hardly a modern edition of Beethoven's works exists that does not list – if not print – versions, as well as, the so-called "final versions."

Adhering to his convictions, Hess not only published the catalog, but also made the works he discovered available to the public. Between 1959 and 1971 he published fourteen supplemental volumes to the old Gesamtausgabe, even though he had printed much of this in individual publications. Naturally not every work in the catalog is available in printed form to date; for many works the sources are too spare. In some other cases, the basis for the inclusion into the catalog was only an assumption or verbal communication from a colleague, which could not be verified. Hess collected every bit of information about lost or unknown compositions and versions that he could find in the literature. In this respect, he strove for completeness of his catalog.

In spite of that, Hess makes sure to point out in the foreword that no one is more aware of the flawed coverage of his catalog than he, and invites the reader to add bits and pieces. The reason for this flaw – if one is allowed to name it thus – is the too-generous definition of "work" that he applied for inclusion in his catalog. While Hess, due to his limited capacity, did not want to include sketches and drafts, he often mentions sketches and other unfinished writings that are created in the process of composition. But the term "work" includes even in its less emphatic forms a certain degree of completeness. Where could one find this in sketches, fragments and discarded versions of parts of single movements? The Hess catalog is thus in itself not free of contradictions, but is still a fascinating book. The editor, James F. Green, invested a considerable amount of work into updating the catalog to the current state of Beethoven research. Hopefully this considerably improved English version will find many readers.

Bonn, January 2003   Sieghard Brandenburg

Foreword to the New Edition

by James F. Green

The burning question that faced Willy Hess and the musical world in the middle of the 20th Century was, "Why a new complete edition?" These scholars were correct in their view that a new edition of Beethoven's collected works was very much needed at that time. In 1959, Hess was able to begin publication, through Breitkopf & Härtel, of a fourteen-volume supplement to the old twenty-five-volume 19th century Gesamtausgabe (collected edition) of Beethoven's works. Almost at the same time, the Beethoven-Haus in Bonn began to issue a new complete "critical edition" that has now spanned some forty years and will eventually consist of forty-six volumes arranged in fourteen series or parts. It was begun in 1961 under the title *Ludwig van Beethoven: Werke: Neue Ausgabe sämtlicher Werke* and is being published by G. Henle, Munich-Duisburg. The need that challenged Hess and his contemporaries has, therefore, largely been accomplished. What confronts musicologists and scholars today is the absence of a thorough and logical catalog of Beethoven's works. This has not been accomplished, nor is it likely to be done soon. In the interim we must rely on old catalogs. For this reason, the updating and correcting of those old catalogs has become essential. It is this task that is the purpose of this new edition of Willy Hess's groundbreaking work. To distill forty-five years of scholarship, to correct old mistakes, and to challenge new scholarship to find answers to still unresolved questions has been an arduous undertaking. While this edition may have its own shortcomings it is still a step forward on a long journey toward fully understanding Beethoven's creative output.

Because of its importance, a translation of the Hess catalog should have been done shortly after the original edition appeared in order make it available to a wider public and a corrected, or updated, edition should have been done at least twenty years ago. This work – taken together with the Kinsky/Halm catalog, which appeared slightly earlier in 1955, and Kurt Dorfmüller's 1978 work, *Beiträge zur Beethoven Bibliography*, which contains corrections to Kinsky/Halm and Hess – form a kind of "trinity" of work's catalogs for Beethoven. All three are necessary for a complete, or nearly complete, view of Beethoven's output. All the catalog numbers fall into roughly three categories: those with opus numbers, those without (as listed by Kinsky/Halm) and those with Hess numbers. There is duplication or overlapping in the Kinsky/Halm and Hess catalogs. Kinsky/Halm used a different approach than Hess for identifying and classifying the works. Kinsky/Halm lists the "published" works regardless of when, or by whom, they were published. Kinsky/Halm first lists the works with opus numbers in numerical order; then the remaining works are listed by instrumental size and type, beginning with the largest. The latter are designated "Werke ohne Opuszahl" (WoO) and assigned a separate sequence of numbers. Hess, on the other hand, listed in his catalog only those works that were not published in the great 19th century collected edition by Breitkopf & Härtel. These two quite different approaches resulted in two very different catalogs; Kinsky/Halm is missing many interesting unpublished works that lay in the sketchbooks or other autograph sources and Hess is missing many important and well known published works.

Several other catalogs have appeared over the years. The first was prepared by Gustav Nottebohm in 1851, but appeared without his name on it; however, it was reprinted in 1868 and in several later editions, all with his name. The catalog of A. B. Marx was published in 1859 as an appendix to his Beethoven biography. In it the works are arranged chronologically. The catalog of A. W. Thayer, the great Beethoven biographer, came out in 1865. It is also arranged chronologically. The catalog by Sir George Grove appeared in 1911. Grove followed the Opus numbers to 138 then added works without opus numbers in a continuous numbering to 256. Catalogs in Italian appeared by Antonio Bruers in 1950 and by Giovanni Biamonti in 1968. The Bruers catalog followed the same continuous numbering format as Grove, but carried the list to 350. The Biamonti catalog suffers from two handicaps: it includes many very small sketch-like pieces that don't properly belong in a catalog of works; and it was printed only in Italian and in very small quantity. The result has been that it is rarely consulted and almost never cited as a reference although it does list 849 works, and more in an appendix of doubtful or attributed works. Interestingly, the third version of the Hess catalog also appeared in Italian, not German, in 1953 in *Annuario dell'Accademia Nazionale di Santa Cecilia*. The first version of the Hess catalog appeared in the fifth volume of the *Schweizerisches Jahrbuch für Musikwissenschaft*, in 1931, and the second edition or version followed in the seventh volume of the *Neues Beethoven Jahrbuch*, in 1937. An addendum to it appeared in the ninth volume, in 1939. For more detailed references to the various editions of the Hess catalog, see the first paragraph of the "Original Forward" below.

A new catalog would be of great value for Beethoven scholarship today. This should be done using a new numbering system designed by expert catalogers and specialists working together with Beethoven scholars employing modern cataloging techniques. The new catalog should be able to add newly discovered works without having them appear out of place, and it should drop, now thoroughly discredited works, like the "Jena Symphony." How this could be achieved I will leave to expert catalogers and scholars. What is important it that someday it be done by shedding old, outmoded conventions or concepts, and by adopting a new more flexible system.

Hess, in the last paragraph of his text, says that he has not examined all the sketchbooks, and a careful look at this catalog shows that whenever he cites sketchbook sources he almost always mentions someone else's research; most frequently Nottebohm's. Hess holds out the happy prospect that future research into the sketchbooks will yield many exciting new little pieces completely ready to perform. To a large extent this is what Professor Biamonti did, to some ridicule, when he listed as "works" many little items that are nothing more than sketches. Some are as little as two bars and don't properly belong in a "work's" catalog.

I believe it is important to understand the stylistic approach that has been adopted for this edition of Hess's catalog. Occasionally, it was necessary to present an interpretive translation of certain passages. At times Hess used a very relaxed casual style full of colloquial expressions alternating with a much more formal and sometimes stilted style. In these cases a literal translation simply did not carry the clarity necessary for understanding what Hess was trying to say. The indulgence of the reader is requested in these instances. For most of the text, Hess used the first person singular to describe information he had received, or found, but he also frequently referred to himself in the third person, especially when referencing one of his own publications. At times, this even occurred in the same entry and it has not been changed. Hess could, at times be cryptic and, on occasion, even obtuse. Wherever possible Hess's original style has been retained; however, every effort has been made to smooth out the problems and bring clarity to the text. Hess cited many sources for which he gave incomplete information; I have attempted to complete those references and reorder the bibliographic information into a consistent form.

For stylistic form I have chosen the standard bibliographic and grammatical style recommended in the *Macmillan Handbook of English*, 5th edition, edited by John M. Kierzek and Walker Gibson, Macmillan, New York 1965, and D. Kern Holoman's book, *Writing About Music: a Style Sheet from the Editors of 19th-Century Music*, University of California Press, Berkeley 1988. I have avoided slavish obedience to "Chicago Style." The use of abbreviations has been kept to a minimum and the reader is urged to consult the list of abbreviations at the beginning of the book. Wherever possible, truncated or one-word sentences have been written out more fully. I have been obliged by the original publisher to keep Hess's text separate from my additions; therefore, the "TN," meaning "translator's note," set in square brackets becomes quite repetitive and the reader's indulgence is begged. Smaller and minor insertions are set off by only the square brackets without the "TN." The translations of titles, which were left in their original language (mostly German), are shown in parentheses. It is my hope that this catalog is easily comprehensible and its information available to every reader, not just the specialist.

Four major collections have changed locations since Hess first prepared his catalog. The Paris Conservatory has transferred all its important musical holdings to the Bibliothèque Nationale in Paris, and likewise the British Museum has transferred its holdings to the British Library in London. The Deutsche Staatsbibliothek (successor to the Preußische Staatsbibliothek), which was divided at the end of World War II into the Deutsche Staatsbibliothek and the Staatsbibliothek Preußischer Kulturbesitz, is now reunited under the name Staatsbibliothek zu Berlin-Preußischer Kulturbesitz. Part of its original collection was removed from Berlin during the war and is now in the Biblioteka Jagiellońska in Cracow, Poland. To add to the confusion, after World War II another name was used to designate the still unorganized Berlin libraries, Öffentliche Wissenschaftliche Bibliothek. This confusing term survives in the Kinsky/Halm catalog of 1955. Lastly, the personal collection of H. C. Bodmer of Zurich was donated to the Beethoven-Archiv in Bonn in 1956 just prior to the publication of the Hess catalog. Occasionally, Hess failed to change all these references to their correct locations.

Hess cataloged not only works of doubtful authenticity but several that may never have existed at all, and some that did exist but are now considered lost. For this new edition I have created an Appendix A, which lists lost works, and an Appendix B, which lists works that may never have been written. Appendix C lists works that were once thought to be by Beethoven but are now known to be by other composers or arrangers. References to these particular entries have been shortened and repeated under the appropriate Appendix. Appendix D presents special information on the Hess entries that relate to the folksong arrangements. It cross-references them to two specialized lists prepared by Barry Cooper and Petra Weber-Bockholdt. The original Concordance has been expanded to include six more catalog systems by important 19th and 20th century scholars.

As with the production of any large reference work, full credit for its production cannot be taken by the editor or translator alone. I first began to translate the Hess catalog in 1997 in small bits and pieces for my own interest. Later, I was encouraged by Jos van der Zanden of Almere, the Netherlands to begin a complete and systematic translation. Without his early encouragement this work would never have been undertaken and for this I am grateful to him. Two individuals, Mark S. Zimmer of Madison, Wisconsin, and Albert Willem Holsbergen of Leiden, the Netherlands, have figured very prominently in the review and editing of this work. They have suggested sources for new and correct information and their comments have proven illuminating. I would particularly like to thank Mark Zimmer for his careful preparation of the first edition of Hess 96, the piano transcription of the beginning of the Seventh Symphony, Op. 92. I wish to acknowledge the very able assistance of Jan Templiner of Hamburg, who carefully proofread the translation and contributed some very important insights into the meaning of Hess's text, especially the explanations of Hess's use of idiomatic expressions and colloquialisms. I want to thank Gerard Dault of Washington, D.C., who examined several draft copies and reviewed the new Concordance and to Annie Moss Moore of Eastbound, Washington who painstakingly tracked down additional corrections to the new Concordance. I am grateful for information supplied to me by Tadahiro Nakamoto of Osaka, Japan. Mention should also be made of the patient understanding and assistance of Vivian Rehman of Breitkopf & Härtel and the enthusiastic willingness of Gerry S. Thomas of Vance Brook Publishing to undertake this project.

I also wish to thank Ira F. Brilliant, who proofread an early draft copy without knowing that this work would be dedicated to him, and to acknowledge the efforts of Gail Tarleton and William Hearn, who proofread the final draft. I gratefully acknowledge the very distinguished Beethoven scholars who examined the numerous draft copies and made suggestions for improvements: Dr. Barry Cooper, Dr. Scott Burnham, Dr. William Meredith, Dr. Ernst Herttrich, Dr. Douglas Johnson, who patiently checked information, and Dr. Sieghard Brandenburg, who graciously agreed to supply this edition with a new introduction.

I wish to thank the following individuals and their respective libraries, archives and institutions who have aided my searches and patiently answered my questions: Friederike Grigat (Beethoven-Archiv); Dr. Jon Newsom, Raymond White and Kevin Levine (Library of Congress); Ingeborg Pechotsch, Dr. Thomas Leibnitz and Dr. Günter Brosche (Österreichische Nationalbibliothek); Dr. Helmut Hell (Staatsbibliothek zu Berlin-Preußischer Kulturbesitz); Eva M. Ondreka (Hessen Rheinhessen Stadt- und Universitätsbibliothek); Rob Ritchie, for his work at the British Library in London; Stephen Roe (Sotheby's); and Thomas Venning (Christies). I would particularly like to single out the assistance of Patricia Stroh of the Ira F. Brilliant Center for Beethoven Studies, whose constant eagerness to check information and verify facts and whose unrelenting cheerfulness has greatly eased my burdens.

Alexandria, Virginia, Spring 2003   James F. Green

Original Introduction,
"Why a New Complete Edition?"

by Willy Hess

No one can doubt that we live in a time of the renaissance of the technique of editing! Not only have new, excellent original editions increasingly replaced arrangements in mainstream music performance, but our standards regarding textual fidelity and completeness have also risen dramatically. The old monumental complete editions of the musical classics, so revolutionary and deserving as they once were, no longer suffice as they once did. Many works that were missing at one time have meanwhile come to light; and many sources that one would have had to do without then are available today, so that essential text revisions have become possible. Where once one had to content oneself with the publication of the final version of a work, the research today demands one complete and accessible publication that includes all the versions. However, it should not include mere sketches, whose publication would overstep the framework of a complete edition, and which should be the object of a specialized edition whose publication would be part of a separate series.

The old Gesamtausgabe (complete edition) of Beethoven's works by the publishing house of Breitkopf & Härtel, Leipzig, which appeared between the years 1862 and 1865 in twenty-four volumes, is no exception here. [TN: a twenty-fifth supplemental volume was issued in 1888.] In essential areas, it needs a textual re-examination. Max Unger has repeatedly pointed out mistakes that were overlooked at the time. – These volumes need a supplement that would include earlier working stages of many important works. For example, Nottebohm provides in his *Zweite Beethoveniana*, p. 472, an earlier setting of bars 21-32 of the D-flat major section of the second movement of the Sonata, Op. 110, which should be taken into consideration, since this is not an unfinished sketch but rather an earlier manuscript version of a finished work. – The six bars of an earlier setting belonging to the finale of the Ninth Symphony which originally stood in the same position as the first fourteen bars of the "Tempo primo" before the very last "poco adagio," should also be included in the new complete edition. – Furthermore we should present the earlier working stages of the Bagatelles Op. 126, as published by Nottebohm, loc. cit., pp. 193-207, and make them accessible, at least in the revision report of a new complete edition, since they represent more than mere sketches.

The small Rondo for piano and orchestra in B-flat major [WoO 6] has only been known up to the present day in the version by Carl Czerny. The autograph (Beethoven Autograph 3 in the Gesellschaft der Musikfreunde in Vienna) shows, however, that it wasn't necessary for him to complete the orchestration, as is widely assumed; but rather upon examination of the autograph we find that the score was completed by Beethoven himself. What Czerny has done, however, is to complete only the partially sketched solo piano part, which was not performance ready. As it has turned out, Czerny has degenerated Beethoven's original text into the virtuosic, overstepping the range of the piano of that time and bombastically decorating what is in itself a simple work. – The solo part of the Violin Concerto still awaits publication in its original form. – Nottebohm, on pp. 74-78, tells us of highly interesting variations in the solo part of the Piano Concerto Op. 58 in G major, which Beethoven subsequently added, apparently for his own performance purposes. These variations should necessarily be included in our current musical practice. – From the "Rondo a Capriccio," Op.129, we now know from studying the autograph, which has reappeared recently in the USA (property of Mrs. Eugene Allen Noble, Providence, Rhode Island), that eight bars are missing between bars 31 and 32 in the printing of the Gesamtausgabe (this mistake was repeated in all subsequent editions); in addition there are numerous smaller deviations. [TN: the autograph of Op. 129, which is now owned by Robert O. Lehman, is on deposit in the Pierpont Morgan Library, New York.] The first corrected printing took place in 1950, in the Urtext edition of the bagatelles done by Otto von Irmer, G. Henle, Munich-Duisburg. [TN: this edition is titled *Klavierstücke*; it is described by the publisher as "comprising all Beethoven's compositions for the piano with the exception of the 32 sonatas, the variations and the dances." Numerous later editions have appeared.] – The oratorio, "Christus am Ölberg" was revised and enriched by Beethoven with an additional chorus in the first half of 1804, that is, approximately one year after the premiere. It will be a matter for the new complete edition to also bring forth the original version, which should not be all that difficult, thanks to the Berlin autograph "Artaria 179," of Beethoven's own amendments. [TN: it is interesting to note that when Hess had the opportunity to publish this early version of the oratorio in the *Supplemente zur Beethoven-Gesamtausgabe* he didn't include it in spite of his assertion that it "should not be all that difficult." The new "Complete Edition," which is now in preparation through the Beethoven-Haus and G. Henle, has not yet published the volume that should contain the oratorio, so it is not certain whether it will contain this early version either. This early version and its dating are discussed in Alan Tyson's article "The 1803 Version of Beethoven's 'Christus am Oelberge'," *The Musical Quarterly*, Vol. LVI, 1970, pp. 551-84.]

In addition to amendments of this kind, there are all the works that are likely absent from the old Gesamtausgabe. Indeed Beethoven had the satisfaction in his old age to see that the greatest part of his complete works were printed, and to know, therefore, that these works were protected from obscurity. This was very much in contrast to approximately the same situation as Haydn and Mozart, not to speak at all of Bach. Nevertheless, with the unhappy auction of his estate, his fate became to have many still unpublished pieces scattered and only little by little to have them reappear again.

Incidentally, the first plan of a complete edition came from Beethoven himself! Already in his first years in Vienna, the composer expressed the wish to Prince Lobkowitz that he would like to be paid a yearly pension by a publisher, for which the publisher would then have the sole right to publish all his works. Beethoven had taken up this plan again and again, and the great central work [Beethoven biography] by Thayer-Deiters-Riemann mentions such suggestions and plans for an index that covers works from 1806 to 1826. [TN: the reference is to a footnote in Thayer II, p. 407. The same comment is found in Thayer/Forbes, p. 339.]

Two especially important and pertinent works should be mentioned in this context. The first is by Max Unger, *Beethoven über eine Gesamtausgabe seiner Werke*, Journal I, from the Veröffentlichungen des Beethovenhauses, Bonn 1920; and the second is by Otto Erich Deutsch, "Beethovens gesammelte Werke. Des Meisters Plan und Haslingers Ausgabe," *Zeitschrift für Musikwissenschaft*, Vol. 13, November 1930, pp. 60-79. Deutsch reported here for the first time on the extensive collection of Beethoven's works bound in sixty-two large red folio volumes, that was compiled for Archduke Rudolph, and which is known under the name *Haslinger-Rudolfinische Sammlung*, and is today the property of the Gesellschaft der Musikfreunde in Vienna. Haslinger planned the first complete edition by using this collection, of which, according to Deutsch, nearly seventy-five individual works have appeared! It would be too much to separately quote the contents of these volumes here; we refer the reader to the descriptions by Otto Erich Deutsch. A very big part of what today are extremely rare journals are located in the collection of Anthony van Hoboken; moreover, the Universitätsbibliothek in Basel indeed possesses the first series, however, it is incomplete. The same edition is mentioned by Marta Walter in "Musikalische Seltenheiten der Universitätsbibliothek Basel," *Sonntagsblatt der Basler Nachrichten*, 28 June 1953. As she states, this old edition has almost completely been brought together by Paul Hirsch in Cambridge.

Haslinger's edition was begun in 1828 and continued over two decades without being completed. Incidently, the complete edition of Franz Liszt through Holle in Wolfenbüttel, which was begun about the middle of the previous century, got stuck in its beginning also. It wasn't until 1862 that a great event happened, that is, the beginning of the Leipzig complete edition by Breitkopf & Härtel. In 1888, the publishing house followed its twenty-four volumes in the series, with a supplemental volume, known as series 25, containing approximately fifty additional works. In 1890 two piano concertos were subsequently appended to the edition as No. 310 and No. 311: a concerto in E-flat major from the year 1784 which survived in a solo piano part, and a concerto movement in D-major, that later turned out to be a work by Johann Joseph Rösler (the same piece is mentioned by Hans Engel in "Der angeblich Beethovensche Klavierkonzertsatz," *Neues Beethoven-Jahrbuch*, Vol. 2, Augsburg 1925, pp. 167-175). And the publishing house Breitkopf brought out in the last addendum to the complete edition under the numbers 312-334, twenty-three folksong arrangements by Beethoven ([prepared by] G. Schünemann in *Neues Volksliederheft 4*, Leipzig 1940), without, however, somehow making a connection between them and the old Gesamtausgabe; only the plate numbers on them indicate it. Further attempts at an extensive supplement have never been done. [TN: this was done by Hess himself in *Supplemente zur Beethoven-Gesamtausgabe*, 14 Vols., Breitkopf & Härtel, Wiesbaden 1959-1971.]

It therefore seems desirable, once and for all, to collect and identify all the works by Beethoven that have appeared since 1888, as well as what has partially appeared in first editions outside of the Gesamtausgabe. The author has undertaken work in this direction for approximately thirty years, by writing over 100 articles and special examinations in a wide range of journals and periodicals. This publishing house and the author hope that with this comprehensive publication, the interest in a new and complete total edition of the works of Ludwig van Beethoven will be carried into the widest circles.

This is done in the conviction that it is one of the first and most important tasks of modern musicology to collect and reveal the complete works of our great masters of music so fully and correctly as to open these works up to a much larger public and to foster greater understanding of their worth.

Original Foreword

by Willy Hess

I first presented a still very incomplete compilation of all the works of Beethoven missing in the Gesamtausgabe in the fifth volume of the *Schweizerisches Jahrbuch für Musikwissenschaft*, Aarau 1931, pp. 163-188, which appeared under the title "Beethovens Werke und ihre Gesamtausgabe." A second and already essentially supplemented edition followed in the seventh volume of the *Neues Beethoven Jahrbuch*, Braunschweig 1937, pp. 104-130, and an addendum to it appeared in the ninth volume, 1939, pp. 75-79. The third edition appeared under the title "Le opere di Beethoven e la loro edizione completa" (translation by Professor Giovanni Biamonti, Rome), in *Annuario dell'Accademia Nazionale di Santa Cecilia* 1951/2, printed in 1953, pp. 301-367, and also as a separate edition in Rome.

A fourth edition should have appeared in 1956 in Max Hinrichsen's *Music Book* in London. However, the publication of this London edition was so delayed that the author decided to reorganize the entire material from scratch, together with the countless addenda and corrections prepared for the London edition since 1955, and to publish this expanded material as an independent work in book form. With that, it became, in contrast to early plans, necessary to make changes; most notably, the "Doubtful and Falsely Attributed Works" were removed from the main catalog and summarized in an addendum. [TN: the fourth edition proposed for Hinrichsen became the Hess edition of 1957, which is what was used as the basis for this book. The present expanded and corrected translation is effectively the fifth edition of the Hess catalog.]

Of course, a big change was brought on by the appearance of the *Thematisch- Bibliographisches Verzeichnis aller vollendeten Werke Ludwig van Beethovens* by Kinsky/Halm, (this catalog is mentioned below under abbreviations). It should be expressly noted that this wonderful work, which one could call "Beethoven's Köchel," is still not at all complete and hence does not render superfluous this summary of everything that the Gesamtausgabe lacks. On the other hand, the present catalog should conveniently satisfy the practical needs of all, and therefore avoid, wherever possible, the philological details that are not absolutely necessary to the enumeration of the works. Thus, in general, I only give the number of bars with unpublished, or otherwise difficultly accessible works; in addition to this, I have generally put value on the listing of all signatures or autographs, where such was possible. But wherever possible, I have indicated all the printed editions of the named works; in other words, my intention here is the collection of the materials for the supplement of the Gesamtausgabe and not primarily an attempt at bibliographical completeness.

The following abbreviations were applied:

a.a.O.: at the stated place. [TN: this abbreviation was not used in this translation.]

Br. & H.: Publishing house of Breitkopf & Härtel, Leipzig, or Wiesbaden. [TN: this abbreviation was not used in this translation.]

GA: Gesamtausgabe [TN: this is the old complete edition of Beethoven's Works, the printing of which was begun in the 1860s and completed in 1888 by Breitkopf & Härtel. This had for nearly a century been the standard edition of Beethoven's works. It is commonly referred to as just the "Gesamtausgabe." In 1961 publication began on a new complete edition titled *L. van Beethoven Werke: neue Ausgabe Sämtlicher Werke*, edited by Joseph Schmidt-Görg and others and published in cooperation with the Beethoven-Haus, Bonn by G. Henle, Munich-Duisburg. It is now commonly called the "New Gesamtausgabe" or the "Critical Edition" or just "Werke."]

Hess 2 as well as 3: Refer to the second and third supplemental Catalogs that I prepared to the Gesamtausgabe. The fourth, its fate still uncertain, is nowhere considered here. [TN: these supplemental Catalogs are those mentioned in the first and second paragraphs of the Original Foreword (see above) and not to Hess's later work titled *Sämtliche Werke: Supplemente zur Beethoven-Gesamtausgabe*, in 14 Vols., published by Breitkopf & Härtel, Wiesbaden, between 1959-71. The fourth edition to which Hess refers is in fact the 1957 edition of this catalog upon which this translation is based.]

Kalischer I-V: Kalischer's complete edition of Beethoven's letters: *Beethovens sämtliche Briefe*, Schuster & Loeffler, Berlin-Leipzig 1906-1908. [TN: this edition of Beethoven's letters was superseded in 1961 with the publication of the three-volume edition *Letters of Beethoven*, translated by Emily Anderson and published by Macmillan & Co., London. In its turn, that edition was overtaken by the publication of the eight-volume edition edited by Sieghard Brandenburg and published as *Briefwechsel Gesamtausgabe*, through the Beethoven-Haus, by G. Henle, Munich 1996-98.]

Kinsky/Halm: *Thematisch-Bibliographisches Verzeichnis aller vollendeten Werke Ludwig van Beethovens* by Georg Kinsky. After his death this work was completed by Hans Halm and published by G. Henle, Munich-Duisburg, 1955.

Kl. A.: Piano transcription. [TN: this abbreviation has been omitted from this translation.]

Nohl, I or II: Ludwig Nohl's *Briefe Beethovens,* Cotta, Stuttgart 1865, and his *Neue Briefe Beethovens,* Cotta, Stuttgart 1867.

Nottebohm, I or II: Gustav Nottebohm's *Beethoveniana,* J. Rieter-Biedermann, Leipzig-Winterthur 1872, as well as his *Zweite Beethoveniana,* Leipzig 1887.

S.: Page. [TN: this abbreviation has been changed to the standard form of "p." for page and "pp." for pages.]

T.: Bar. [TN: this abbreviation was not used in the translation.]

Thayer, I-V: The important major work about Beethoven by Thayer-Deiters-Riemann, Breitkopf & Härtel, Leipzig. 1st volume, 1917; 2nd volume, 1922; volumes 3-5, 1923. [TN: the page numbers referred to are to these editions only. There are a few earlier and several later editions of Thayer's biography of Beethoven.

Thayer No. X: the number is meant to indicate the entry as listed in Thayer's *Chronologisches Verzeichniss der Werke Ludwig van Beethovens*, Schneider, Berlin 1865.

All remaining sources are quoted with the full name. The Bodmer collection is today in the Beethoven-Haus, Bonn. References to [Ludwig] Schiedermair's *Der junge Beethoven,* always refer to the first edition (1925). All works that are listed are absent in the Gesamtausgabe, even if they have been lost or have only been passed on as fragments. [TN: this is not always quite true. Hess did make some mistakes in these listings and some of the entries are in the Gesamtausgabe. All such occurrences are noted in the appropriate entry.] In addition to that I have, in general, not taken sketches into account, since this would be a project in itself and would properly be done together with a complete publication of all the sketchbooks.

Even with all the will that one can summon, we can never expect such a project to become complete. Of this, nobody is more aware than the author himself. I have as such posed open-ended questions in the hope that through the cooperation of my readers, some answers may be found, because the collecting of material that can truly be regarded as complete and final exceeds the strengths of a single person. That even a relative completeness could, nevertheless, be reached, this author owes to the unselfish help of renowned Beethoven researchers. My thanks are expressed before all to my friend, Professor Giovanni Biamonti in Rome, and also to Mr. Donald W. MacArdle (Dallas, USA), Dr. Hans Halm (Munich), Professor Dr. Otto Erich Deutsch (Vienna), Dr. Max Unger (Volterra-Zurich), Mr. Fritz Kaiser (Darmstadt), and likewise also Dr. Dagmar Weise (Beethoven-Haus, Bonn) for always willingly giving me information. There is a need for me to express further thanks to Dr. Hedwig Kraus (Gesellschaft der Musikfreunde, Vienna), as well as to Prof. Dr. L. Nowak (Nationalbibliothek, Vienna) and to Dr. Fritz Racek (Stadtbibliothek, Vienna) for the great kindness shown to me in 1954, when these individuals in Vienna relieved and lightened my work in the libraries and manuscript collections under their care. I also ask the assistants that I don't mention by name to please accept my sincere thanks.

Winterthur, in the spring of 1957,   Willy Hess

References and Abbreviations

Anh.

refers to the German word *Anhang* meaning appendix. Used by Kinsky/Halm and by Hess to describe the doubtful works.

Anderson:

refers to the three-volume edition, *Letters of Beethoven*, translated by Emily Anderson, published by Macmillan & Co., London 1961.

BL:

stands for the British Library, London.

BN:

stands for the Bibliothèque Nationale, Paris.

Brandenburg:

refers to the eight-volume edition *Briefwechsel Gesamtausgabe*, edited by Dr. Sieghard Brandenburg and published through the Beethoven-Haus, by G. Henle, Munich 1996-98.

C/C:

stands for Cooper/Compendium and refers to *The Beethoven Compendium*, edited by Barry Cooper, Thames & Hudson, London 1991.

C/F:

stands for Cooper/Folksongs and refers to *Beethoven's Folksong Settings: Chronology, Sources, Style*, by Barry Cooper, Clarendon Press, Oxford 1994.

Dorfmüller:

refers to *Beiträge zur Beethoven Bibliographie*, edited by Kurt Dorfmüller, G. Henle, Munich 1978.

Kalischer I-V:

refers to A. C. Kalischer's *Beethovens sämtliche Briefe*, published in five volumes by Schuster & Loeffler, Berlin-Leipzig 1906-1908.

Kinsky/Halm: refers to *Thematisch-Bibliographisches Verzeichnis aller vollendeten Werke Ludwig van Beethovens* by Georg Kinsky. After his death this work was completed by Hans Halm and published by G. Henle, Munich-Duisburg 1955.

MacArdle/Misch: refers to the work *New Beethoven Letters* by Donald W. MacArdle and Ludwig Misch, University of Oklahoma Press, Norman, Oklahoma 1957.

Mh: refers to a now obsolete numbering of the Bodmer collection done by Max Unger. Published in *Eine Schweizer Beethovensammlung Katalog*, Verlag der Corona, Zurich 1939.

Misch: refers to Dr. Ludwig Misch's, "Pseudokanons und Rätselkanons von Beethoven," in *Die Musikforschung*, Vol. 3, Journal 3/4, 1950.

Nohl I, or II: refers to Ludwig Nohl's *Briefe Beethovens*, Cotta, Stuttgart 1865 and to his *Neue Briefe Beethovens*, Cotta, Stuttgart 1867.

Nottebohm I, or II: refers to Gustav Nottebohm's, *B e e t h o - veniana*, J. Rieter-Biedermann, Leipzig and Winterthur 1872, as well as *Zweite Beethoveniana*, C F. Peters, Leipzig 1887.

SBB: stands for the Staatsbibliothek zu Berlin-Preußischer Kulturbesitz, Berlin.

SBG I-XIV: refers to the *Supplemente zur Beethoven-Gesamtausgabe*, edited by Willy Hess and published in fourteen volumes by Breitkopf & Härtel, Wiesbaden 1959-71.

SBH: means *Sammlung Beethoven-Haus* and is a

catalog of the holdings of the Beethoven-Haus prepared by Hans Schmidt. It was published in the *Beethoven-Jahrbuch*, Jahrgang 1969/70, Beethoven-Haus, Bonn 1971.

SV: means *Sizzenverzeichnis* (sketch catalog) prepared by Hans Schmidt and published in the *Beethoven-Jahrbuch*, Jahrgang 1965/68, Beethoven-Haus, Bonn 1969.

Thayer, I-V: refers to the important biography *Beethovens Leben* by Alexander W. Thayer and edited by Herman Deiters and Hugo Riemann, Breitkopf & Härtel, Leipzig. Volume 1, 1917; Volume 2, 1922; Volumes 3-5, 1923.

Thayer/Forbes: refers to *Thayer's Life of Beethoven,* revised and edited by Elliot Forbes, Princeton University Press, Princeton, New Jersey 1964, first edition in two volumes.

TN: means "translator's note." These comments are enclosed in square brackets. Small insertions are simply enclosed in square brackets without the "TN."

WoO: means "Werke ohne Opuszahl" (Work without Opus number) as listed by Kinsky/Halm.

MAIN CATALOG
Miscellaneous Orchestral Works

1 Original ending of the first movement of the Eighth Symphony, [Op. 93]. At the premiere it was about thirty-four bars shorter; Beethoven later canceled out the last ten (or possibly eight?) bars and replaced them with the ending known today. Nottebohm I, p. 25, gives the original timpani part. See Alfred Orel's "Der ursprüngliche Schluß des ersten Satztes in Beethovens achter Symphonie," in *Schweizerische Musikzeitung*, Vol. 90, February 1950, pp. 50-53, where Orel presents the whole ending in score on p. 51. Both of the rest-bars which are shown by Orel are missing in Nottebohm, though this may be a copying error by Nottebohm. Orel states that in Ms. 19 in the Paris Conservatory (part of the first violin part – at the end of the first movement – of the 8th Symphony) also belongs to this first version. [TN: the Paris Conservatory has transferred all of its holdings to the BN.] Today the autograph score is in private hands, which Orel does not name. [TN: today the autograph is in two locations. The first, second and fourth movements are in the SBB, while the third movement is in the Biblioteka Jagiellońska, Cracow, Poland; however, there is on a single page, SBH 560, in the Bodmer Collection in the Beethoven-Haus, the original ending with ten bars crossed and the new ending added. Hess published only the original ending of the first movement in the SBG, Vol. IV, 1961, p. 70.]

2 Twelve Minuets, composed in 1799. Copies of the orchestral parts were found in 1872 by A. von Perger in the archive of the Künstler-Pensionsinstitut in Vienna and

were transferred to the Österreichische Nationalbibliothek (Ms. 16925), which also possesses a full
score prepared by Perger (Ms. 18488). The Minuets
recorded by Thayer in his catalog as No. 290, "Nos. 3,
9, and 11" are actually score copies of 3, 9, and 11
from this cycle. They were formerly in Berlin, but are
possibly held in trust in the Universitätsbibliothek,
Tübingen (Artaria No. 139). [TN: these scores have
now been returned to the SBB and are no longer in
Tübingen.] Two score copies for [Minuet] No. 1 are
known: one is owned by the British Museum (Add. Ms.
31.750); the other is in the archive of the Gesellschaft
der Musikfreunde in Vienna (XV 29369). [TN: the
British Museum is now the BL. Minuet No. 1, along
with three other pieces in Add. Ms. 31.748, were ascribed to Mozart until 1919 when Georges de Saint-
Foix identified one as WoO 12, No. 1 and ascribed the
others (Kinsky/Halm Anhang 3, 6 and 8) to Beethoven.
In 1941, C. L. Cudworth and D. R. Wakeling discovered that the three Anhang pieces were arranged from
Leopold Kozeluch's *La Ritrouata Figlia di Ottone II*
(1794). See the references in entries A 16, A 18 and A
20 in this catalog.] The autographs are unknown and
performances in Beethoven's lifetime don't seem to
have taken place. The first edition was published by J.
Chantavoine in 1903 in a piano version and in 1906 in
full score through *Au Ménestrel*, Heugel & Cie., Paris,
but with substantial changes in some places to the
original [musical] text. The first edition of the [cor-
rect] original text was done by Willy Hess in *Musik-
Archiv*, No. 183, Nagels Verlag, Kassel 1953. [TN: this
set of Minuets is listed in Kinsky/Halm as WoO 12.
Shin Augustinus Kojima believes them to be by Beethoven's brother Karl. For more information on their
identification, see two articles by him: "Kaspar Anton
Karl van Beethoven als Musiker - Leben und Werk," in
Annuario: Instituto giapponese di cultura in Roma,
Italy, Vol. XIV (1977-78), pp. 79-108; and

"Zweifelhafte Authentizität einiger Beethoven zugeschriebener Orchestertänze," in *Bericht über den Internationalen Beethoven-Kongreß Berlin 1977*, Deutscher Verlag für Musik, Berlin 1978, pp. 307-322. This dance set was published by Hess in the SBG, Vol. IV, 1961, p. 7.]

3 Twelve Ecossaises for piano or for orchestra. These twelve Ecossaises for piano were found in the Artaria estate. It is likely that they were originally composed for orchestra. They are missing today. Hence, Hugo Riemann's remark (Thayer II, p. 62), that six of the twelve Ecossaises from this set are still unpublished (he probably believes the published ones to be the six printed in the GA, Series 25, No. 302); however, this presumption cannot be verified. [TN: this is an oblique reference to WoO 83 which was published in the GA as No. 302.] On no account however, can they be Kinsky/Halm, WoO 16. See "Doubtful and Falsely Attributed Works," A 5, for more about this. [TN: in spite of Hess's emphatic statement that these twelve Ecossaises cannot be WoO 16, he later changed his 1957 opinion and did admit in the second edition of his biography of Beethoven that he was just "uncertain whether they are identical with WoO 16" and then listed them in the works catalog of the same book as being the same set. See *Beethoven*, Amadeus Verlag, Winterthur 1976, p. 335. Dorfmüller also lists them as being the same as WoO 16; see p. 357. See also WoO 16 in Kinsky/Halm, p. 452 for a more detailed account of the history of these Ecossaises and entry A 5 in this catalog.]

4 An Ecossaise in G major for Wind Band. According to Kinsky/Halm, [which lists this as] WoO 23, it is possible that this piece was composed about 1810 [and it appears] in the GA, Series 25, as No. 306, as a transcription for piano by an unknown arranger of a work

originally written for wind instruments, although the [original] score has not yet been found. Thayer reports on page 171 of his *Chronologisches Verzeichniss*: "This piece [was] played as wind band music in the Prater about the year 1810, and retained in the memory of (Wenzel) Krumpholz and, according to his testimony, it was later written down by Carl Czerny." [TN: this entry needs some clarification. If Hess meant entry 4 to be the lost version for wind instruments, then its inclusion in this catalog has validity. If, on the other hand, he meant the piano version written out by Czerny based on Krumpholz's remembrance of it, then it is in fact in the GA and should not be listed here. Hess fails to mention that this piece in Czerny's piano version was first published about 1834 in Tobias Hasliniger's *Wiener Musikalisches Pfennig Magazin*, Volume 1, No. 27, p. 108. According to Kinsky/Halm, p. 461, "The version in the GA was based on a copy made by Nottebohm of a copy owned by L. v. Sonnleithner." Presumably this refers to Leopold Sonnleithner, nephew of Joseph Sonnleithner (librettist of the first version of *Fidelio*). We know Beethoven, who mentions Leopold in a letter of 1824, was acquainted with him. See Paul Nettl's *Beethoven Handbook*, F. Ungar Publishing Co., New York, 1956, p. 241. It is not clear whether Sonnleithner has copied Czerny's version, or whether he had some sort of access to the original autograph for wind instruments upon which he based his own piano version. It is also possible that he was in possession of Czerny's copy, since Kinsky/Halm simply says "a copy owned by L. v. Sonnleithner." It is also possible that Sonnleithner owned a copy of the *Musikalisches Pfennig Magazin*, which was already fifty years old and may have been difficult to obtain from any other source by the time Nottebohm was preparing volume 25 of the GA in the mid 1880s.]

5 Twelve German [Dances], presumably performed in Vienna about 1796-7. Known only in a piano version revised by Beethoven, Thayer No. 291, autograph Artaria 137 of the Staatsbibliothek, Berlin. [TN: now the SBB.] The first edition was published by Otto Erich Deutsch, through Strache in Vienna, 1929; Deutsch dated the composition about 1800. Reprinted by Edwin Fischer and Georg Schünemann, through Eichmann, Berlin in 1937. [TN: this is listed as WoO 13 in Kinsky/Halm, p. 447.]

6 March in F major for Wind Band ("Marsch für die böhmische Landwehr") (March for the Bohemian General Armed Forces). Composed in 1809. The autographs are in Berlin (Artaria 144) and in Vienna in the possession of the Deutscher Ritterorden. The first edition of the original was published by Willy Hess in the *Beethoven-Jahrbuch*, Beethoven-Haus, Bonn 1953-4. The score, published by Schlesinger about 1818-9 as "Marsch für das Yorck'sche Korps," (March for the York Corps), is an arrangement by someone else. An arrangement prepared by Beethoven appeared in the GA, Series 25, No. 287 I. See also entry No. 99 of this catalog. [TN: this is listed under WoO 18 in Kinsky/Halm, p. 456. Hess entry 6 is a first version of WoO 18 while WoO 18 is the second version of the same work. See Dorfmüller, p. 35.]

7 Zapfenstreich (Military Tattoo) No. 1 in F major. [This is] identical with the previous entry, but with the addition of a small trio. The autograph, Artaria 145, is in Berlin. A copy of the trio [only] in another hand is found in the autograph, Artaria 144. The first edition was edited by W. Hess for the *Beethoven-Jahrbuch*, Beethoven-Haus, Bonn 1953/4. [TN: this is also listed under WoO 18 in Kinsky/Halm, p. 456. Hess, by his assignment of a separate entry number for this piece is indicating that this entry should be considered as the

whole work including the trio, and entry 6 should be considered the earlier version without the trio. This entry should be considered the third version of this march, with Hess 6 being the first and WoO 18 being the second. See Dorfmüller, p. 35. According to Barry Cooper, the trio, which is in B-flat, was written in 1822. See C/C, p. 224.]

8 March for Archduke Anton in F major, likewise for Wind Band. The autograph, which carries the title "Zapfenstreich No. 3" (see below), is the property of the Gesellschaft der Musikfreunde, Vienna. It is the oldest existing manuscript [for the work]; from it Beethoven worked out his second manuscript, which is today the property of the Deutscher Ritterorden in Vienna. Some corrections and a small shortening took place in it. A copy of this second manuscript is also in the possession of the Gesellschaft der Musikfreunde. The first edition, with all the variants in both settings, was published by W. Hess in the *Beethoven-Jahrbuch*, [Vol. I,] Beethoven-Haus, Bonn 1953/4, [pp.260-274] (an addendum to this first edition appeared in the *Beethoven-Jahrbuch,* [Vol. II,] Beethoven-Haus, Bonn 1955/6, pp.120-121). An instrumental simplification of the march prepared by Beethoven appears in the GA, Series 25, No. 287 II. [TN: this is listed under WoO 19 in Kinsky/Halm, p. 456. This entry should be considered the first version of WoO 19.]

9 Zapfenstreich (Military Tattoo) No. 3 in F major. This is identical with the first version of the preceding entry. To this work belongs a little trio in F minor titled "Trio to No. 3," which was found together with a draft, in the autograph Artaria 146 in Berlin (today all three autographs, Artaria 144 to 146, are in Tübingen). [TN: all three autographs have now been returned to the SBB.] The first edition was published by W. Hess in the *Beethoven-Jahrbuch*, [Vol. I,] Beethoven-Haus, Bonn

1953/4, [pp.269-274]. [TN: this is listed under WoO 19 in Kinsky/Halm, p. 456. Hess entry 9 should be considered the third version of this march, with WoO 19 being the second version and Hess entry 8 being the first version. See Dorfmüller, p. 35. According to C/C, p. 224, the trio was written in 1822.]

The minuets and ländler for two violins and bass, which we have until now included under the chamber music works for string instruments, could just as well be placed here with the orchestral works.

Concertos and Solo Works
with Orchestral Accompaniment

10 Violin Concerto in C major (fragment of a first movement). Composed about 1790-2. The autograph is in the collection of the Gesellschaft der Musikfreunde in Vienna. The first edition, in a completion by Joseph Hellmesberger, was published by Friedrich Schreiber, Vienna, 1879, in score and piano transcription. Hellmesberger allowed himself many arbitrary alterations to the surviving part of the score, but a newer attempt at a completion by Juan Manén (Universal-Edition, Vienna; piano transcription 1933; score 1943) also alters the original score. The press release that circulated about 1933, stating that Manén had found a previously unknown work of Beethoven for violin and orchestra in the library of a Spanish cloister is a complete fabrication. The work in question is the present one, which was printed in an accurate edition by Ludwig Schiedermair in 1925 (appendix to *Der junge Beethoven,* Quelle & Meyer, Leipzig). [TN: this work is listed as WoO 5 in Kinsky/Halm, p. 434. Published by Hess in the SBG, Vol. III, 1960, p.44.]

11 Violin Romance No. 3. A work described as such was alluded to by W. Altmann as having been offered to the publisher [Sigmund Anton] Steiner in 1816 (foreword to the Eulenburg edition of the Violin Concerto), ". . . but this offer is not proof that he (Beethoven) also truly had it ready. The late Beethoven researcher Erich Prieger knew that this third romance existed in private hands and hoped that he would be able to find it." Unfortunately, this hope has not been fulfilled so far. [TN: this work was not listed in a price list sent to Steiner in 1816, but rather in a list of works prepared

by Beethoven for his own reference and later offered to C. F. Peters in 1822. On this, Alan Tyson writes: "In an appendix to the third volume of his biography of Beethoven, Thayer cites a price list Beethoven had drawn up for a number of his unpublished (and in a couple of cases still unwritten) works. (See Thayer III, pp. 487-88; reprinted unchanged in Thayer-Deiters-Riemann III, pp. 619-20. Omitted in Thayer/Krehbiel and Thayer/Forbes.) Thayer appears to have known it only from a transcript made by Otto Jahn, and his printed text contains some errors. Fortunately it is possible to correct them, for the list is today in the SBB, catalogued as 'Mus. Ms. Autogr. Beethoven 35, 80.' The list carries no date – not surprisingly, since as a document it was probably intended for Beethoven's eyes alone. Thayer printed the list along with Beethoven's correspondence with Steiner and Haslinger from the years 1815-17, and added a somewhat enigmatic footnote to say that according to indications in the Steiner and Streicher correspondence, the document belonged to the end of 1816. Thayer's dating was not challenged by Nottebohm. (Nor obviously by Hess.) Today, however, it is plain that the list must be placed over five years later. The clearest evidence for a later date is contained in a letter that Beethoven wrote to the Leipzig publisher C. F. Peters on June 5, 1822." This letter is Anderson 1079 and Brandenburg 1468. This work is listed on the price list as "Romanze für Violin solo" at 15 ducats and offered in the letter at the same price as "Violin-Romanze (Solo mit ganzem Orchester)." The only known works fitting that description are Beethoven's Op. 40 and Op. 50, both published many years earlier. Tyson speculates that, "The only known composition for violin and orchestra unpublished at this time was the violin concerto WoO 5, written in Bonn c.1790-92. All that has survived of it is a fragment of the first movement, though since the score breaks off at the end of a gathering (bundle of pages), it is likely that there was once more of it. Perhaps its slow movement was still in existence when the list was compiled, and was the "Romanze" referred to here." See Alan Tyson "A Beethoven Price List of 1822," in *Beethoven Essays: Studies in Honor of Elliot Forbes*, Harvard University Press, Cambridge, Mass., 1984.]

12 Concerto for Oboe and Orchestra in F major. Completed by Beethoven in his early years in Vienna and sent to Bonn. Formerly in the possession of the publisher Anton Diabelli (Thayer, No. 281), the work has disappeared without a trace; however, the Beethoven-Haus, Bonn possesses a page [SBH 772] with the incipits of the three movements (*Handschriftenkatalog*, Schmidt-Görg No. 135). See also a reference by Fritz von Reinöhl in "Neues zu Beethovens Lehrjahren bei Haydn," *Neues Beethoven-Jahrbuch, Vol. VI*, Henry Litolff's Verlag, Braunschweig 1935, pp. 36-47. [TN: the surviving sketches are in the "Kafka Sketchbook" in the BL; what is left is fragmentary and consists of an Allegro moderato and a Rondo: Allegretto. According to C/C, p. 220, this was written about 1790-93, while Joseph Kerman gives the composition date as 1792 or 1793 in *Autograph Miscellany, ca. 1786 to 1799*, British Museum, London, 1970, Vol. I, p. xxvii. A reconstruction based on the surviving sketches of the slow movement was done for oboe with piano accompaniment by Charles Lehrer, Amherst, Massachusetts, and published by Nova Music, London 1983. Two reconstructions for oboe and orchestra have been undertaken, one by A. Willem Holsbergen of Leiden and the other by Cees Nieuwenhuizen of Alkmaar, both in the Netherlands. The orchestral version by Holsbergen has been recorded by L'Orchestre de Bretagne under the direction of Stefan Sanderling. It is scheduled for release by ASV records in late 2003.]

13 Romance Cantabile for piano, flute and bassoon accompanied by two oboes and strings in E minor; written about 1792-3, and surviving as a fragment only. The autograph is in the British Museum (Add. 29801, ff 74b, through 80b). [TN: "Add. 29801" is the so-called Kafka Sketchbook, now in the BL.] The first edition and a completion was published by Willy Hess, Breitkopf & Härtel, Wiesbaden 1952. [TN: C/C, p. 221, suggests that this Romance Cantabile dates from c.1786, while Joseph Kerman gives the composition date as 1786 or 1787 in *Autograph Miscellany, ca. 1786 to 1799*, British Museum, London 1970, Vol. I, p. xxvii. Its provenance suggests that this complete section in E minor and one page of the "segue maggiore" section were part of a once complete autograph of a slow movement, which may also have been part of a complete concerto, the rest of which is now lost. Kinsky/Halm suggests that this work, like WoO 37, may have been written for the Westerholt-Gysenberg family, who were friends of Beethoven's in Bonn. See Kinsky/Halm, p. 479. This movement was also published by Hess in the SBG, Vol. III, 1960, p. 33.]

14 Piano Concerto in B-flat major, [Op. 19] first version, composed 1794-5 and played in this version by Beethoven more than once, but unfortunately now lost. See the references in Thayer II, p. 85, and Max Unger in *Neues Beethoven-Jahrbuch* VI, Henry Litolff's Verlag, Braunschweig 1935, p. 106. The Beethoven autograph Ms. 61 in the Paris Conservatory contains a page of this first version in score, and the Beethoven autograph Ms. 70 of the same library contains sketches to a cadenza for the first movement of this first version. Additional cadenza sketches [are found] in the so-called "Kafka Sketchbook" (British Museum). [TN: the Paris Conservatory has transferred its holdings to the Bibliothèque Nationale, Paris, and the British Museum has also transferred its holdings to the British Library,

London.] See Nottebohm II, p. 66. [TN: this version is mentioned under the Op. 19 entry in Kinsky/Halm, p. 45. The cadenza sketches mentioned above are listed in the present catalog under entry 79. Two pages of this first version were published in score by Hess in the SBG, Vol. III, 1960, p. 70. Barry Cooper, in "A Long-Running Revision: Second Piano Concerto," from *Beethoven and the Creative Process,* Oxford University Press, Oxford 1990, describes the "Second Piano Concerto as a work with a long period of gestation. About twenty years passed between the probable date of the first autograph score (the late 1780s) and the last phase of composition (1809). In light of this, the idea of just a first and a second (final) version may be too simplistic." There is an extensive analysis of the history of the writing of this concerto by Geoffrey Block in "Some Gray areas in the Evolution of Beethoven's Piano Concerto in B-flat major, Op. 19," in *Beethoven Essays: Studies in Honor of Elliot Forbes*, edited by L. Lockwood and P. Benjamin, Harvard University Press, Cambridge 1984, pp.108-26. Of particular interest is the chronological table (pp. 123-6) showing the sketches, continuity drafts and autographs for this concerto. This same problem is also discussed by Hans-Werner Küthen in "Probleme der Chronologie in der Skizzen und Autographen zu Beethovens Klavierkonzert Op. 19," in *Beethoven Jahrbuch*, Vol. 9, (1973/77), Beethoven-Haus, Bonn, pp. 263-292.]

15 Piano Concerto in D major, fragment from the year 1815. This consists of a substantial number of score pages, some completely worked out and some only sketchy, which definitely should be put in order and included in the GA. The autograph is in Berlin, Artaria 184, 60 pages. [TN: a performance edition of the first movement was done by Prof. Nicholas Cook and Kelina Kwan in cooperation with the Deutsche Staatsbibliothek, Berlin, and is based on the autograph

Artaria 184. Cook writes, "Beethoven made about 70 pages of sketches for the first movement and started writing out a full score; this runs almost uninterrupted from the beginning of the movement to the middle of the solo exposition, although the scoring becomes patchy as the work proceeds and there are signs of indecision or dissatisfaction on the composer's part. This torso of a movement represents one of the most substantial of Beethoven's unrealized compositions." There is also an extensive discussion of this piece by Lewis Lockwood in "Beethoven's Unfinished Concerto of 1815: Sources and Problems" in *The Creative World of Beethoven*, edited by Paul Henry Lang, W. W. Norton, New York 1971, pp. 122-44, including the comment that, since it is so fragmentary, it does not appropriately belong in this [Hess's] catalog. Sketches for this concerto are found in several sketchbooks and miscellanies. More information can be found from Nicholas Cook in "Beethoven's Unfinished Piano Concerto: a Case of Double Vision?," *Journal of the American Musicological Society*, Vol. 42, (1989), pp. 338-374. See also the response by Lewis Lockwood in the same Journal, Vol. 43 (1990). Another article by Cook appeared as "A performing edition of Beethoven's Sixth Fortepiano Concerto?," *The Beethoven Newsletter*, Vol. 8, No. 3-Vol. 9, No. 1, San Jose State University and the American Beethoven Society, San Jose, California, 1994, pp. 71-80.]

16 Original beginning [of the] Choral Fantasy, Op. 80. At the first performance on 22 December 1808, the work did not yet have the introduction for solo piano that we know today; the latter originated in the second half of the year 1809. See Nottebohm II, p. 272 and Thayer III, p. 109. During the printing of this catalog, Fritz Kaiser (of Darmstadt) brought the following facts to my attention: in Beethoven's own handwriting [there] exist three string parts (violin I, viola and bass). They

are mentioned in Kinsky/Halm [p. 213], and are today located in the Hessian Landesbibliothek, Darmstadt; [they were] formerly in the archive of Breitkopf & Härtel. They are, in reality and truth, parts to a forgotten orchestral prelude of the work, which is now, as is well known, for piano alone. Justifiably, Kaiser now poses these questions: "Did Beethoven, at first, plan an orchestral prelude (whether with, or without, piano)? Was this orchestration not ready at the time and was a prelude improvised for piano alone which has eventually remained?" The heading "finale" at the first entrance of the orchestra also appears to suggest that the previous part was conceived as a full movement for orchestra.

In this context, Kaiser points out two more sources for further investigation:

1. A handwritten score of the complete work in the Stadt - und Universitätsbibliothek, Frankfurt am Main, which is possibly the earliest score of all.
2. A handwritten piano transcription with additions in Beethoven's own handwriting, which was recently auctioned at a Stargardt-Auktion in Marburg-Lahn [Catalog 532, May 1957, Lot 265.] It came from a private Swiss collection [Sammlung Viardot] and was acquired for the Beethoven-Archiv, Bonn. [TN: cataloged as SBH 721.]

In addition to the above-mentioned parts, we should also note that a facsimile of the violin part of this work appears in Wolfgang Schmieder's *Musikerhandschriften in drei Jahrhunderten*, Breitkopf & Härtel, Leipzig 1939, p. 20. Concerning it, Schmieder remarks on page 60: "The sheet of music reproduced is a violin part to the introduction of the Choral Fantasy, Op. 80. In this respect it is of particular interest, since the first edition of this work, which originated under Beethoven's supervision, is for piano alone, without any accompaniment. The violin part follows the piano accompaniment very precisely." [TN: this was published by Hess in the SBG, Vol. X, 1967, p. 75, where, according to Mark Zimmer, "This orchestral score essentially doubles the extant piano introduction for much of its duration." Another edition with a foreword and revisions, which included the string parts, appeared from Edition Eulenburg, London-Zürich-New York 1966.]

Chamber Music for Wind Instruments

17 Allegro and Minuet in G major for two flutes. Composed by
   Beethoven on 23 August 1792, for his friend [J. M.]
   Degenhart. The autograph is in Berlin (Artaria 135).
   The first edition was in Thayer I (the 2nd edition,
   1901); the performance edition in parts was published
   in 1902 by A. G. Kurth through Breitkopf & Härtel.
   Another edition was published by Zimmermann in
   Leipzig. [TN: no edition by Zimmermann in Leipzig
   could be located, but one edited by Kurt Walther was
   published by Zimmermann, Frankfurt, c.1933. This
   work is listed in Kinsky/Halm as WoO 26 on p. 465.
   Kinsky/Halm suggests that the initials stand for
   "Johann Michael" and that he was a law student in
   1787, while Max Braubach gives the name as "Johann
   Martin" in *Die Stambücher Beethovens und der
   Babette Koch*, Beethoven-Haus, Bonn 1995, p. 141.
   There is an inscription at the top of the autograph that
   reads "für Freund Degenharth von L. v. Beethoven. /
   1792 / d 23 n / august / Abends 12." The day and time
   may be in Degenhart's hand. Beethoven appears to
   have misspelled his friend's name and it occasionally
   appears in the Beethoven literature as "Degenhardt."
   Also interesting to note is that because of the date, this
   piece could be Beethoven's last composition written
   while still in Bonn. This was published by Hess in the
   SBG, Vol. VII, 1963, p. 7.]

18 Variations on Mozart's "La ci darem" for two oboes and
   English horn. Composed about 1795-6. The first edi-
   tion was edited by Fritz Stein through Breitkopf &
   Härtel, Leipzig 1914. The autograph is in Berlin
   (Artaria 149). [TN: this work is listed in Kinsky/Halm

as WoO 28 on p. 467. This was published by Hess in the SBG, Vol. VII, 1963, p. 11.]

19 Quintet for oboe, three horns and bassoon in E-flat major [SV 8]. This survives only as a fragment; pages are missing at the beginning and end. This work is apparently identical to Thayer's No. 282, which is listed as an "incomplete sextet for oboe, clarinet, three horns and bassoon" from the former Artaria Collection. Actually, the autograph score (Artaria 185, formerly in Berlin, and missing today) contains the space for an (unwritten) part in B-flat for clarinet. Time, key signature, everything is stated, but not a single note is present. The first performance was given in 1862 with completions by [Leopold Alexander] Zellner; the first edition with these completions was published by W. Hess through B. Schott's Söhne, Mainz 1954. After completion of this first edition, I still found another version in the archive of the Gesellschaft der Musikfreunde, Vienna, two scores and parts for a movement under the title "Serenade" (Signatur VIII 49858, in copy, not in autograph). [TN: C/C, p. 227, gives this information: "The first movement (4/4; beginning is missing) – Adagio mesto (2/4) – Menuetto Allegretto (3rd movement, incomplete); 1793?" Published again by Hess in the SBG, Vol. VII, 1963, p. 24.]

20 Eleven Viennese dances for seven or eight wind instruments. Composed in the summer of 1819. The autograph is missing. Transcription-like parts were found by Hugo Riemann in the Archive of the Thomasschule, Leipzig. The first edition was by Riemann in 1907 through Breitkopf & Härtel. See the reference in Thayer IV, pp. V-VIII; and Riemann's study, "Beethovens Mödlingertänze vom Jahre 1819," in the magazine, *Zeitschrift der Internationalen Musikgesellschaft*, Vol. IX, November 1907, pp. 53-65. [TN: this work is listed as WoO 17 in Kinsky/Halm, p. 453,

where it is given as being for seven instruments and with the title, "Mödlinger Tänze." They were published by Hess in the SBG, Vol. VII, 1963, p. 34. In C/C, p. 224, Barry Cooper has the following interesting comments: "Spurious. According to the extremely unreliable [Anton] Schindler, Beethoven wrote a set of waltzes for a local band at an inn near Mödling during the summer of 1819. In 1905, Hugo Riemann found in Leipzig a set of parts for eleven dances and concluded that, as they were well written, they must be those referred to by [Anton] Schindler. Since the set shows several differences from genuine Beethoven sets of dances (for example, in having a much less satisfactory key sequence), it can be dismissed on both internal and external grounds." Hess seems to have generally agreed with Riemann that these are genuine. Recent scholarship has clearly moved away from this assumption and it would be better to consider this set of dances as more appropriately belonging in the section titled "Doubtful and Falsely Attributed Works."]

21 Fragment of an arrangement for 9-10 instruments of the "Andante con Variazioni" from the Septet [Op. 20]. Artur Holde reports on such an attempt by Beethoven in the *Österreichische Musikzeitschrift*, 1952, pp. 303-304. The eight pages were given to Napoleon III by Prince Metternich, and from there they were acquired by Charles F. Tretbar and then came into the possession of Henry Ford. From there, these pages came on the market anew from his estate. Where they are now, Holde is not able to say. [TN: these pages have found their way into the collection of the Beethoven-Haus, Bonn.] This piece is discussed by Artur Holde in "Beethoven-Handschriften in Amerika," *Österreichische Musikzeitschrift*, 1952, pp. 301-304. The American Beethoven scholar, Donald W. MacArdle, writes the following information to me concerning this interesting fragment:

"I am informed that it was sold by the Ford Estate through the Parke-Bernet Galleries (probably America's leading auctioneer of *objets d'art*) on 13 May 1952. The catalog description was: BEETHOVEN, LUDWIG van: Manuscript Musical Score in two fragments. The first is signed: 'v. Beethoven'. 16 pp., oblong small folio. In a leather folder. - This has been attested by several important foreign musical authorities to be beyond a doubt in the early handwriting of Ludwig van Beethoven. The first leaf is unnumbered, the others are numbered '6, 7, 8, 9, 10, 11 and 12'. The first leaf, which is the first fragment, is entitled 'Andante con Variazioni', and constitutes the beginning of his popular Septet opus 20. This leaf is arranged for nine instruments. The seven leaves of the second fragment form the finale of the same work, scored for ten instruments. This group, then, is not one arrangement but two attempts. It is interesting to note that the long cadenza in the Finale, given to the violin in the original Septet, is given in this arrangement to the clarinet. Beethoven wrote the Septet when he was only thirty years old, and these arrangements were evidently made soon after."

[TN: much of this information is challenged by Myron Schwager in "Beethoven's Septet, Opus 20: An Arrangement for Military Band," in *The Creative World of Beethoven*, edited by Paul Henry Lang, W. W. Norton, New York 1971, pp. 225-239. Schwager gives a rather extensive history and analysis of the work; however, the most pertinent comments that concern this catalog entry are, "Based on erroneous information given by MacArdle . . . the assumption is made that these are 'two attempts.' Since each of the fragments contains parts for eleven separate instruments, however, it is probable that they belong to a single arrangement; it is unknown whether a completed one ever existed. The error in determining the number of instruments appears to have been made in counting the staves, rather than the parts. In the variation movement, the horns occupy a single stave as do the bassoons. In the finale, only the horns share a single stave." Schwager also doubts the authenticity of this arrangement based on a detailed analysis of the handwriting. Schwager's article also appeared in the *Musical Quarterly*, Vol. 56, 1970, pp. 727-741.]

Chamber Music for String Instruments

22 Duet (Sonata movement in E-flat major for viola and cello), titled "Duett mit 2 obligaten Augengläsern" (Duet with Two Obligatory Eyeglasses), composed in 1795. The autograph is in the Kafka Sketchbook in the British Museum (Add. Ms. 29801 ff. 135-137). [TN: now the BL. The Kafka Sketchbook has been edited by Joseph Kerman and published as *Autograph Miscellany, ca. 1786 to 1799*, British Museum, London 1970.] The first edition was by Fritz Stein through C. F. Peters, Leipzig 1912. [TN: this work is listed as WoO 32 in Kinsky/Halm, p. 472. A second edition of this, as well as editions of the two following pieces was published by Hess in the SBG, Vol. VI, 1963, p. 7. In that edition, all three entries, that is, 22-24, are grouped together and referenced to WoO 32, thus further reinforcing the belief that they are all intended to be movements of the same work and not three separate works.]

23 Minuet in E-flat major for the same instruments as above [viola and cello]. The autograph is in the same sketchbook (Folio 119). [TN: see the reference to the Kafka Sketchbook above.] The first edition was published by Karl Haas through Peters/Hinrichsen in London 1952. Haas suspects that this is a second movement to the "Augengläserduett." [TN: see the translator's note on number 22 above.]

24 Fragment of a slow movement, 23 bars, C major for the same instruments (viola and cello), autograph in the same sketchbook (Folio 137). The first edition was published by W. Hess in *Musica*, November 1953, in facsimile and in transcription. See also the reference in Willy Hess's [article,] "Beethovens Augengläserduett

- ein Torso?," in the same magazine, where the supposition is put forward that this C major fragment is the planned second movement and that the minuet is the third movement of the "Augengläser" duets. Also discussed is the possibility that Beethoven planned a finale to complete the work. [TN: see the translator's note on number 22 above.]

25 Early version of the String Trio Op. 3 in E-flat major. [TN: the surviving autograph dates from 1795; see D. Johnson, *Beethoven's Early Sketches in the 'Fischhof Miscellany' Berlin Autograph 28*, 2 Vols., Ann Arbor, 1980, pp. 138-40.] The autographs of the first five movements are missing, the one of the finale is in the collection of the Library of Congress, Washington. Unpublished. [TN: this was published by Hess in the SBG, Vol. VI, 1963, p. 18 where it is clearly listed by him as a "first version of the finale."] The same piece is mentioned by Carl Engel in "Beethoven's Opus 3 an envoi de Vienne?," *The Musical Quarterly*, Vol. XIII, No. 2, April 1927, pp. 261-279. That autograph includes ten pages and has the heading "Finale, Allegro." Four hundred fifty-nine bars, plus one bar deleted after both the 220th and the 397th. Engel has two pages of facsimiles shown between pp. 260-261. [TN: A. Willem Holsbergen writes, "It is questionable whether one can truly call this a 'first version of the finale.' The differences are so small, that it seems better to regard it as just a copy of the finale, which contains three variants (at bars 236/7, 309/310 and 362-369)." Cooper states that this "probably does not represent an early version of the finale;" see C/C p. 237. See also E. Platen's remarks in "Streichtrios und Streichduo," *Beethovens Sämtliche Werke*, VI/6, G. Henle, Munich 1965, p. vii.]

26 Six minuets for two violins and bass. Listed in Thayer as No. 293, [and] surviving in copies of the parts in Berlin

(Artaria 141). Kinsky, who published these works in 1933 through Schott in Mainz, states that these pieces had originated about 1795. [TN: this work is listed as WoO 9 in Kinsky/Halm, p. 441. See the article by Shin Augustinus Kojima, "Zweifelhafte Authentizität einiger Beethoven zugeschriebener Orchestrtänze," in *Bericht über den Internationalen Beethoven-Kongreß Berlin 1977*, VEB Deutscher Verlag für Musik, Leipzig 1978, pp. 308-11, where the authenticity of this set of dances is discussed. These were published in the SBG, Vol. VI, 1963, p. 42.]

27 Seven ländlerische Tänze (Ländler Dances) for the same instruments as above [i.e., two violins and bass]. Although existing only in Beethoven's piano setting (GA Series 18, No. 198) [WoO 11], no doubt can exist, however, that these pieces also were originally written for two violins and bass, and are related to GA Series 18, No. 197 [WoO 15 for solo flute] and Series 25 No. 291 [WoO 15 for two violins and bass]. - Whether Dr. Sonnleithner's supposition is correct that the 6 Minuets, GA Series 18, No. 194 [WoO 10] were also originally written for orchestra cannot be verified without additional findings. See also Kinsky/Halm under WoO 10. [TN: while Hess urges the reader to view the entry for WoO 10 for more information, these dances are actually listed as WoO 11 in Kinsky/Halm, p. 444. Thayer lists these unpretentious dances as being written 'before 1799.' Hess gives a fuller account of his reasons for believing that they were orchestral versions of these dances in an article in the *Schweitzerische Musikzeitung und Sängerblatt*, Vol. 70, 1930, p. 886. Sketches for dance No. 5 were auctioned by Stargardt in Marburg in February 1975, catalog 605, lot 660 with a facsimile. The sketch page is now in the Beethoven-Haus, Bonn cataloged as NE 96.]

28 A second trio for the Scherzo of Op. 9, No.1. [TN: Cooper states in C/C, p. 238, that this trio in A-flat major for the Scherzo, which dates from c.1797-8, may have been subsequently rejected from the autograph score. See also Douglas Johnson's *Beethoven's Early Sketches in the 'Fischhof Miscellany' Berlin Autograph 28*, 2 Vols., Ann Arbor 1980, pp. 327-8.] The autograph is in the Beethoven-Haus, Bonn. The first edition was by Arnold Schmitz in Volume 3 of the *Veröffentlichung des Beethoven-Hauses*, Beethoven-Haus, Bonn 1924. [TN: this was published by Hess in the SBG, Vol. VI, 1963, p. 48. This second trio is also discussed by Emil Platen in the forward of *Beethovens Sämtliche Werke*, Vol. VI, Pt. 6, Streichtrios und Streichduos, G. Henle, Munich 1965.]

29 Prelude and Fugue in E minor for two violins and cello. This piece originated about 1795, during the time of Beethoven's studies with [Johann Georg] Albrechtsberger. The autograph, including the sketches, is [the] property of the Gesellschaft der Musikfreunde in Vienna. Published for the first time in complete form based on the original autograph by W. Hess in *Nagels Musik-Archiv No. 188*, Nagels Verlag, Kassel 1955. For other incorrect and former editions, see entry 31 [of this catalog]. The first page of the work is printed in facsimile on p. 70 of Willy Hess's *Beethoven*, Büchergilde Gutenberg, Zurich 1956. [TN: this was published by Hess in the SBG, Vol. VI, 1963, p. 32. The Prelude to this piece is derived from the first of three *Nachahmungssätze* (imitation movements) that are discussed in entries 237 and 245. They were published in their piano form in SBG, Vol. VI, 1963, p. 32. The remaining two *Nachahmungssätze* were each used as the preludes to entries 30 and 31. The *Nachahmungssätze* exist as works for keyboard. They were transcribed by Beethoven for use with entries 29, 30 and 31.]

30 Prelude and Fugue for String Quartet in F major. See note on entry 29 above. The first edition is by Willy Hess in *Nagels Musik-Archiv No. 187*, Nagels Verlag, Kassel 1955. [TN: Cooper in C/C, p. 238, gives the composition date as 1794-5. This was published by Hess in the SBG, Vol. VI, 1963, p. 54.]

31 Prelude and fugue for String Quartet in C major. See note on the two previous entries. The first edition was published by Willy Hess in *Nagels Musik-Archiv No. 186*, Nagels Verlag, Kassel 1955. Earlier editions of these three works [are]: in Ignaz Ritter von Seyfried's work *Beethovens Studien*, Tobias Haslinger, Vienna, 1832; the F major prelude, pp. 172-181; the F major fugue, pp. 217-227; the E minor prelude, pp. 167-171; the E minor fugue, pp. 197-203; and the C major fugue, pp. 292-299. These editions should, however, be used with great caution, since Seyfried indiscriminately altered the musical text. - Gustav Nottebohm published in his book, *Beethovens Studien,* Leipzig-Winterthur, 1873, the E minor prelude, pp. 63-7; the F major fugue, pp. 132-141; and the C major fugue, pp. 158-166, following Beethoven's original text in almost all the variations and working stages. - In 1926 Alfred Pochon published through Carl Fischer in New York two performance editions, one titled "Three fugues" which unites the F major prelude, C major fugue and F major fugue into a cycle, while the other brings together as "Sonata a tre, in six movements," the last movements being the E minor prelude and fugue; all of these texts are corruptions after Seyfried. We will occupy ourselves again with this "Sonata a tre." [TN: it is listed again in this catalog under "Doubtful and Falsely Attributed Works," No. A 9.] - Concerning the exact composition details, I refer the reader to the *Revisionsberichte* (revision reports) of my editions mentioned earlier. The C major prelude appears there for the first time in print at all (see illustration page

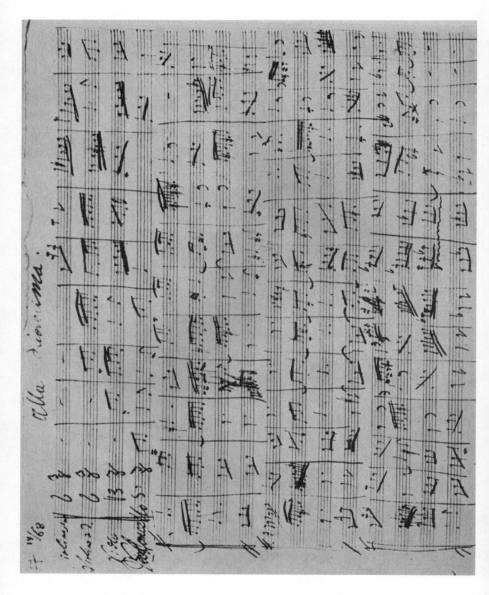

Hess 31, First page of the Nachahmungssätz (prelude to the figure) in C major for String Quartet, facsimile of the autograph.

26). [TN: this fugue is part of a set of fugues written for Johann Georg Albrechtsberger and is listed a second time in this catalog as entry 243, No. 3. See below. This was published by Hess in the SBG, Vol. VI, 1963, p. 66.]

32 First version of String Quartet Op.18, No. 1. [TN: dedicated to Karl Amenda.] Finished in May or June 1799, the autograph is in the Beethoven-Haus, Bonn [SBH 714]. An edition of the development part of the first movement was published by Carl Waack in "Beethovens F-dur Streichquartett op. 18, No. 1 in seiner ursprünglichen Fassung," in *Die Musik*, Vol. 2, March 1904, p. 418. A complete first edition was published by Joseph Wedig in the Veröffentlichungen des Beethoven-Haus, Vol. 2, Bonn 1922. [TN: this was published by Hess in the SBG, Vol. VI, 1963, p. 74, and in *Beethovens Sämtliche Werke*, Vol. VI, Pt. 3, Streichquartette I, G. Henle, Munich 1963, as Anhang 1 with a facsimile of the first page of the autograph. The autograph was purchased in 1913 through the auction house of Leo Liepmannssohn, from Anna Kawall of Riga, a descendant of Amenda; see catalog 43, p. 76. The title page of the first violin part was shown in the catalog. Various other pages were also shown in facsimile in R. Bory's *Ludwig van Beethoven*, Zurich 1960, p. 91; J. Schmidt-Görg and H. Schmidt, *Ludwig van Beethoven*, Braunschweig 1969, p. 94; H. C. Robbins Landon, *Beethoven*, Zurich 1970, p. 63. At least part of the autograph is in the hand of a copyist; see A. Tyson, "Notes on Five of Beethoven's Copyists," in the *Journal of the American Musicological Society*, Vol. XXIII, No. 3, 1970, p. 446.]

33 Minuet for String Quartet in A-flat major, 71 bars, unpublished. [TN: this piece, SV 214, which was written about 1790-2, was published in an article "Ein Menuett von L. van Beethoven für Streichquartett" in

the *Beethoven-Jahrbuch 1961/64*, Beethoven-Haus, Bonn 1966, pp. 85-6, with three pages of facsimiles edited by Paul Mies. The *Beethoven-Jahrbuch* edition also contained a set of the parts as loose sheets inserted in the rear of the book.] The autograph is in the Paris Conservatory, Beethoven Ms. 61. [TN: now the BN.] The piece is without a trio and it exists only as a first movement. [TN: this work also exists in a piano version which is listed in this catalog as entry 88. The normal structure for a minuet of this type is: Minuet, plus Trio, plus Minuet Da Capo. A. Willem Holsbergen writes, "There is in the Kafka sketchbook a Trio (for piano) which has been identified as belonging to Hess 88 (thus creating a complete piece). There doesn't seem to be a trio for the quartet version of this minuet, if one ever existed." This quartet movement was also published by Hess in the SBG, Vol. VI, 1963, p. 50.]

34 String Quartet in F major, [an arrangement of] the Piano Sonata, Op. 14, No. 1. This was written in 1801-2. [TN: this is dedicated to Baroness Josephine von Braun.] The original edition appeared in May 1802 in parts by the Kunst- und Industriekomptor, reprinted in 1802 by N. Simrock in Bonn; in 1815 by Riedl, Vienna; in 1822 by Steiner & Co., Vienna; and again in 1826 by Tobias Haslinger. A further reprint was organized by Gustav Nottebohm through N. Simrock in 1875. Newer editions, also London reprints, could be verified. [TN: Kinsky/Halm, p. 33, lists two London editions: one by Clementi & Co., 1807; and another by Clementi, Banger, Hyde, Collard & Davies in 1810.] Nevertheless, this highly interesting arrangement was not included in the GA with the string quartets! W. Altmann brought it out again in 1905 through Breitkopf & Härtel and in 1911 a pocket score of the same edition followed from Eulenburg. [TN: this was published by Hess in the SBG, Vol. VI, 1963, p. 121.] The same piece is mentioned by W. Altmann in "Ein vergessenes

Streichquartett Beethovens," (A Forgotten String Quartet by Beethoven), in *Die Musik*, Vol. 5, No. 4, November 1905, pp. 250-257 (with the printing of the finale in the quartet version and an inferior piano version). [TN: Michael Broyles, in an article in the *Journal of the American Musicological Society*, Vol. XXIII, No. 3, Fall 1970, beginning on p. 405, speculates that this version may have in fact been written, or at least sketched, before the piano version.]

35 String Quartet Arrangement of the B minor Fugue [No. 24] from Part One of Bach's *Well- tempered Clavier*. [This is] an unpublished fragment. The arrangement includes bars 1-20 and 28-32. The autograph (one sheet, inscribed on both sides) is the property of the Gesellschaft der Musikfreunde in Vienna. [TN: it is catalogued by them as A 81.] The composition dates from 1817. The same piece is discussed in this author's article "Eine Bach- und Händelbearbeitung Beethovens," *Schweizerische Musikzeitung*, Vol. 94, April 1954, pp. 142-143. I have included there all the deviations from Bach's musical text so that this arrangement is available to the public in a practical [form]. [TN: Richard Kramer gives the date for this as "before the end of 1802." See "Beethoven and Carl Heinrich Graun" in *Beethoven Studies*, edited by Alan Tyson, W. W. Norton, New York 1973, p. 20. However, in a footnote on the same page, Kramer speculates that it may be "late 1801" based on sketches that appear on the same sheet with the Bach piece. Curiously, while Hess mentions that he published a detailed description of this piece in Vol. 94 of the *Schweizerische Musikzeitung*, he fails to mention that he published an earlier article in the same publication that included a facsimile of this piece. See also, W. Hess's "Eine Bach-Bearbeitung Beethovens," *Schweizerische Musikzeitung*, Vol. 93, 1953, pp. 402-405.]

36 String Quartet Arrangement of the fugue from the Overture to Handel's "Solomon," 69 bars. It is unpublished.
   The autograph is in Berlin, Grasnik 13. [TN: Barry
   Cooper gives the composition date as c. 1798 in C/C,
   p. 275. This was published together with a facsimile in
   the *Österreichische Musik Zeitschrift,* Vol. 14, No. 12,
   December 1959. Another facsimile appears with the
   article "Eine Bach- und Händelbearbeitung
   Beethovens" in *Beethoven-Studien* by Willy Hess,
   Beethoven-Haus, Bonn, G. Henle, Munich-Duisburg
   1972 pp. 60-63.]

37 Mozart's Fugue, KV 426. Beethoven also wrote this out in
   score. See also the reference in Otto Jahn's *Mozart,*
   edited by Hermann Abert, Vol. 2, Breitkopf & Härtel
   Leipzig, (6th Edition, 1924), p. 158. Unpublished.
   Further details are not known to me. [TN: it is apparent that Hess took this entry from the Jahn-Abert reference completely on face value. A careful examination of the original manuscript (which is now divided
   between the Beethoven-Haus, Bonn and the Robert O.
   Lehman Collection in the Pierpont Morgan Library,
   New York) reveals that this is actually a copy by Beethoven of Mozart's original version for two pianos of
   the fugue (KV 426) which was later arranged for string
   orchestra (KV 546) by Mozart himself. There is a wide-
   spread notion that Mozart wrote KV 546 for string
   quartet rather than orchestra, but Mozart writes,
   "bassi" (i.e., plural), therefore indicating orchestra,
   not quartet. See Edition Eulenburg, No. 369, or A. Einstein's *Mozart, His Character, His Work*, Oxford University Press, Oxford and New York 1962, p. 273. What
   Hess has done is to place a Beethoven copy of a Mozart
   work for two pianos (KV 426) with the works for string
   quartet because he believed it to be KV 546, which is
   Mozart's version for strings. The manuscript has not
   been dated with any certainty, but it is possible that
   Beethoven studied this in preparation for writing Op.

134, which was originally a fugue for string quartet that he transcribed for piano four-hands. There are thirty-six minor deviations in the copy compared to Mozart's original, most of them mere slips of the pen; however, several could be considered "improvements" by Beethoven. This is not the only work by Mozart that Beethoven copied. There is another in the Pierpont Morgan Library that is a, "Fair copy of the last bars of the finale, probably copied in the 1790's" of Mozart's String Quartet in A major, KV 387. See *The Mary Flagler Cary Music Collection*, Pierpont Morgan Library, N. Y. 1970, p. 17. Richard Kramer states that "the copy of KV 387 can be dated 1799-1800." There are also portions of KV 387 in the Beethoven-Haus cataloged as NE 119. Beethoven also copied Mozart's Andante from KV 464. That autograph is now in the Stiftelsen Musikkulturens Främjande in Stockholm. See Richard Kramer's article " 'Das Organische der Fuge': On the Autograph of Beethoven's String Quartet in F Major, Opus 59, No. 1" in *The String Quartets of Haydn, Mozart and Beethoven: Studies of the Autograph Manuscripts*, Harvard University Press, Cambridge 1980, pp.230-1.]

38 String Quintet Arrangement (two violins, viola and two cellos) of Bach's B-flat minor Fugue, No. 22 from Book 1 of the *Well-tempered Clavier*. This work originated about 1801-2; the autograph is in Berlin, Grasnick 14. W. Hess has published a facsimile and critically examines the style in *Schweizerische Musikzeitung*, Vol. 93, October 1953, pp. 402-405. [TN: this arrangement of Bach's fugue appears to have been done for purposes of Beethoven's own studies. About the same time, Beethoven also made quartet arrangements of fugues by Handel. This was published by Hess in the SBG, Vol. VI, 1963, p. 143.]

39 String Quintet in F major. [This is] unpublished and missing. [TN: this is known only from posthumous writings.] A copy of this youthful work of Beethoven was
   sent in 1826 to Prince Galitzin. See the reference by
   Wilhelm von Lenz in *Beethoven [Eine Kunststudie]*,
   Vol. 5, [Ernst Balde,] Hamburg 1860, p. 341. [TN: see
   also Martin Staehelin "Another Approach to Beethoven's Last String Quartet Oeuvre: The Unfinished
   String Quintet of 1826/27," in *String Quartets of
   Haydn, Mozart and Beethoven: Studies of the Autograph Manuscripts*, Harvard University Press, Cambridge 1980, pp. 304-311.]

40 String Quintet Movement [two violins, two violas and
   cello] in D minor. Composed in 1817 as a prelude to a
   fugue (which Beethoven didn't complete). The autograph (Artaria 185a) used to be in Berlin and has been
   missing since the [Second World] War. The first edition was published by W. Hess in *Schweizerische
   Musikzeitung*, Vol. 95, October 1955, pp. 424-7. [TN:
   there are apparently three sources for this work. The
   first is Artaria 185a, which is not lost, but still in
   Berlin. There was great confusion on the whereabouts
   of many things after the War and this was actually in
   East Berlin. Either Hess had no knowledge of what was
   in the East, or he was denied access to verify it. Now
   that the two Libraries (East and West) are merged, it
   is no longer "missing." It is cataloged as SV 9 and
   listed by Hans Schmidt in "Verzeichnis der Skizzen
   Beethovens" in *Beethoven-Jahrbuch VI*, Jahrgang
   1965/68, Beethoven-Haus, Bonn 1969, p.19. This is
   incorrectly listed in Dorfmüller as SV 8, p.394, but
   correctly listed as SV 9 on p. 41. Another autograph
   sketch-leaf fragment was acquired by the Beethoven-
   Haus in 1978, and is catalogued as NE 114. See *Beethoven Jahrbuch X*, Jahrgang 1978/1981, Beethoven-
   Haus, Bonn 1983, p. 330. Hess may have had no
   knowledge of this source, since it is only a fragment

and was in a private collection in Oslo, Norway before coming to the Beethoven-Haus. The third source is the Boldrini Sketchbook. The spelling is given in Hans Schmidt's list as "Poldrini" because Beethoven misspelled it. He cataloged it as SV 71; see *Beethoven-Jahrbuch VI*, p. 47. This sketchbook was part of the Artaria collection and was cataloged as No. 75 by Guido Adler in 1890. Hans Schmidt gives the location as Berlin, but says that it has been "missing since 1945." Hess may have confused this with Artaria 185a; we can't be sure. Compounding this confusing set of sources is the statement by Douglas Johnson that, "It must have left the (Artaria) collection sometime between 1890 and 1893, however, for it is missing from August Artaria's catalogue in the latter year, and it was not part of the Artaria collection that came to the Berlin Royal Library in 1901." Why Schmidt would state that the Boldrini Sketchbook had been in Berlin and was lost "since 1945" is a mystery, since it appears that Berlin never received it in 1901. See *Beethoven Sketchbooks: History, Reconstruction, Inventory*, University of California Press, Berkeley-Los Angeles 1985, pp. 347-50. According to C/C, p. 239, only the Prelude is complete and the Fugue breaks off after four bars. It is interesting to observe that although the contents of the Boldrini Sketchbook were described in some detail by Gustav Nottebohm, Hess makes no mention of it in this entry. He was very familiar with all of Nottebohm's writings. See Nottebohm II, pp. 157-63 and 349-55.This was published by Hess in the SBG, Vol. VI, 1963, p. 147.]

41 String Quintet in C major, fragment of a first movement. (Introduction "Andante maestoso," 26 bars) written in the autumn of 1826. The autograph is missing. [TN: an autograph sketch-leaf was acquired by the Beethoven-Haus, Bonn about 1976 and is catalogued as NE 101.] In 1838, Anton Diabelli published arrangements that

he did for piano two-hands and four-hands. A reprint was published by G. Lange in *Musikgeschichtliches*, Berlin 1900. Remarkably, this arrangement by another was also included in the Urtext edition of Beethoven's bagatelles by Otto von Irmer, G. Henle, Munich-Duisburg 1950. [TN: the correct title of Irmer's publication is *Klavierstücke*. The two-hand piano transcription is known as WoO 62 and, while not numbered separately, the four-hand version is mentioned under WoO 62 in Kinsky/Halm. The two-hand version appears in publications and other references as Beethoven's "Letzter musikalischer Gedanke" (Last Musical Thought), since it was probably the last piece he worked on before his final illness and death in March 1827. See Kinsky/Halm, p. 508. This entry by Hess is meant to be the original string quintet version, not either of the piano versions given in Kinsky/Halm. Hess published both the two- and four-hand versions in the SBG, Vol. VIII, 1964, p.144.]

42 Small Piece for two Violins, A major, 7 bars. Written on 29 April 1822, for the violinist Alexandre Boucher. The autograph is in the Paris Conservatory. [TN: now the BN, and was part of the Malherbe Collection.] The first printing was as a facsimile in *Revue internationale de musique,* from 1 March 1898, and printed in score in Frimmel's *Ludwig van Beethoven*, first edition, Berlin 1901, p. 65; and in the fourth edition, Berlin 1912, on p. 73. In the former editions of this catalog, [meaning Hess 2, or Hess 3] the piece was listed under the piano pieces because of the way it is written; however, it is probably for two violins since the recipient was a violinist. [TN: this piece is listed as WoO 34 in Kinsky/Halm, p. 475.] - In our time the small piece has recently been reprinted as No. 326 of the work *New Beethoven Letters* by Donald W. MacArdle and Ludwig Misch, University of Oklahoma Press, Norman, Oklahoma 1957, p. 383. See also the reference to MacArdle/Misch in entry 257.

Chamber Music with Piano

43 Sonata Movement in C major for Mandolin and Cembalo. Composed in 1796 in Prague. The autograph is in the Archiv Clam-Gallas in Friedland. The same is true for the two following pieces. The first edition was by A. Chitz in *Merker*, Vol. 3, Journal 12, June, 1912. See also A. Chitz' *Beethovens Kompositionen für Mandoline* [in the same publication as above], pp. 446-450. [TN: Hess separates this piece from entry 45 below. It is listed in Kinsky/Halm as WoO 44, p. 488, where this Sonata movement and the Theme with Variations are joined to form one work. The Sonata is given as a Sonatina in that listing.]

44 Adagio, ma non troppo for the same instruments [piano and mandolin]. According to a message from Fritz Kaiser, the first edition was published by O. Bahlmann through Schuberth, Leipzig 1938. A second edition was published by Karl Michael Komma as Vol. 2 of the series *Sudetendeutsches Musikarchiv*, Edmund Ullmann Verlag, Reichenberg 1940. The piece represents the final setting of GA Series 25, No. 296. [TN: Hess 44 is a slightly variant version of WoO 43b; see Kinsky/Halm, p. 487. More information is available on this and other mandolin pieces from Alexander Buchner in "Beethovens Kompositionen für Mandoline" in *Beethoven Jarhbuch III*, Jahrgang 1957/58, Beethoven-Haus, Bonn 1959, pp. 38-50.]

45 Andante con variazioni in D major for the same instruments [piano and mandolin]. The first edition was by K. M. Komma in *Sudetendeutsches Musikarchiv*, Vol. I, Edmund Ullmann Verlag, Reichenberg 1940. [TN:

this piece is listed in Kinsky/Halm as the second part of WoO 44, p. 488.]

Beethoven's complete mandolin pieces turned up published again by Erich Repke in the *Thüringischer Volksverlag,* Weimar 1952. Further, there are compositions for mandolin that are not listed here; they are said to have existed based on evidence from old archive catalogs that disappeared after the First World War; [this information is from] (a communication of the archivist Dr. Bergel to Dr. Komma).

46 Fragment of a Sonata for Piano and Violin, A major. This is unpublished. Only two sheets exist, apparently torn out of a larger collection. None of the movements is complete. [TN: a transcription (not a true completion) was published by Hess in the SBG, Vol. IX, 1965, p. 115.] Ludwig Schiedermair in *Der junge Beethoven*, p. 172, writes of it: "It is questionable whether the fragment of a sonata for piano and violin that survives in the Preußische Staatsbibliothek [TN: this is now the SBB.], originates from Beethoven's youth. An untitled fragment of a three-part movement from the Artaria Collection in Vienna, however, could be attributed to the youthful Beethoven based on the character of the handwriting." [TN: the quotation from Schiedermair needs clarification. The collection was assembled by Domenico Artaria, the Viennese publisher, mostly from purchases made at the sale of Beethoven's estate. This collection is now dispersed, with most of it eventually going to Berlin; some of it is lost and none of it remains in Vienna.] However, these two works are doubtless identical; the untitled three-part fragment, No. 131 of the former Artaria Collection, is the above fragment of a violin sonata. The description in Thayer I, p. 171, fits exactly. The autograph contains three pages and one line of musical text. The work is not listed in Thayer's *Chronologisches Verzeichniss,* and Nottebohm's supposition that the autograph has been

recorded under Thayer No. 29 as "Duo for the Musical Clock" is also incorrect. The "Spieluhr Duet" consists of two movements in C major, which are noted in the alto and tenor clefs. It carries the Artaria Number 186 and is also kept in Berlin today, in fact in Beethoven's autograph, whereas the above fragment represents a copy. [TN: Cooper in C/C, p. 230, gives the composition date as, "c.1790-2. Fragmentary: parts of a first movement (3/8) and a finale (4/4)." A true completion was executed by the Dutch composer and musicologist, Albert Willem Holsbergen in 1998. He gives a detailed analysis of the completion process on the Internet website at: <*www.unheardbeethoven.org*>.]

47 Trio for Piano, Violin and Cello after [the String Trio], Op. 3. This original arrangement breaks off after forty-three bars of the second movement. The first edition with a description was published by Wilhelm Altmann in the *Zeitschrift für Musikwissenschaft*, Vol. 3, December 1920, pp. 129-158. The autograph, formerly with Hans Prieger, [is] now in private hands in Frankfurt am Main. [TN: this autograph became the property of H. C. Bodmer who gave it to the Beethoven-Haus, Bonn in 1956 where it is catalogued as SBH 713. Mark Zimmer comments on this by saying, "Hess (in later writings) was able to date the work between 1800 and 1817. My inclination is to give the transcription an earlier date since it seems unlikely that Beethoven would revisit such an early work as late as 1817 without performing major surgery upon it." This was published by Hess in the SBG, Vol. IX, 1965, p. 51.]

48 Allegretto in E-flat major for piano, violin and cello. Probably from the earliest part of the Bonn period. The first edition was published by Jack Werner through Elkin & Co., London 1955. The autograph is in the British Museum in the "Kafka Miscellany" (unfortunately the editor gives no more information about its source).

[TN: now in the BL. Cooper in C/C, p. 230, gives its composition as c.1790-2; the autograph is together with a fragment of a trio section in folios 129r and 129v of the Kafka Sketchbook [SV 185]; see also Kerman's *Autograph Miscellany, ca. 1786 to 1799*, British Museum, London 1970, Vol. II, pp. 177-82, and 291. This Allegretto was published by Hess in the SBG, Vol. IX, 1963, p. 30.]

49/50 Two Piano Trios (E-flat and B-flat major). [Wilhelm von] Lenz in *Beethoven et ses trois styles,* Paris 1909, p. 450, [and in the] German edition, Hamburg, 1860, pp. 362-63, states that these two small trios were composed in 1786 and published by Dunst in Frankfurt. Ries is supposed to have attested to their authenticity. There has been no trace of these trios to this day; but W. W. Cobbett in his *Cyclopedic Survey of Chamber Music I*, London 1929, p. 85, also mentions two piano trios by Beethoven that are supposed to have existed before the Trios Op. 1. One is faced with a puzzle. [TN: it is apparent that Hess never saw a copy of any of the editions of these two trios. If he had, he would surely have realized that they are the same pieces that are listed as WoO 38 and WoO 39 in Kinsky/Halm, pp. 480-2, and that they were published in the Gesamtausgabe as No. 86 = Series 11, No. 8 and No. 85 = Series 11, No. 7. Dorfmüller, p. 361, confirms the correct identification of these two works. The puzzle is solved!]

Works for Piano, Two-Hands

51 Rondo in C major for piano, composed in 1783. The first edition was published anonymously in Bossler's *Blumenlese für Klavierliebhaber*, Speyer 1783. A newer publication was by Max Friedländer in *Jahrbuch der Musikbibliothek Peters,* Vol. 6, 1899. Friedländer has convincingly proven the genuineness of this piece. See Max Friedländer's *Ein unbekanntes Jugendwerk Beethovens*, loc. cit., p. 68 ff. A copy of the piece is found on pp. 70-75. Additional reprints appear in *Neue Musikzeitung,* Vol. 21, No. 13, Stuttgart-Leipzig 1900, and in G. Lange's *Musikgeschichtliches,* Berlin 1900. Furthermore, this work was included in this author's [W. Hess] collection *Leichte Klavierkompositionen Beethovens,* Musikverlag zum Pelikan, Zürich 1947, and also in Otto von Irmer's Urtext edition of the Beethoven bagatelles [TN: correct title *Klavierstücke*], G. Henle, Munich-Duisburg 1950. [TN: this piece is listed as WoO 48 in Kinsky/Halm, p. 495. Published by Hess in the SBG, Vol. IX, 1965, p.7.]

52 Piano Sonata in C major. Thayer mentions an unknown sonata under No. 286, which, according to the Gräffer-Katalog of Beethoven's works, should have appeared with Mollo in Vienna. Even the incipit is given. No trace has been located of this sonata; however, this would not be the first case of a published work which has remained untraceable. (See also entry Nos. 49, 50 and 55). [TN: since Hess wrote this book, all three of these entries have been located and identified, but entry No. 52 has still not been found.]

53 Sonata Movement and Allegretto in F major for [Franz Gerhard] Wegeler, from the Bonn period. A facsimile appeared in *Beethovens Briefe,* by L. Schmidt, Simrock, Berlin 1909. The autograph is in the collection of Julius Wegeler, Koblenz. [TN: the entire Wegeler collection is now in the Beethoven-Haus, Bonn. Another facsimile of the autograph of this piece together with *Kaplied,* entry 63, appeared in an exhibition catalog prepared by Michael Landenburger, *Aus der Samlung Wegeler*, Beethoven-Haus, Bonn 1998, pp. 16-17.] Wegeler's note, "Für mich von Beethoven geschrieben und bezeichnet." (For me by Beethoven written and marked.) This could also mean that it is a copy of the work of a third [person] prepared by Beethoven for Wegeler. However, Kinsky/Halm has expressed no misgivings and listed the piece as WoO 50. [TN: what Hess implies, but fails to make clear, is that since this Sonata precedes entry 63 of this catalog in the autograph manuscript and because that entry is a transcription with finger markings of a song by C. D. F. Schubart, then this Sonata may also be a transcription of a work by Schubart (or possibly someone else) transcribed and fingered by Beethoven.] A new edition of this bagatelle [Sonata Movement] was again published in the bagatelle collections of Hess and Irmer. See the reference under entry 51. [TN: this reference is to Hess's collection, *Leichte Klavierkompositionen Beethovens,* Musikverlag zum Pelikan, Zürich 1947, and to Otto von Irmer's Urtext edition, *Klavierstücke*, G. Henle, Munich-Duisburg 1950.]

54 Variations on a Theme, "Freudvoll und leidvoll" by [Karl] Amenda. If these variations were composed at all, they have vanished without a trace. See also Thayer II, p. 119.

55 Variations on *Venni amore* (Righini), first version. These variations appeared with Götz in Mannheim in 1791,

and were dedicated to the Countess Hatzfeld. This first version of the work is said to be different in its essentials from the latter one that came out in 1801 [or 1802] through Traeg; however, no copy has been found. [TN: this piece is listed as WoO 65 in Kinsky/Halm, p. 513; however, the assignment of a separate catalog entry should be eliminated. These are basically identical works, not first and second versions. Cooper writes: "For many years, no copies of the original 1791 edition of this work were known, and the earliest source was an edition of 1802; it was generally believed that Beethoven must have revised the work that year, on the grounds that he could not have written such an advanced work as early as 1791. When the original edition was rediscovered it proved everybody wrong, for it showed that no changes were made in the second edition, and that Beethoven had developed his compositional style much earlier than previously imagined." See the program notes for the Deutsche Grammophon's *Complete Beethoven Edition*, Vol. 6, p. 31. Also note that Kinsky/Halm gives the publication date of WoO 65 (Hess 55) as 1802, not 1801, which Hess probably took from Nottebohm, who gives it as 1801. Based on information from Thayer, it was believed that the lost 1791 edition was published by Götz in Mannheim; however when the 1791 edition was discovered, it turned out to be published by Schott in Mainz. The 1791 edition was discovered in the Music Collection of the Gemeente Museum in s'Gravenhage, the Netherlands, by Clemens von Gleich, who was Curator. In a letter to me Dr. von Gleich tells that the edition is now "housed in Nederlands Musiek Instituut, Den Haag" and that it is still the only known copy of this edition.]

56 Bagatelle in G minor, 13 bars. According to a verbal message from Dr. Hans Halm, this piece is identical with the one that, according to Albert Leitzmann in

Beethovens Persönlichkeit, Insel Verlag, Leipzig 1914, p. 354 and in footnotes on p. 352 and p. 427, was written in October 1825 for a Lady Clifford. In actual truth, however, it was composed for Sarah Burney Payne on 27 September 1825. The present owner of the autograph [is] Louis Krasner (1904-1995), Syracuse, New York, USA. [TN: according to information given to me by Douglas Johnson, sometime in the late 1970s Krasner decided to have protective covers custom made for this piece and for several other autographs (not by Beethoven) that he owned. Accordingly, they were sent to a book binder or restorer, who after opening the package removed the other autographs but overlooked the Beethoven, and discarded the box, packing materials and the Beethoven autograph. Johnson served as an expert witness in the lawsuit that resulted from this careless error. The Beethoven autograph has never been recovered.] The first edition was published by Ludwig Misch in *Neue Zeitschrift für Musik*, Vol. 117, April 1956, pp. 196-7. A facsimile was published beside p. 440, as an addition to letter 427, by MacArdle/Misch, *New Beethoven Letters*, University of Oklahoma Press, Norman 1957, also referred to in entry No. 257 of this catalog. [TN: this is listed as WoO 61a in Kinsky/Halm, p. 507. Also published by Hess in the SBG, Vol. IX, 1965, p. 29.]

57 Sketches for a Bagatelle in C major. These sketches [SV 280] are nearly performance ready, also see below. Presented in Nottebohm II, p. 208, [this is] found with the sketches for Op. 126. [TN: the autograph is in the Gesellschaft der Musikfreunde in Vienna, A 50. Since these sketches are found between sketches for the Six Bagatelles for Piano, Op. 126, they may be dated May/June 1824. See Jos van der Zanden's "Beethovens Bagatellen Op. 126: Bemerkungen zu iher Entstehung," *Die Musikforschung,* Vol. 39, No. 1, Jan.-

March 1986, pp. 13-17. This piece was published by Hess in the SBG, Vol. IX, 1965, p. 29.]

58 Piano Etude in B-flat major, composed about 1800, and it is performance ready. Printed in Nottebohm II, pp. 361-2. [TN: found among sketches for larger works but probably not intended for publication. This piece and the one below were transcribed selectively in the writings of Nottebohm and many were published by Joseph Kerman in *Autograph Miscellany, ca. 1786 to 1799*, British Museum, London 1970, 2 Vols., which gives their composition dates as c.1790-8. Found on pp. 153v and 153r in the autograph and p. 165, Vol. 2 in the transcription. This was published by Hess in the SBG, Vol. IX, 1965, p. 13. A. Willem Holsbergen, who has examined the original sketch sources for this piece, says that there are more sketches than Hess was aware of and that it continues beyond his ending point. It appears more likely that this is a theme with variations rather than a single etude.]

59 Piano Etude in C major, composed about 1800, and it is performance ready. Printed in Nottebohm II pp. 361-2. See note on entry 58 above. [TN: this was published by Hess in the SBG, Vol. IX, 1965, p. 13.]

60 A performance-ready sketch for piano in A major. See the following number! [TN: concerning this and other small piano pieces, Mark Zimmer writes, "The Allemande for Piano, WoO 81, as well as Hess 60, Hess 61 and Biamonti Nos. 268-284 are all found on two sketch sheets kept in the Beethoven-Archiv in Bonn, SBH 631 (SV 88). The quantity of diverse material that can be crowded in such a small space is truly remarkable!"]

61 Anglaise [for piano] in D major. This and the previous piece (both originated about 1800) are in an autograph

[TN: this piece has several catalog numbers. It is BH 114 from an old catalog and SBH 631from a newer one. It is also SV 88.] in the Beethoven-Haus and were printed for the first time by Arnold Schmitz [in *Beethoven. Unbekannte Skizzen und Entwürfe. Untersuchung, Übertragung, Faksimile*], Volume 3 of the Veröffentlichungen des Beethoven-Haus, Bonn 1924, as drafts II and XXI. [TN: this and the previous piece may have been written as early as 1793. This was published by Hess in the SBG, Vol. IX, 1965, p. 23.]

62 Allegretto in B minor. Composed on 18 February 1821 for F. Piringer. About 1905, the autograph was the property of the Oberrechnungsrat (Chief Financial Counselor) Victor V. Marquet in Vienna. Where is the piece today? [TN: we still don't know the present whereabouts of this piece, but it was auctioned in March 1988 by the German auction house J. A. Stargardt; see Catalog 641, p. 325 for the listing and p. 327 for a facsimile.] The first edition was in Adolf Robitschek's *Deutsche Kunst- und Musikzeitung* from 15 March 1893 through Frimmel. The first page was printed in facsimile in the biography by Frimmel [titled] *Beethoven*, 3rd edition, 1908, p. 66, or 4th edition, p. 68. Reprinted by Willy Hess in *Schweizerische Musikpädagogische Blätter,* No. 23, 1930, and [again by Hess in "Ist die Gesamtausgabe von Beethovens Werken Volständig?"], in *Die Musik*, Vol. 33, No. 1, December 1940, p. 81. The piece was also included in the bagatelle collections of Hess and Irmer mentioned under entry No. 51. [TN: this reference is to Hess's collection *Leichte Klavierkompositionen Beethovens,* Musikverlag zum Pelikan, Zürich 1947, and to Otto von Irmer's Urtext edition *Klavierstücke*, G. Henle, Munich-Duisburg 1950. This is listed as WoO 61 in Kinsky/Halm, p. 507.]

63 Piano setting of Christian Friedrich Daniel Schubart's *Kaplied* (Cape Song). As far as the manuscript, origination and first edition are concerned, the same information is true as that given for No. 53. [TN: what Hess means is that both this entry and entry 53 (WoO 50) are found in the same manuscript, with entry 53 preceding this one in that manuscript. Entry 53 also has finger markings by Beethoven.] No editions are known, however. Publication in a future GA would be worthwhile, however, be it only for the sake of the finger markings that are directly from Beethoven. This piece [is important because it] also represents an arrangement from Beethoven's pen. [TN: this was published by Hess in the SBG, Vol. IX, 1965, p. 11. A facsimile of the autograph of *Kaplied* and of entry 53 appeared in an exhibition catalog prepared by Michael Landenburger, *Aus der Samlung Wegeler*, Beethoven-Haus, Bonn 1998, pp. 16-17. The autograph of this piece, which was once owned by Franz Gerhard Wegeler, is now in the Beethoven-Haus, Bonn.]

64 Three-part Fugue in C major. Composed about 1794. The autograph is in the British Museum, Add. Ms. 29801, folio 158. [TN: now in the BL.] Described and published by A. E. F. Dickinson in *The Musical Times*, February 1955, pp. 76 to 79, and in an addendum in the June issue, p. 320. Also printed by the same author as a supplement to *Musik im Unterricht* as "Eine vergessene Fuge Beethovens," November 1955, p. 339. [TN: this was published by Hess in the SBG, Vol. IX, 1965, p. 15.]

65 Small Concerto Finale in C major. Composed in 1820 [as a piano arrangement of] the closing stretta of the C minor [Piano] Concerto [Op. 37]. [It was done] for the third volume of F. Starke's *Wiener Piano-Forte-Schule*, printed in the third part as No. 24, p. 62, Vienna 1821. Reprinted by Th. Frimmel in *Der Merker*, Vol. VIII, 1

January 1917, pp. 24-26. Another edition appeared in Hess III, in the annual *Santa Cecilia 1951/2* (printed 1953), pp. 318-9, and in a separate printing on pp. 20-21. [TN: this was published by Hess in the SBG, Vol. IX, 1965, p. 27.]

66 Second version of the Allegretto in C minor, GA Series 25, No. 299, 164 bars. [TN: the first setting is listed as WoO 53 in Kinsky/Halm, p. 499.] It is unpublished and the autograph is in Berlin, Grasnick 25. [TN: this was published by Hess in the SBG, Vol. IX, 1965, p. 17. According to A. Willem Holsbergen: "The main differences with WoO 53 are in the second phrase of the trio and in the coda. In bar 26 a D-natural indicates a deliberate clash between E-flat and D; however, the D-natural is more likely a mistake and should be a D-flat as in the equivalent bar after the trio (bar 116)."

67 Virtually playable drafts of two German Dances, in F major and F minor, each about 16 bars. Unpublished. The autographs are in the Bodmer Collection, Zurich. [TN: the Bodmer Collection is now in the Beethoven-Haus, Bonn. These two dances are catalogued as SBH 639 (SV 106) and listed as "2 Tänze." This was published by Hess in the SBG, Vol. IX, 1965, p. 26. According to A. Willem Holsbergen: "These two German dances, Hess 67, date from about 1811-12. The indication 'Nr. 1 D.C.' at the end of the one in F minor makes it clear that these two dances belong together, the second one functioning as a trio."]

68 Little Waltz (German Dance) in C minor, 16 bars. Unpublished. This work was composed about March 1803. The autograph (Mh 71) is in the Bodmer Collection. [TN: the Bodmer Collection is now in the Beethoven-Haus, Bonn and this autograph has been renumbered SBH 637 and SV 118. This was published by Hess in the SBG, Vol. IX, 1965, p. 24.]

69 Allegretto in C minor [for piano]. The unpublished autograph (Beethoven Ms. 82) is in the Paris Conservatory.
[TN: now the BN.] This is a fragment [SV 234] existing
as a beginning of seventy-three bars and an ending of
nineteen bars. It was composed about 1797. [TN: according to Cooper in C/C, p. 247, "This piece was written c.1795-6, revised in 1822; and perhaps originally
intended for the Piano Sonata Op. 10, No. 1." According to Jos van der Zanden, "The classification of this
piece as a *bagatelle* is justified by the indication '*Nr.9*'
in the manuscript, presumably written by Beethoven
in 1822." See van der Zanden's program notes to *Beethoven: Sketchbook Miscellany, Contrapuntal Studies
& Fugues*, an LP album produced by Raptus Records,
Amsterdam 1986, and his expanded article on this
piece "Ein weiteres 'Ingharese' von Beethovens?" in
Bonner Beethoven-Studien, Vol. 1, Beethoven-Haus,
Bonn 1999, pp. 112-130. This article includes facsimiles of the four autograph pages and a transcription.
This piece was published by Hess in the SBG, Vol. IX,
1965, p. 19.]

In his book *Ein Skizzenbuch von Beethoven aus dem
Jahre 1803*, Breitkopf & Härtel, Leipzig 1880, Nottebohm
mentions the following piano pieces (until now unpublished):
[TN: these pieces are taken from a Sketchbook known as
Landsberg 6. Johnson, Tyson and Winter give this information
in *The Beethoven Sketchbooks: History, Reconstruction, Inventory*, University of California Press, Berkeley 1985, p. 137:
"Landsberg 6, the so-called *Eroica* sketchbook, was formerly
in the Preußische Staatsbibliothek in Berlin but could not be
traced at the end of World War II. Long believed to be in Poland, it was located, after more than thirty years, in the
Biblioteka Jagiellońska in Cracow, Poland, where it remains at
this time (1984)." It is still there today (2003).]

70 The beginning of an Adagio (page 116 of the sketchbook).
[TN: Mark Zimmer has supplied me with the following

information on this entry: "Marked 'Adagio ma non molto' and 'piano' is written beneath the first notes. It appears on the same page as sketches for 'Vestas Feuer,' Hess 115, and a version of Gellert's 'Vom Tode,' which is very different from that which became Op. 48, No.3. This is a fragment of seven bars, in the key of G major. This Adagio quickly moves through several keys before resolving at G major and thus seems to sound more like a transition, rather than a 'beginning' as Nottebohm describes it. Unpublished as of this date (2001). This fragment hardly warrants an entry as a "composition," any more than do the many other such fragments to be found scattered liberally throughout the sketchbooks." Entries such as this one and several others that are so very fragmentary make one wonder if Hess ever really examined them, or simply listed them because they were cited by a reliable authority like Nottebohm.]

71 Unknown piano piece (page 117). [TN: Mark Zimmer has supplied me with the following information on this entry: "This fragment consists of 11 bars in the key of G. It appears to be an introduction which breaks off almost immediately after restless, chromatic 16th notes are introduced. As in the case with entry 70 (above), this piece is too fragmentary to be considered a composition or to warrant being given a catalog number. It is marked 'Molto adagio' and is written in cut time. It consists of a four-bar figure which is repeated, then three bars which begin with a repeat sign but the phrase is incomplete. At the end, Beethoven marks both the treble and bass staves with a circle with an X through it, indicating that the sketch is continued elsewhere, but no obvious continuation has yet been discovered. Hess 71 is found on a page with sketches denoted 'Sonata con violoncello' and marked 'Adagio,' but Hess 71 appears to have been written at a different time than the cello sonata sketches."]

72 Theme with the beginning of a Variation [for Piano], (p. 159). [TN: this piece dates from 1803. It was published by Hess in the SBG, Vol. IX, 1965, p. 24, and again by Jos van der Zanden in *12 Piano Miniatures from the Sketchbooks*, Raptus Editions, Amsterdam 2000.]

Two additional piano pieces are found in *Sketchbook F 91* [Landsberg 7] of the former Preußische Staatsbibliothek, Berlin [TN: now the SBB], prepared by Lothar Mikulicz [in *Ein Notierungsbuch von Beethoven*] and published by Breitkopf & Härtel in 1927 [reprinted by G. Olms, Hildesheim-New York 1972]:

73 Melody [for Piano] in C major, 16 bars [SV 61], nearly performance-ready (in the sketchbook on p. 63, and in transcription on p. 59). [TN: written about 1800, this was published by Hess in the SBG, Vol. IX, 1965, p. 22.]

74 Allegro [for Piano] in E-flat major, 12 bars [SV 61] (in the sketchbook on p. 66, and in transcription on p. 62). [TN: written about 1800, this was published by Hess in the SBG, Vol. IX, 1965, p. 22.]

75 Theme for Archduke Rudolph (on the words, *O Hoffnung, du stählst die Herzen, du milderst die Schmerzen*). G major, 4 bars. The autograph (one loose single page) is in the Deutsche Staatsbibliothek, Berlin [TN: now in the SBB]. The autograph of the variations by the Archduke is the property of the Prince Archbishop's Library at Kremsier. The theme was composed in the spring of 1818. In 1819 it appeared with forty variations by the Archduke through Steiner & Co., Vienna. [TN: according to Thayer and others, this theme comes from Christoph August Tiedge's *Urania*. See Thayer No. 216. Hans Volkmann believes this comes from Beethoven himself in his "doloribus" (sadness). See Volkmann's *Beethoven in seinen Beziehungen zu*

Dresden, Deutscher Literature-Verlag, Dresden 1942, p. 236. Susan Kagan writes, "The similarity in titles undoubtedly accounts for the confusion, but since the text of 'O Hoffnung' is not to be found in Tiedge's collection, and its origin is uncertain, there is the strong possibility that Beethoven himself wrote the words." See *Archduke Rudolph, Beethoven's Patron, Pupil, and Friend*, Pendragon Press, Stuyvesant, New York 1988, p. 71. A facsimile of the autograph by Beethoven appears on p. 70 of the same edition. This piece is listed as WoO 200 in Kinsky/Halm, p. 200.]

Cadenzas for the Piano Concertos

76 Draft of an unknown cadenza to the C major Concerto [Op. 15]. The autograph [SV 31] is p. 30 of the Berlin Beethoven Autograph 28 (now [in the] Universitätsbibliothek, Tübingen). [TN: this autograph has now been returned to the SBB and is no longer in Tübingen.] See also Nottebohm II, where on p. 67, an excerpt of it is printed. I have to thank Mr. Fritz Kaiser (Darmstadt) for a copy of the whole sketch. [TN: this sketch or continuity draft, which dates from the 1790s, is found in what is now known as the "Fischhof Miscellany." It was transcribed and published by Douglas Johnson in *Beethoven's Early Sketches in the 'Fischhof Miscellany,'* 2 Vols., Ann Arbor, Michigan 1980.]

77/78 Two cadenzas for the C major Concerto [Op. 15] (one for the first and one for the second movement). According to Kalischer, they were composed for Anna Fröhlich (see the footnote on p. 66 of the new edition, 1907, of *Aus dem Schwarzspanierhaus*). [TN: this edition was reprinted in 1970 by Olms, Hildesheim. An edition was published in English by Maynard Solomon under the title *Memories of Beethoven*, Cambridge University Press 1992, in which he chose to omit the footnote by Kalischer.] It is obvious that these two cadenzas can't be the same as those that were printed in the GA, because all three of those are meant for the first movement. Possibly the above mentioned sketch [entry 76] is a sketch to the first of these two cadenzas? Furthermore, another cadenza must have existed, since Beethoven wouldn't have been able to play one of the known ones at performances prior to 1804 because of the smaller range of the pianos at that time. However, it is possible that Beethoven never even wrote down those first cadenzas, but freely improvised them. [TN: Hess does not give the source for these sketches for the cadenzas but it does seem that they are in found in two sources. First, from the Kafka Miscellany transcribed by Joseph Kerman in *Autograph Miscellany from the Kafka Sketchbook ca. 1786 to 1799*, British Museum, London 1970, pp. 72 and 138, and second, from the Grasnick Sketchbook I, p. 2, transcribed by Erna Szabo in *Ein Skizzenbuch Beethovens aus den Jahren 1798-99*, Ph.D. dissertation, Bonn University, 1951. It is not likely that Beethoven wrote a cadenza for the second movement. It's more likely for the third movement. The fault may lie in Fröhlich's memory of them. It had been more than 40 years since she had seen them when she related the information to Kalischer, or he may not have understood her correctly. The very existence of these cadenzas is known only from Kalischer's footnote. It's clear that Hess never saw a single note for either cadenza – how they relate to any of the existing cadenzas, or sketches for cadenzas, or whether they're totally new compositions, is impossible to say. It is entirely possible that these cadenzas are the same as those printed in the GA, in spite of Hess's assertion that they are not.]

79 Unknown Cadenza for the first version of the Piano Concerto in B-flat major [Op. 19]. Drafts to such a cadenza are found in the Kafka Sketchbook, London (see also Nottebohm II, p. 66) and in the Paris Conservatory (Beethoven Ms. 70) [TN: now in the BN]. The completed cadenza, which was unquestionably played by Beethoven, has not survived. [TN: it appears Hess's assessment of the sources for this cadenza was not complete, nor was he aware that an autograph, SBH 525, in the Beethoven-Haus is probably the completed copy of the cadenza. The completed cadenza is part of

the Bodmer collection and was cataloged by Max Unger as Mh 13. The drafts or sketches for this cadenza (if in fact it is one, and not two separate ones) is found in several places. The Kafka Sketchbook gives us sketches on pages 46 and 89 for an earlier cadenza. These sketches are on the same type of paper that was used between 1792-93. Another sketch appears on page 45 that is on paper dated about 1793-1796 and which Kerman notes may be for a different cadenza. See the transcription published by Joseph Kerman in *Autograph Miscellany from the Kafka Sketchbook ca. 1786 to 1799*, British Museum, London 1970. See also the article by Geoffrey Block, "Some Gray areas in the Evolution of Beethoven's Piano Concerto in B-flat major, Op. 19," in *Beethoven Essays: Studies in Honor of Elliot Forbes*, edited by L. Lockwood and P. Benjamin, Harvard University Press, Cambridge 1984. Of particular interest is the chronological table (pp. 123-6) showing the sketches, continuity drafts and autographs for this concerto.]

80 Cadenza for the first movement of the C minor Piano Concerto [Op.37]. It is unpublished, 145 bars, including a *Vi-de* after bar 88 that draws attention to a shorter twenty-bar-long ending. Max Unger, to whom I owe my knowledge of this piece, doesn't want any more details divulged about his discovery for the time being. At the moment, Unger is not able to say whether the sketches to an unknown cadenza for this concerto in the Bodmer Collection (Mh 71 in Unger's catalog) [TN: now numbered SBH 637 and SV 118] are identical with the ones mentioned above. This still needs to be checked. [TN: according to an entry by Giovanni Biamonti in *Catalogo cronologico e tematico delle opere di Beethoven*, Turin 1968, p. 393, he received a letter from Hess stating that this cadenza was written by Sigismund Thalberg, "L'altara cadenza scritta per lo stesso tempo, di cui al. n. 80 del catalogo Hess, non e

di Beethoven, ma di Thalberg, come da recente comunicazione dello Hess medesimo." Unger must have surely suspected that this cadenza was not really by Beethoven; it is the only plausible reason why he would have withheld information from Hess. Even more surprising is Hess's willingness to include it in this catalog without more information.]

81 Cadenza for the first movement of the [Piano] Concerto [No. 4] in G major [Op. 58; c.1809], 12 bars, unpublished. [TN: this cadenza was published in the SBG, Vol. X, 1969, p. 74, and published in NGA, Vol. VII.] Bodmer Collection, Mh 16. [TN: the Bodmer Collection, which is now in the Beethoven-Haus, Bonn, has been renumbered and this manuscript is now SBH 540.]

82 Transition "senza misura" to the Rondo of the [Piano] Concerto [No. 4 in] G major [Op. 58]. Written about 1809. It is unpublished and in the Bodmer Collection, Mh 17. [TN: this cadenza was published in the SBG, Vol. X, 1969, p. 74, and published in *Beethovens Sämtliche Werke*, Vol. VII. The Bodmer Collection, which is now in the Beethoven-Haus, Bonn, and this autograph has been renumbered as SBH 541.] Max Unger makes the following comment about this in "Von ungedruckter Musik Beethovens," *Zeitschrift für Musik,* November, 1935: "This belongs in place of another version that is found at the end of page 253 of the version printed in the GA. It's likely the master wrote this unpublished setting after he composed the concerto and probably thought it was better."

83 A very short cadenza to the Rondo of the [Piano] Concerto [No. 4] in G major [Op. 58; c.1809], 6 bars. This is unpublished and in the Bodmer Collection, Mh 18. [TN: this cadenza was published in the SBG, Vol. X, 1969, p. 74, and also published in NGA, Vol. VII. The

Bodmer Collection is now in the Beethoven-Haus, Bonn, and this autograph has been renumbered as SBH 542.]

84 Transition to the soloist's second entrance in the Rondo of the piano version of the Violin Concerto [Op. 61]. Headed, "Second entrance into the Rondo's theme." It is to be inserted at the 92nd bar of the Rondo. This is unpublished and in the Bodmer Collection, Mh 22. [TN: this cadenza (or transition) was published in the SBG, Vol. X, 1969, p. 73. The Bodmer Collection is now in the Beethoven-Haus, Bonn. This manuscript has been renumbered as SBH 547.]

85 Another cadenza to the Rondo of the piano version of the Violin Concerto, [Op. 61]. It consists of 15 bars, insofar as bar-lines are present at all, and belongs between bars 279 and 280 of the Rondo. Unpublished. [TN: this cadenza was published in the SBG, Vol. X, 1969, p. 73.] The autograph is Berlin Mus. Ms. Beethoven Autograph 28, p. 11 (according to the friendly communique of Fritz Kaiser), today it is in the Universitätsbibliothek, Tübingen. [TN: this autograph, commonly known as the "Fischhof Miscellany," has been returned to the SBB and is no longer in Tübingen.] (See the illustrations on pages 56 and 57.)

According to Max Unger's explanations, all the cadenzas, with the exception of No. 79, originated in 1809. [TN: since entry 80 is now believed to be by Sigismund Thalberg, the assignment of the date 1809 may not apply to that entry as well. In assigning the date and excluding entry No. 79, Hess also seems to have overlooked entry No. 76, which is a sketch for a cadenza that dates from the 1790s.]

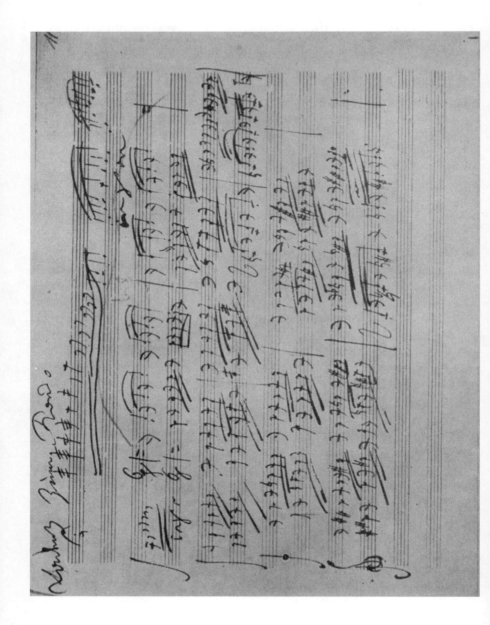

Hess 85, Cadenza to the Rondo of the piano setting of the Violin Concerto, facsimile of the autograph, first page.

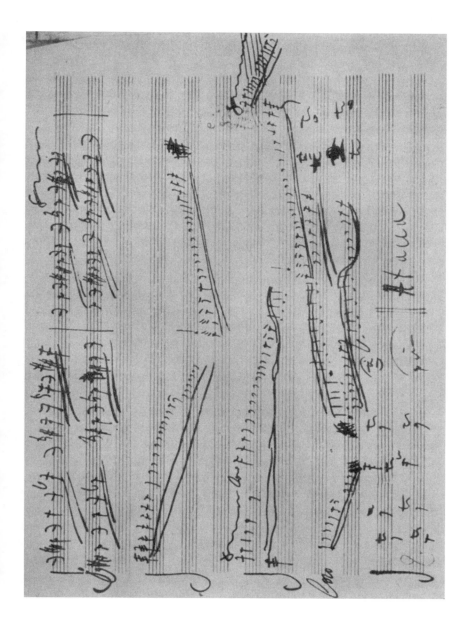

Hess 85, Cadenza to the Rondo of the piano setting of the Violin Concerto, facsimile of the autograph, second page.

Original Piano Arrangements by Beethoven

Although Beethoven in general did not concern himself with the writing of piano versions of his works, there are a number of such treatments from his pen available, which can now be proven [authentic, and] should be included in the new GA:

86 The Fugue Op. 134 for piano, four-hands is a transcription of the *Große Fuge* for String Quartet, Op. 133. This was written in the summer of 1826 at Gneixendorf. The autograph is missing except for the last seventeen bars, which are in the collection H. C. Bodmer (Mh 25). [TN: the Bodmer Collection is now in the Beethoven-Haus, Bonn, and the manuscript has been renumbered as SBH 573.] The first edition was published by Artaria in Vienna, 1827. A newer printing was published in Litolff's edition of Beethoven's four-handed compositions. [TN: this edition is *Sämmtliche Compositionen für das Pianoforte zu vier Händen*, Braunschweig c. 1870, and other later editions. According to Quirino Principe, in program notes for Stradivarius CD, No. 33464, "Beethoven initially wanted to entrust the work (meaning, the preparation of the four-hand transcription) to the pianist Anton Halm (1789-1872), but he was not happy with the too drastic division of the parts between the first and second performer." Beethoven then undertook the transcription himself.]

87 March for 6 wind instruments, GA Series 25 No. 292. [TN: this is a piano transcription of WoO 29, originally written for wind instruments. This was published by Hess in the SBG, Vol. VIII, 1964, p. 97.] The piano version is in the Berlin Beethoven Autograph, Grasnick 25.

The first edition was by W. Hess in *Schweizerische Musikpädagogische Blätter*, No. 1, 1931. It was included in my bagatelle collection, previously referred to under entry No. 51; not, however, in Otto von Irmer's bagatelle collection. [TN: this reference is to Hess's collection, *Leichte Klavierkompositionen Beethovens,* Musikverlag zum Pelikan, Zürich 1947, and to Otto von Irmer's Urtext edition *Klavierstücke*, G. Henle, Munich-Duisburg 1950.] A transcription of this march by another person for piano two hands is located in the *Sudetendeutschen Monatsheften*, issue of 6 June 1936. Thus the editor, Ernst Günthert, was not aware of Beethoven's original version. [TN: Mark Zimmer writes of this piece: "Composed about 1797-1798. Another version of this same march appears in the 'Grenadiersmarsch' for mechanical clock, Hess 107, composed by Haydn (first part) and Beethoven (transition and second part)." See <*www.unheardbeethoven.org*>.]

88 [Piano arrangement of] Minuet in A-flat for String Quartet, listed [in this catalog] as No. 33. The [previously] cited Parisian manuscript also contains a piano version. [TN: the Parisian manuscript cited is Beethoven Ms. 61 [or SV 214], formerly in the Paris Conservatory and now in the BN. According to Cooper, this was written between 1790-2; see C/C, p. 274.] This unpublished partial draft seems to have been written before the original quartet setting. [TN: this was published by Hess in the SBG, Vol. VIII, 1964, p. 14. A corrected edition was done by J. Zürcher in *Musikforschung* 19, 1966, p. 304ff. According to Mark Zimmer: "While Hess lists this piano minuet as a piano arrangement, there exists a 'Mineur' for the piano version which apparently never existed for the string quartet version of this little dance. The 'Mineur' is found in the Kafka Miscellany in the British Library, London, which states that it is, 'for the minuet in A-flat.'"]

89 *Ritterballett* (Knightly Ballet). The complete piano arrangement, written by Beethoven himself, has not yet
appeared in publication. No. 1 of this work is presented in facsimile in the program notes of the elev-
enth Chamber Music Festival of the Beethoven-Haus,
Bonn 1913; Nos. 2 and 3 were printed in facsimile in
Beethovens Handschrift, edited by Max Unger, Veröffentlichung der Beethovenhauses Bonn, Vol. 4,
Quelle & Meyer, Leipzig 1926. Nos. 4 through 7 were
added in facsimile to Schiedermair's work, *Der junge
Beethoven*; No. 8 has remained unpublished. Auto-
graph of the whole work is in the Beethoven-Haus,
Bonn. [TN: the orchestral version is listed in
Kinsky/Halm as WoO 1. The piano arrangement is
mentioned on p. 428, where No. 4, the "Minnelied," is
described as being in an unknown hand. Alan Tyson,
in "Notes on Five of Beethoven's Copyists," in the
Journal of the American Musicological Society, Vol.
XXIII, No. 3, Fall 1970, p. 466, states that the
"Minnelied" is in the handwriting of Ferdinand Ries.
The original autograph was destroyed by an accidental
fire in a storage room of the Beethoven-Haus in 1960.
Photocopies of the original exist. The entire piano
transcription was published by J. Rieter-Biederman,
Leipzig/Winterthur 1872, and more recently by Hess
in the SBG, Vol. VIII, 1964, p. 7. Giovanni Biamonti in
*Catalogo Cronologico e Thematico Delle Opere Di
Beethoven*, ILTE, Torino, 1968, p. 31, says that the
Rieter-Biederman edition was in a reduction for piano
by Ferdinand Dulcken. It may not actually be the Beethoven reduction. According to Thayer, there were
once vocal elements to this work that are now lost.
Hess has listed these "lost" vocal parts as entry 116 of
this catalog. In 1927, the Beethoven-Haus exhibited
the piano reduction as "Musik zu einem Ritterballett
mit Gesang," with no explanation of how, or by what
means, it has vocal parts. See *Das Beethoven-Haus in*

Bonn und seine Sammlungen, by F. A. Schmidt and Fr. Knickenberg, Bonn 1927, p. 94.]

90 [Piano Arrangement of the Ballet], *Die Geschöpfe des Prometheus* (The Creations of Prometheus), [Op. 43]. The piano transcription for two-hands, which appeared in 1801 by Artaria as Op. 24, is authentic according to a statement by Carl Czerny. [TN: the source for this statement appears to be found in a collection of "Anekdoten und Notizen über Beethoven," written by Czerny between September and November of 1852, and published by Otto Jahn. This assertion is cited in Thayer II, p. 237, and in all subsequent editions of Thayer. This work was published by Hess in the SBG, Vol. VIII, 1964, p. 44. The autograph is in the Beethoven-Haus, SBH 747. It is part of the Bodmer Collection, and was formerly cataloged as BMd 1.]

91 "Opferlied" (Offering Song), Op. 121b. [TN: arranged for soprano, choir and piano accompaniment instead of orchestra.] Beethoven's original piano arrangement appeared in 1825 with Schott, Mainz. The autograph is in Berlin today; earlier it was in the Petter Collection, then later in Landsberg. [TN: this was also published by Hess in the SBG, Vol. V, 1962, p. 64. This is the last of five settings of this song. The first being Hess entry 145, the second is WoO 126, while the third and fourth versions are both known as Op. 121b.]

92 "Bundeslied" (Fellowship Song), Op. 122. [TN: an arrangement for two soloists, three-part choir and piano accompaniment.] Regarding publication and autograph, the same as for Op. 121b applies. It was possible to establish that these two piano transcriptions which were published by Schott [Mainz 1825], are really original arrangements because a copy prepared by me of the two autographs agrees almost completely with

the named editions. [TN: this was also published by Hess in the SBG, Vol. V, 1962, p. 71.]

Piano settings of the song "Freudvoll und leidvoll" from the music to Egmont:

93 A simplified setting [of Freudvoll only] in A major. The autograph is in the collection of Louis Koch (Schloß Wildegg, Switzerland). The first edition was by Max Unger in *Von ungedruckter Musik Beethovens*, Zeitschrift für Musik, November 1935. It is not possible to verify for whom this arrangement was intended. In a letter to me, Fritz Kaiser suspects (probably correctly) that maybe it is only a sketch, since it lacks the four-bar ritornello at the beginning. [TN: this sketch and a completion were published again by Hess in the SBG, Vol. V, 1962, p. 60. The Koch collection is now dispersed, with some parts of it going to Hans Rahmer, Hamburg-Langenhorn, part in the Cary Collection in the Pierpont Morgan Library, New York, and still other parts missing. This autograph is now in the Floersheim Collection, Basel, Switzerland. See C/C, p. 224.]

94 Piano version in G major [of Clärchen's Lied, No. 4 of "Egmont" Op. 84, 1810]. This setting is found as a supplement in the (incomplete) Berlin autograph of the Egmont music. Unpublished. [TN: this was not published by Hess in the SBG, he wrote, "because it brings nothing new." It was, however, published in the new complete edition, *Beethovens Sämtliche Werke*, Vol. XII, Pt. 1, Lieder und Gesänge, G. Henle, Munich 1990, p. 271.]

95 Piano version in F major [of Clärchen's Lied, No. 4 of "Egmont" Op. 84, 1810.] This setting is found as a supplement in the (incomplete) Berlin autograph of the Egmont music. Unpublished. [TN: this was not published by Hess in the SBG, he wrote, "because it

brings nothing new." This was published in the *Beethovens Sämtliche Werke*, Vol. XII, Pt. 1, Lieder und Gesänge, G. Henle, Munich 1990, p. 250. A facsimile of the second page of four pages was published in an article by Helga Lühning in *Questiones in Musica: Festschrift für Franz Krautwurst*, Hans Schneider, Tutzing 1989, pp. 351-386.]

96 Seventh Symphony, [Op. 92,] the first 46 bars of the first movement [in an incomplete piano transcription]. This is unpublished. [TN: this was published in facsimile by Hess as the frontispiece of the SBG, Vol. VIII, 1964, however a transcription of it has never been published until now. The first edition, transcribed and prepared by Mark Zimmer, is included in this edition of the New Hess Catalog beginning on page 245.] The autograph is in the Paris Conservatory (W. 7, 1). [TN: this piece is now in the BN.] It is mentioned by Max Unger in "Die Beethovenhandschriften der Pariser Konservatoriumsbibliothek," *Neues Beethoven-Jahrbuch VI,* Verlag des Beethovenhauses, Braunschweig 1935, pp. 114 and 119. [TN: page 119 is a misprint. The reference begins on page 114 and extends across the double page spread to page 115, not page 119. There is no reference to this work on page 119.]

97 Wellingtons Sieg, oder die Schlacht bei Vittoria [Op. 91]. Published in 1816 by S. A. Steiner, Vienna; this piano transcription is by Beethoven. The same piece is mentioned in Kinsky/Halm, p. 255. [TN: this was published again by Hess in the SBG, Vol. VIII, 1964, p. 99.]

98 Scherzo of the Piano Trio Op. 1, No. 2 [in a version for piano alone]. The autograph of a piano setting was previously in the Artaria collection. The same piece is mentioned in Thayer I, p. 404. Where is this autograph today? This is unpublished. [TN: apparently,

when Hess prepared this entry he was not completely familiar with the contents of the Kafka Miscellany in the British Library, London where this piece, which is 64 bars, is found on pages 126r and 126v. This was later published by Hess in the SBG, Vol. VIII, 1964, p. 13. The Kafka Sketchbook was published both in facsimile and transcription by Joseph Kerman in *Autograph Miscellany from the Kafka Sketchbook ca. 1786 to 1799*, 2 Vols., British Museum, London 1970.]

99 Military March in F major. [TN: this piano arrangement of the march, WoO 18, was written in 1809 according to C/C, p. 274.] Max Unger found in the Paris Conservatory an autograph of the piano version of this march listed under No. 6 (Beethoven Ms. 41), and published it under the title "Yorck'scher Marsch" through Reinecke, Leipzig, undated (probably about 1942). [TN: see Unger's catalog in *Neues Beethoven-Jahrbuch VI*, Henry Litolff's Verlag, Braunschweig 1935, pp. 99-101. This was published by Hess in the SBG, Vol. VIII, 1964, p. 98, where it was titled "Marsch für die böhmische Landwehr."]

100 [Piano version of] Twelve German Dances for orchestra [WoO 8] (GA Series 2, No. 17). Beethoven's original piano version appeared in 1795 through Artaria in Vienna. [TN: the piano version was published by Hess in the SBG, Vol. VIII, 1964, p. 15.]

101 [Piano version of] the Twelve Minuets for orchestra [WoO 7] (GA Series 2, No. 16). Beethoven's original piano version appeared in 1795 through Artaria. Both versions [entries 100 and 101] should originally have been included in Series 18, as Nos. 201 and 202 of the GA. However, this was not published at that time, although no doubts existed as to the genuineness of these versions. The editions by Artaria have been reprinted many times, but probably not always quite

correctly. [TN: the piano version was published by Hess in the SBG, Vol. VIII, 1964, p. 24.]

102 [Piano version of] Nine Contretänze from the Twelve Contretänze [WoO 14] (GA Series 2, No. 17a), where they appeared through Mollo in Vienna in 1802 in this order: Nos. 8, 7, 4, 10, 9 and 1. The Berlin autograph (Artaria 140) shows these six numbers in a copy revised by Beethoven, plus Nos. 2, 5, and 12, which apparently remained unpublished. Whether the piano setting (dances) originates from Beethoven must remain an open question. The old GA was supposed to contain the six numbers mentioned as Series 18, No. 197, plus, as No. 200 of the same series, the piano arrangement of the Military March in D Major (Series 2, No. 15). This didn't happen, and four numbers of the edition (199-202) remained unused. We don't have any clues to indicate that the piano arrangement of the cited march ("Marsch zur großen Wachtparade") comes from Beethoven. [TN: this fractured set of piano transcriptions has a very confusing and conjectural history. I am indebted to Mark Zimmer for the following information: "Only the first six of the set of 12 were published in the piano version (Mollo, Vienna 1802); however, a copyist's score also contains three more. It is doubtful that Beethoven ever wrote a piano version for the other three dances. The numbering of the piano versions does not follow the numbering of the orchestral versions. According to Barry Cooper, Nos. 1 and 9 date from 1791 in Bonn, No. 3 probably dates from 1795, while Nos. 4, 5 and 7 date from late 1801. No. 2 is derived from the ballet music for 'Die Geschöpfe des Prometheus, Op. 43' and was used again in the finale of the Third Symphony. According to Shin A. Kojima Nos. 8 and 12 from WoO 14 (that is to say, Nos. 1 and 9 from Hess 102), '. . .are possibly arranged by Karl van Beethoven, Ludwig's brother, based on sketches by Ludwig.'" For more information

on the complex history of these dances, see the information presented by Shin Kojima in the "Kritischer Bericht" portion of the *Beethovens Sämtliche Werke*, edited by Martin Staehelin in cooperation with the Beethoven-Archiv, Bonn, Abteilung II, Band 3, G. Henle, Munich 1980. The piano version of the initial six contradances was published by Hess in the SBG, Vol. VIII, 1964, p. 40, and the second set of three in the same volume, beginning on p. 42.]

Works for Mechanical Musical Instruments

103 Adagio in F major for Mechanical Clock. Described and published by A. Kopfermann in *Die Musik*, Vol. 1, No. 2, March 1902, pp. 1059-1061, with an addendum to it in Vol. 1, No. 3, April 1902, p. 1193. [TN: listed as WoO 33, No. 1 in Kinsky/Halm, p. 474. This piece was published by W. Hess in a version for nine wind instruments, Breitkopf & Härtel, Leipzig 1957.]

104 Scherzo in G major for Mechanical Clock. The first edition was done by Gustav Becking in *Das Scherzothema bei Beethoven*, Breitkopf & Härtel, Leipzig, 1921. [TN: listed as WoO 33, No. 2 in Kinsky/Halm, p. 474.]

105 Allegro in G major for Mechanical Clock. The first edition was published by Willy Hess in *Ricoriana: Nuova Serie*, Vol. 3, No. 5, Milan, May 1957, pp. 226-7, and mentioned again in the article "Beethoven e lo Spieluhr," on pp. 228-9. [TN: listed as WoO 33, No. 3 in Kinsky/Halm, p. 474.]

Autographs and editions of these three pieces: all three are located in the Beethoven Autograph, Grasnick 23, which originated in 1799, and were written for the mechanical clock of the Kunstkabinett of Count Deym (Hofstatuarius Müller). Schünemann has, without basis, dated each from 1792. Editions [in arrangements] are: Adagio for Cello and Piano from J. van Lier, in D major, Steingräber 1902; an edition for piano alone appeared in the Stockholm magazine *Damernas Musikblad* in 1902, by Victor Patrik Vretblad. An edition for violin and piano by the same arranger appeared between 1906-1910 in Dahlström's *Orgel- und Pianomagasin*, Stockholm. This arrangement is listed in Hess 3 as No. 270. The information that this "unknown adagio for violin and piano" is really about an arrangement of the mechanical clock adagio, I owe to Mr. Donald W. MacArdle (USA). It is also likely that the unknown adagio mentioned by Marion Scott (*Beethoven*, Dent & Sons, London 1934, p. 250) for string quartet is identical with the mechanical clock adagio, since the Deutsche Staatsbibliothek is indicated as the owner of the autograph, and no other adagio than the mechanical clock adagio is known there. An error is all the more likely, since the mechanical clock adagio is written on four clefs. Hess 3 lists this adagio mentioned by Marion Scott as No. 271. An arrangement for one each, flute, oboe, clarinet, bassoon, and horn, written by the Kapellmeister Böhme, was performed in Bonn in 1902 and remains unpublished. It is probably this arrangement that Max Unger made reference to when he mentioned a version of the adagio for wind instruments (mentioned in Hess 3, under No. 16). The same piece is mentioned in *Die Musik*, Vol. 1, No. 15/16, 1902, p. 1474. Nowhere is [there] evidence of an original version for wind instruments by Beethoven. A setting for flute, two oboes, two clarinets, two bassoons and two horns by Willy Hess appeared in an edition by Breitkopf & Härtel, Wiesbaden 1957. [TN: to be perfectly clear, please note that the reference to "Hess 3" in this entry is to the third version of Hess's catalog, which was printed in Italian in Rome in 1953, and not to entry 3 of this catalog. See the reference in the first paragraph of the original forward to this catalog.]

The Scherzo and Allegro. These were published in an arrangement for piano two-hands by J. Chantavoine, under the title *Deux airs pour boîte à musique*, Au Ménestrel, Heugel & Cie., Paris 1902; and again, also for piano, in the *Sudetendeutsche Monatshefte*, Vol. 6, June 1936. A piano transcription of all three pieces, together with the two following works, was brought out by Georg Schünemann, under the title *Ludwig van Beethoven. Stücke für die Spieluhr*, B. Schott's Söhne, Mainz 1940.

106 Allegro and Minuet in C major. Unpublished. The autograph (Artaria 186) is in the Deutsche Staatsbibliothek, Berlin [TN: now the SBB]. Compare what
was said under No. 46 above. It is possible that these
two movements originated in Bonn and were intended
for a mechanical clock; however, this is not definitely
known. Schünemann's association [of this] with the
handwriting in Grasnick 23 is completely arbitrary.
The notation in the Alto and Tenor clefs is conspicu-
ous. For information on the edition for piano, see
above. [TN: listed as WoO 33 No. 4 and No. 5 in
Kinsky/Halm, p. 474. This was published by Hess in
the SBG, Vol. VII, 1963, p. 56. These two pieces were
also published by Hess as "Sonatine für Viola und Violoncello," Amadeus Verlag, Winterthur 1976.]

107 Grenadiermarsch [in F major] for mechanical clock. It
was published and described by Georg Kinsky in
Beethoven-Almanach, Bosse Verlag, Regensburg 1927,
pp. 320-332. The piece was taken partly by listening
[TN: presumably Hess means listening to the mechanical clock itself.] and partly through mechanical trans-
fer of cylinder No. 7 of the mechanical clock No. 2061
in the former Heyer Museum in Cologne, titled,
"Granadiers Marsch arranchiert von Herrn Ludwig von
[sic!] Beethoven." It has turned out that the first
twenty bars come from Haydn, and that they represent
the transcription of a march presented for pairs of
clarinets, horns and bassoons. There then follows a 16-
bar transition, probably provided by Beethoven, and
then the transcription of his March [WoO 29], GA
Series 25, No. 292, transposed to F major. Haydn's
original was in E-flat major. The same piece is mentioned by E. F. Schmid in "Haydn und die Flötenuhr,"
Zeitschrift für Musikwissenschaft, Vol. 14, Journal 4,
January 1932, pp. 193-221.

108 *Wellingtons Sieg oder die Schlacht bei Vittoria*, the original version for Mälzel's panharmonikon. The "Battle of Vittoria" was, as is generally known, written first for Mälzel's panharmonikon and later transcribed for large orchestra. The original score of the second part in a revised copy is located in Berlin, Artaria Autograph 181, with Beethoven's handwritten heading, "Auf Wellingtons Sieg bei Vittoria 1813 geschrieben für Hr. Maeltzel [sic] von Ludwig van Beethoven." The instruments in this score written for the panharmonikon are: piccolo, large flutes, oboes, clarinets, bassoons, contrabassoon, horns, "clarini" trumpets [TN: these are high pitched trumpets in D or E-flat.], trombone, timpani, triangle, cymbals, small and bass drums, and organ base pedal. The piece begins with the "allegro con brio" of the Siegessymphonie, GA, p. 49, bar 4. Bars 23-28 of this first setting are printed in Hess 3 on pp. 326-327, and in a separate edition on pp. 28-29; the rest of it has remained unpublished. [TN: the complete second part was published by Hess in the SBG, Vol. IV, 1961, p. 71.]

Works for the Stage

109 *Leonore*, Opera in 3 Acts (first version of *Fidelio* 1805). The first edition of the piano version was published by Erich Prieger through Breitkopf & Härtel, Leipzig 1905. A second edition was published in 1907. The score was published in two volumes in 1908-1910 as a private edition. Both editions were without the spoken dialogue. In 1922, the remainder of the piano version and the hiring of the performance material was taken over by Tischer & Jagenber, in Köln-Bayenthal. The complete libretto appeared in 1805 with Pichler in Vienna; furthermore, a reprint (without place and year) must also have been published in Vienna and appeared under the title *Gesänge zu der Oper Fidelio Frey nach dem Französischen bearbeitet von Joseph Sonnleithner in drey Aufzügen. Musik von Ludwig van Beethoven.* A copy is in the possession of the Wiener Stadtbibliothek (Signature A 109 625). Professor Otto E. Deutsch has compared that edition with the official script by Pichler, and he notes only minor deviations. A new edition of the official libretto was published as No. 115 of Breitkopf & Härtel's music books (presumably 1905), with the alterations probably made by Beethoven during the composition, included in the footnotes. Another edition of the libretto appeared in Adolf Sandberger's "Beethoven-Aufsätze," Vol. 2 of *Ausgewählte Aufsätze zur Musikgeschichte,* Munich 1924. Finally, Koschny published the duet "Um in der Ehe froh zu leben" (In Order to Live Happily in Marriage), in a piano version with two solo instruments in 1908, Breitkopf & Härtel, Leipzig. [TN: the complete first version of *Fidelio* (*Leonore*) was published by Hess in the SBG, Vol. XI (first and second acts), and Vol. XII (act three), 1967.]

110 *Leonore*, Opera in 2 Acts (second version of *Fidelio* 1806). The score remains unpublished. [TN: this score was partly published by Hess in the SBG, Vol. XIII, 1970, beginning on p. 1. However, in Vol. XIII, Hess published only those portions that were new or different from the first version, with extensive cross-references to Volumes XI and XII for those portions that were the same in both versions. The score for the Overture (*Leonore*,) No.1 was not included, since it had been published in the Gesamtausgabe by Breitkopf & Härtel in the 19th century; and Hess did not include those arias numbered 1, 2, 3, 6 and 15, since they are essentially the same as those found in other versions of *Fidelio* (detailed notes on the differences do appear in the *Revisionsbericht* at the end of the volume), nor did he include arias number 5 and 7 because they were identical to those from the 1805 version of *Fidelio* and were printed in Vol. XII.] The piano version appeared:

1807: Trio, "Ein Mann ist bald genommen" (A Man Is Taken Soon); canon quartet, "Mir ist so wunderbar" (A Wondrous Feeling Fills Me); and duet, "Um in der Ehe froh zu leben" (In Order to Live Happily in the Marriage). Published by Giovanni Cappi, Vienna.

1810: The whole opera with exception of the Overture and both the finales [appeared] under the title "Leonore, Oper in zwey Aufzügen von L. van Beethoven." Breitkopf & Härtel. (Arranged by C. Czerny.)

1815: New edition with the addition of the Overture. Titled: "Ouverture und Gesänge aus der Oper: Fidelio (Leonore) von L. van Beethoven Klavierauzug. Neue ausgabe." Also published by Breitkopf & Härtel.

1841: Pizarro's Aria with chorus. "Auf euch nur will ich bauen" (I Only Want to Rely on You) from the first finale. Breitkopf & Härtel published the piece on Schindler's urging as a piano reduction (plate number 6893).

1851: A complete piano version was prepared by Otto Jahn without spoken dialogue; however, the numbers were in the sequence of the first setting and generally followed the then-known deviations of the first setting from the second setting.

The libretto appeared in 1806 by Anton Pichler in Vienna, together with the one of 1805, and was first reprinted in my work, *Beethovens Oper Fidelio und ihre drei Fassungen*, Atlantis-Verlag, Zurich, 1953, where I have pointed out additional details concerning this work. In this book, the reader will find, on pp. 197-202, a table of all the autographs that are known today of the first and second setting of *Fidelio*. As an addendum to it, see "Die Wiener Handschriften zur ersten und zweiten Fassung von Beethovens, Fidelio" in *Die Musikforschung* VIII/2, 1955, pp. 208-9.

It is desirable that the score of the first version of *Fidelio* [TN: that is, *Leonore*] with the complete libretto will be included in the new complete edition. One supplemental volume would then have to encompass the deviations of 1806 and also make accessible some early studies and interim settings, since they cannot (like the two early versions of the Marzelline aria; see below) appear as independent works. These early studies and interim settings are given here:

111 Duet, "Nur hurtig fort, nur frisch gegraben" (Just Work Swiftly, Only Freshly Dug). An early setting discarded by Beethoven. Unpublished. [TN: published by Hess in the SBG, Vol. XII, 1967, p. 561.] It was never played and probably can only be considered as an early study,

although it is in Beethoven Autograph 6 in Berlin, where it is available in a copy by an unknown hand (as far as I can judge). [TN: this is now generally considered to be in Beethoven's hand and not in that of a copyist.] It deviates largely from Prieger's text of the first version in the instrumentation and numerous details. The same piece is mentioned on pages 155/6 in my work, *Fidelio,* quoted above.

112 Rocco's "Gold" aria from 1806. This aria was removed in 1806; however, a copy is located in Beethoven Autograph 26, folio 1, in Berlin. It matches the version from 1805, except for the absence of trumpets and timpani; furthermore it has another text (derived from Breuning) and small alterations in bars 35 and 79 of the second oboe. Therefore, [it can be assumed] it was originally planned to also use this aria in 1806. The new complete edition should note the few variations to the 1805 version. The aria is printed in Otto Jahn's piano version of the second setting of the opera from 1806. The same piece is mentioned on p. 52 in my work *Fidelio,* quoted above. [TN: this was published by Hess in the SBG, Vol. XIII, 1970, p. 137.]

113 Marzelline's Aria, [with the] shortened ending from 1814. The above-mentioned Beethoven Autograph 26 of the Berlin Library contains a copy of this aria in the 1806 setting, in which Beethoven has written down the 1814 alterations. These are an attempt at a radical shortening of the ending; one bar after the "piu moto," Beethoven inserted a *Vi-de* which leads to a three-bar-long ending, that I have published in a piano version in *Die Musik,* Vol. 30, No. 2, 1938, p. 517, and in score on p. 254 of my work *Fidelio*. [TN: this work was published by Hess in the SBG, Vol. XIII, 1970, p. 169. There is an extensive study of all the versions of Marzelline's Aria is presented by Philip Gossett in "The Arias of Marzelline: Beethoven as a Composer of

Opera," in *Beethoven-Jahrbuch*, Vol. X, Beethoven-Haus, Bonn 1983, pp. 141-183.]

114 Dresden addition to the second finale of the 1814 [version of] *Fidelio*. The 1823 copy of the *Fidelio* score, which was made for Dresden [performances], contains, like the 1806 version, nine bars [sung by] Fernando before the final chorus. The text is: "Hinweg mit diesem Bösewicht, uns Freunde, winket süße Pflicht. Auf, lasset laut in diesen Hallen der Wonne Jubel hoch erschallen" (Away with this villain, we friends have a sweet duty. Oh, let us in these halls resound loudly in blissful jubilation). This composition is unquestionably more beautiful than the one from 1806. It doubtlessly was written by Beethoven. For further information, read Hans Volkmann, *Beethoven in seinen Beziehungen zu Dresden*, Deutscher Literaturverlag, Dresden 1942, p. 106 (where the nine bars were printed in the piano version), and pp. 240-243, where the Dresden copy is described in detail. [TN: it is not really certain that Beethoven knew of, or requested, this revision to the 1814 version of *Fidelio*. The nine bars of the recitative appear in the 1806 version, but were cut in 1814, only to reappear in this copy made for the Dresden performances in 1823. Beethoven did receive a request for a copy of the opera for use in Dresden. See Thayer/Forbes, p. 863: "Beethoven had to borrow it from the Kärntnertor Theatre, whose musical archives were in the care of Count Gallenburg. Through Schindler, Gallenburg sent word to Beethoven that he would send the score provided two copies were on hand; if not, he would have a copy made." Evidently there were not two copies on hand, because a new copy was prepared and sent to Dresden. It is not certain whether Beethoven ever asked for the change (or restoration, to be more precise) in this scene or whether he even knew of it. No one is certain that he reviewed the copy before it was

sent to Dresden. All that is certain is that the Dresden copy contains this addition. A. Willem Holsbergen writes on this point: "Without wanting to add to the considerable confusion surrounding this recitative, let me remind you that Treitschke wrote somewhere, that one of his changes in the libretto of the 1814 version of *Fidelio*, was to change the place of the last scene from the dungeon to the courtyard. The words from the recitative 'diesen Hallen' (in this Hall) no longer applied, so that may have been the reason to cut this recitative in 1814." It seems clear that whatever copy of the score was used to prepare the Dresden score, it contained this original line or phrase. It is not known whether, in the 1823 Dresden performances, the last scene was placed back in the dungeon or was presented in the courtyard (thus ignoring the words 'diesen Hallen')." This was published by Hess in the SBG, Vol. XIII, 1970, p. 170.]

115 "Vestas Feuer," first scene of an unfinished opera with a libretto by [Emanuel] Schikaneder. Sketched in 1803. Published with a supplement by Willy Hess after the autograph [SV 60] found in the collection of the Gesellschaft der Musikfreunde, [by] Bruckner-Verlag, Wiesbaden 1953, today known as Alkor-Edition, Kassel. Thayer II still mentions this music on pp. 408-9, under the title, *Alexander in Indien*. See also the reference in Raoul Biberhofer, "'Vestas Feuer,' Beethovens erster Opernplan," *Die Musik,* Vol. 22, No. 1, 1929/30, pp. 409-414, as well as Willy Hess's "Vestas Feuer von Beethoven und Schikaneder," *Schweizerische Musikpädagogische Blätter*, January 1954, p. 3-10. The publication of the piano version, as well as the complete libretto, is imminent. [TN: Hess issued his piano version with Alkor-Edition, Kassel 1968. There are twenty pages of sketches and a 275-bar first scene written out in full score, apart from a

few gaps in the instrumental parts. It was also published by Hess in the SBG, Vol. XIII, 1970, pp.143-68.]

116 Vocal components of the Ritterballett. Thayer I, p. 308, tells us that there were vocal parts to the Ritterballett that are now lost. In a footnote [also on p. 308 of Thayer I] on this subject, Hugo Riemann expresses the supposition that a page auctioned in London in 1910 as, "Beethoven Autograph. A Four-part a cappella Song from the Bonn Period," may have contained the "Minnelied" (love song) from this work. Perhaps later findings will clarify this matter. [TN: there is much more information in Riemann's footnote than Hess presents. The auction took place "about" 1910, not "in" 1910 as Hess states. For this edition, Rob Ritchie of London undertook a thorough search to locate the auction record in the microfilm files of the British Library. He could find no trace of any item matching this description being auctioned in London between mid-1909 and early 1911. Hess does not tell us that Riemann didn't actually see the "four-part a capella song." According to Riemann, it was examined and copied by Edward Speyer (1839-1934), who supplied his findings to Riemann. See the reference to Edward Speyer in entry 133. There existed both a text and a couplet. The text runs:

> "Doch liebt gleichwohl Amynt und spricht, daß nichts so süß wäre.
> Voll Ungewißheit fleh' ich dir, geib [sic] du o Liebe, selber mir Verstand, zu entscheiden."
> (However, Amynt nevertheless speaks to us of love, that nothing could be so sweet.
> Full of uncertainty I give you, Oh love, my mind itself to judge.)

The couplet is given as:

Bringt Liebe, Lust, bringt sie Gefahr,
   Sagt der Amynt der Mutter wahr.
(If love brings desire, it brings danger,
   The Mother of Amynt predicts the future.)

Riemann suggests that the text could be for the "Minnelied" (Romance No. 4), and the couplet, which fits the melody very well, could be used as a refrain for the "Deutscher Gesang" (German Song No. 2), which is repeated several times in the ballet. In 1927, the Beethoven-Haus exhibited the piano reduction (see entry 89) as "Musik zu einem Ritterballett mit Gesang" (that is, 'with song'), but with no explanation of how, or by what means, it has vocal parts. See: *Das Beethoven-Haus in Bonn und seine Sammlungen*, by F. A. Schmidt and Fr. Knickenberg, Verlag des Beethoven-Hauses, Bonn 1927, p. 94.]

117 Music to [Christoph] Kuffner's tragedy *Tarpeja*. The old GA contained only the Triumphal March (GA Series 2, No. 14). [TN: listed as WoO 2a in Kinsky/Halm, p. 429.] One piece titled "Introduzione dell'secondo atto" (Berlin, Beethoven Autograph, Artaria 152), which, according to Otto Jahn, may be a part of the *Tarpeja* music. Georg Schünemann has without questioning adopted this conclusion, and published the two pieces – Introduction and Triumphal March – in 1938 through B. Schott's Söhne, Mainz. Schünemann suspects, in his foreword to that edition, that even further pieces existed which are now lost. [TN: the second part, "Introduzione del'secondo atto," listed in Kinsky/Halm as WoO 2b, p. 430, is now believed by most Beethoven scholars to be a discarded introduction to the second act of *Leonore*, which was in three acts in 1805. What appears to be a definitive article on the identity of this entry was written by Clemens Brenneis, "'Intorduzione del II^{do} Atto' und die

'Leonore' von 1805," *Beitrage zur Musikwissenschaft,* Vol. 32, Issue 3, 1990, pp. 181-303.]

118 *Die Weihe des Hauses* (The Consecration of the House), a festival play. [TN: this was adapted from *Die Ruinen von Athen*, Op. 113.] [The music for] this festival play was composed in 1822 (text by Carl Meisl), and has never been published completely in this grouping. It includes the following musical pieces:

> Overture [published as] Op. 124, GA Series 3, No. 24.
> No. 1 = Op. 113, No. 1 with a new text. It is unpublished in this version.
> Nos. 2-4 = Op. 113, Nos. 2-4. (According to Nottebohm's supposition.)
> No. 5: Chorus "Wo sich die Pulse jugendlich jagen," GA Series 25, No. 266. [TN: listed as WoO 98 in Kinsky/Halm, p. 556.]
> No. 6: Chorus Op. 114, GA Series 20, No. 207a.
> No. 7 = Op. 113, No. 5. [TN: with the text shortened.]
> Nos. 8-9 = Op. 113, Nos. 7-8 with a partly new text. They are unpublished in these versions.

The first listing of all the components of this work was printed by Nottebohm in No. 25 of the *Allgemeine Musikalische Zeitung* of 1873, and reprinted in Nottebohm II. It is desirable that in the new Gesamtausgabe, this work, at least in a piano version and with the complete text, would be included. [TN: Hess published the score for the opening number of this work and a complete text in his SBG, Vol. XIII, 1970, pp.171 and xxii.]

Concert Arias and Songs with Orchestra

119 "No, non turbarti!," Scene and Aria for soprano and string orchestra (1801). [TN: this is listed in Kinsky/Halm as WoO 92a, p. 548.] The text is from Pietro Metastasio's cantata, "La tempesta." The autograph is in Berlin, Artaria 165. The first edition was published by Willy Hess in the Bruckner-Verlag, Wiesbaden, 1948 [or 1949], today known as the Alkor-Edition, Kassel. The edition brings together Beethoven's original work and one including Salieri's corrections put underneath a piano transcription by Willy Hess. [TN: a footnote by Hess in *Beethoven Studien*, Beethoven-Haus, Bonn, through G. Henle, Munich-Duisburg 1972, p. 265, says that Thayer and G. Adler give the title incorrectly as "turbati" instead of "turbarti." Because Hess took his information from two different sources, he didn't realize that this entry is the same as number 138 in this catalog. See entry 138 below.]

120 "Nei giorni tuoi felici," duet for Soprano and Tenor with Orchestra. Text from Metastasio's "Olimpiade." Composed between the end of 1802 and early 1803. The autograph is in Berlin, Artaria 168. The first edition was published by Willy Hess through Ernst Eulenburg, Leipzig, 1939. This edition is in large and small score format, with a piano transcription by W. Hess. - The aria, "Veggo languir chi adoro," referred to in Hess 2 and 3 as No. 82, is most likely sketches to this duet. Recently, some of these sketches have actually appeared in the USA. [TN: the sketches referred to by Hess are indeed in the USA. They are at Stanford University, Stanford, California, and are numbered SV 371 and Otto B. Albrecht 223A. See Dorfmüller, p. 8.] Lot

number 20 in the Manuscript Auction Catalog, No. 37 of Leo Liepmannssohn, Berlin, is probably also some of these [sketches,] not an unknown aria [as is mentioned in the catalog]. [TN: the piano transcription by Hess was reissued separately by Eulenburg in 1966. This is listed in Kinsky/Halm as WoO 93, p. 549.]

121 Marzelline's aria, "O wär ich schon mit dir vereint" (Oh, I Long to Be Already United with You), C major setting. [This is] the earliest setting. [TN: this aria was prepared in 1806 or earlier as part of the revision of *Fidelio*; however, Beethoven decided to use the original 1805 version instead.] A piano transcription appeared in Otto Jahn's edition of the 1806 setting of *Fidelio*, (Leipzig, 1851, see entry No.110), as well as in the second edition of Erich Prieger's piano transcription of the first version of *Fidelio*, Leipzig 1907 (see the entry under No. 109). A copy is in the Staatsbibliothek, Berlin, Beethoven Autograph 26. [TN: now the SBB.] The score is unpublished. [TN: this was published with an Italian text by G. Biamonti in *Revisita Santa Cecilia*, Vol. 4, Rome August 1956. It was also published by Hess in the SBG, Vol. II, 1960, p. 35, with the original German text. In the *Revisionsbericht* of the SGB, Hess quotes what is written by Anton Schindler on the first page of the manuscript, "Diese Bearbeitung ist nach Beethovens Äusserung die allereste unter den Vieren." (This arrangement is, according to Beethoven himself, the very first of the four.) If Schindler is to be believed, then this entry must predate the following one, and if Rachel Wade is correct, then this entry must have been written no later than 1805, and perhaps a little earlier. See the TN on entry 122 below.]

122 The same aria; an early setting in C minor. As for No. 121 the same circumstances apply; however, the score was published by Willy Hess in *Rivisita Santa Cecilia*, Vol.

4, August 1956, and again in the *1954/5 Yearbook of the Accademia Santa Cecilia,* Rome 1956. Both settings are individual compositions; they beautifully increase the small number of Beethoven's concert-arias. Neither one of the two arias belongs to one of the three settings of the opera *Fidelio*. They seem from the start to have been immediately put aside, just as the Overture Op. 138 was. [TN: this setting was published by Hess in the SBG, Vol. II, 1960, p. 46. Rachel Wade wrote an excellent analysis of Beethoven's *Eroica* Sketchbook, published in *Fontes Artis Musicae*, Vol. 24, 1977. From her inventory of the sketchbook, it is apparent that work on entry 122 occurred as early as 1805.]

123 "Kriegslied für die zum heiligen Krieg verbundeten deutschen Heere" (War Song for the German Armies Allied for the Sacred War). The text is by Zacharias Werner (1768-1823). According to Max Unger, such a work was to have been composed by Beethoven for voices and orchestra about 1813-4. The same piece is also mentioned by Max Unger in "Ein verschollenes Kriegslied von Beethoven" in the *Frankfurter Zeitung* of 15 June 1940, second morning edition. Also, Thayer III, p. 418, mentions this piece, of which no trace has been located.

Songs and Arias with Piano Accompaniment

(If not otherwise stated, [each song is] always for one voice with piano accompaniment.)

124 A wedding song for Anna Giannatasio Del Rio (January 1819). "Auf, Freunde, singt dem Gott der Ehen" (Oh, Friends, Sing to the God of Marriages). The text is by Anton Joseph Stein. This song is in A major, for a solo voice and four-part choral refrain. The autograph is in private hands in England. [TN: this autograph is now in the Royal College of Music, London.] The first edition was published by John Oxenford, with an English text through Ewer & Co., London, 1858. [TN: this was partly published in facsimile (bars 22-33) by Hess in *Beethoven*, Amadeus-Verlag, Winterthur 1976, p. 197.] The same piece is mentioned by C. B. Oldman in "A Beethoven Friendship," *Music and Letters* XVII/4, October, 1936, pp. 328-337. [TN: this is listed in Kinsky/Halm as WoO 105, p. 567, in two settings (this one and the one listed below as entry 125).]

125 The same song, in a C major setting with unison choral refrain. (Presumably a second setting.) The autograph is in the Hessische Landesbibliothek, Darmstadt. The first edition was [published] in the yearbook *Der Bär*, Breitkopf & Härtel, 1927. The same piece is mentioned in the introduction by W. Hitzig to the first edition, as well as by W. Hess in "Beethovens Chorlieder mit Klavierbegleitung," *Neue Zeitschrift für Musik*, Vol. 118, Journal 3, March, 1957, pp. 152-155, with a photocopy of the English first edition of the A major setting. [TN: a newer edition was published by Hess in the SBG, Vol. V, 1962, p. 55. This is listed in

Kinsky/Halm as WoO 105, p. 567, in two settings (this one and the one listed above) as entry 124.]

126 Punschlied, "Wer nicht, wenn warm von Hand zu Hand" (Who Not, When Warmly from Hand to Hand). The author of the text is unknown; composed about 1790. The autograph, Artaria 171, is in Berlin. The first edition was through L. Schiedermair as an appendix to *Der junge Beethoven*, Quelle & Meyer, Leipzig, 1925. [TN: a newer edition was published by Hess in the SBG, Vol. V, 1962, p. 39. This is listed as WoO 111 in Kinsky/Halm, p. 573.]

127 "Un liento brindisi," for Soprano, two Tenors and Bass [with text by] Abbate Clemente Bondi, composed in 1814. [TN: Hess gives the title as "Johannisfeier Kantate" in *Beethoven Studien*, Beethoven-Haus, Bonn, through G. Henle, Munich-Duisburg 1972. The opening line of text is used here as a title. This small cantata was written for Johannes Malfatti on the occasion of his name day in 1814.] The autograph is missing; a transcription from the estate of Otto Jahn is in the possession of the Deutsche Staatsbibliothek, Berlin (Autograph Mus. Ms. 1245/1), where the original Italian text has been replaced with a German text. [TN: now the SBB.] Based on this, the first edition was published by Willy Hess in *Jahrbuch der Literarischen Vereinigung*, Winterthur, 1945, pp. 247-266. It also appeared in a separate edition. [TN: this separate edition appeared under the title *Ludwig van Beethoven: Kantata für Sopran, zwei Tenöre und Baß mit Klavierbegleitung*, also printed at Winterthur in 1945.] Thayer [gives the German text and] separately gives Bondi's original text on p. 194 of his *Chronologisches Verzeichniss* as an addendum to his entry No. 185. [TN: a newer edition was published by Hess in the SBG, Vol. V, 1962, p. 42. An extensive discussion of the work by Harry Goldschmidt appeared in the

Beethoven-Jahrbuch, Bonn 1972. The same article was reprinted in *Beethoven Studien I: Die Erscheinung Beethoven*, edited by Harry Goldschmidt, VEB Deutscher Verlag für Musik, Leipzig 1974, pp. 177-197, followed by a complete edition of the score, pp. 199-220; also included in this publication is the German text on p. 221 and facsimiles of pp. 115-121 of the Dessauer Sketchbook showing the manuscript with the addition of superimposed bar numbers. This is listed as WoO 103 in Kinsky/Halm, p. 565.]

128 "An Laura" (Friedrich von Matthisson) "Freud' umblühe dich auf allen Wegen" (May Joy Bloom Around You on All Paths) [was] composed about 1790. The autograph is in the Beethoven-Haus, Bonn. The first edition was published by G. Kinsky in the *Heyer-Katalog*, IV, 1916, pp. 3-5 of the musical supplements. The same piece is mentioned by G. Kinsky in "Ein neuentdeckes Lied Beethovens" in the *Allgemeine Musikalische Zeitung*, 10 January 1913. [TN: a newer edition was published by Hess in the SBG, Vol. V, 1962, p. 7. This is listed as WoO 112 in Kinsky/Halm, p. 574.]

129 "Que le temps me dure" [First version] (text by J.-J. Rousseau). [Written] about 1792. The first edition was published by Jean Chantavoine in the second March issue of *Die Musik*, 1902. Max Unger published the sketch again in the *Zeitschrift für Musik,* November 1935; he also attempts to do a performance-ready realization of Beethoven's largely complete sketches. The entry numbers 129-131 are also mentioned by Jean Chantavoine in "Zwei französische Lieder Beethovens," in *Die Musik*, Vol. 1, No. 2, March 1902, beginning on p. 1078; and they are mentioned by Max Unger, "Zwei Entwürfe nach einem Gedicht von Jean-Jacques Rousseau," in *Zeitschrift für Musik*, Vol. 102, November 1935, beginning on p. 1200. [TN: a newer edition was published by Hess in the SBG, Vol.

V, 1962, p. 11. This is listed as WoO 116 in Kinsky/Halm, p. 577.]

130 Second version of same song, "Que le temps me dure" (see above) with the setting being in the major key. Unger also published the sketches to this as well as his attempt at a completion; please see [entry 129] above. Autographs of both settings are in the Deutsche Staatsbibliothek, Berlin. [TN: now the SBB. A newer edition was published by Hess in the SBG, Vol. V, 1962, p. 13. This is also listed as WoO 116 in Kinsky/Halm, p. 577.]

131 "Plaisir d'aimer" (author unknown). Drafted in 1799, the sketches [start] on p. 52 and continue on the following pages in the Grasnick Sketchbook (Gr. 1) in the Deutsche Staatsbibliothek. [TN: now the SBB.] The first edition was by J. Chantavoine in "Zwei französische Lieder Beethovens," in *Die Musik*, Vol. 1, No. 2, March 1902, beginning on p. 1078. [TN: a newer edition was published by Hess in the SBG, Vol. V, 1962, p. 27. This is also listed as WoO 128 in Kinsky/Halm, p. 590.]

132 "Der edle Mensch sey hülfreich und gut" (Let Noble Men Be Helpful and Good). Text by Goethe. Found in a family [autograph] album for the Baroness Cecilie von Eskeles, later Countess Wimpffen, composed on 20 January 1823. The autograph is in the Gesellschaft der Musikfreunde, Vienna. The first edition was by August Schmidt in *Allgemeine Wiener Musikzeitung,* Vol. 3, from 23 November 1843, beginning on p. 589. Reprinted by Otto E. Deutsch in "Eine vergessene Goethe Komposition Beethovens," *Philobiblon V*, Vienna 1932, beginning on p. 173, and again by Gustav Lange in *Musikgeschichtliches*, Berlin 1900, p. 16, and probably only given correctly through Max Unger in *Ein Faustopernplan Beethovens und Goethes*, Bosse Verlag, Regensburg 1952, p. 31. Kalischer IV also pres-

ents this small piece under No. 867. [TN: a newer edition was published by Hess in the SBG, Vol. V, 1962, p. 38. Another edition was published by Michael Hamburger in *Beethoven: Letters, Journals and Conversations*, Thames and Hudson, London and New York 1951 (reprinted 1984 and 1992), p. 187, with an English translation and no WoO or Hess number given. This is also listed as WoO 151 in Kinsky/Halm, p. 622, where the word in the title is given as "sei" not "sey."]

133 "Das liebe Kätzchen" (The Dear Kitten); see the following number. [TN: this is a setting of an Austrian folksong for soprano with piano accompaniment. Written about March 1820. It and entry 134 were sent in a letter dated 18 March 1820 to Nicolaus Simrock in Bonn. The letter containing both songs was acquired by Wilhelm Speyer of Frankfurt a. M. about 1825. They passed into the collection of Edward Speyer of Shenley, near London, about 1865 and were listed as part of his collection in Theodor Frimmel's *Beethoven Jahrbuch*, Vol. 2, Georg Müller, Munich and Leipzig 1909, p. 306. They were acquired by H. C. Bodmer and are now part of the Beethoven-Haus collection where they bear the catalog number SBH 399. The old Bodmer catalog number was Br 227. The Simrock letter is listed in Anderson as No. 1013 and in Brandenburg as No. 1372. An edition was published by Hess in the SBG, Vol. V, 1962, p. 38. See entry 134 for more publication information.]

134 "Der Knabe auf dem Berge" (The Boy on the Mountain). Beethoven had sent this and the previous Austrian folksong written for piano and voice (vocal line in the piano part) to the publisher Nicolaus Simrock in Bonn on 18 March 1820. The autograph (Br 227) is in the Bodmer Collection. [TN: the Bodmer Collection is now in the Beethoven-Haus, Bonn. See entry 133 above for more details on the history of these two songs.] The

first edition appeared in *Niederrheinische Musik-zeitung* from 23 September 1865, and was again published in Nohl II, as No. 232, and also in Thayer IV, pp. 193-5 and 583-4. [TN: an edition was published by Hess in the SBG, Vol. V, 1962, p. 38.]

135 "La tiranna," according to Kinsky/Halm was composed about 1798. The autograph is missing, as well as the Viennese edition. [TN: Kinsky/Halm states that a Viennese edition may never have been printed.] It appeared with an English text by William Wennington after 1800 in London with Broderip & Wilkinson, Hodsoll & Astor & Co. Kinsky/Halm makes this comment on it: "Anyway, the present edition would likely be the earliest English edition of a composition of Beethoven." See also the reference in J. H. Blaxland "Eine unbekannte Canzonnetta Beethovens," *Zeitschrift für Musikwissenschaft,* Vol. 14, No. 1, October 1931, pp. 29-34. [TN: a newer edition was published by Hess in the SBG, Vol. V, 1962, p. 16. This is also listed as WoO 125 in Kinsky/Halm, p. 587.]

136 "Neue Liebe, neues Leben" ("Herz, mein Herz, was soll das geben") (New Love, New Life) (Heart, My Heart, What Has That Given). The text is by Goethe, and the first version is from 1798-9. The autograph is unknown. The first edition was published [as song No. 1] in *III (Drei) Deutsche Lieder. In Musik gesetzt von L. van Beethoven,* N. Simrock, Bonn 1808. See also the reference by Otto Erich Deutsch in "Ein vergessenes Goethelied von Beethoven," *Die Musik,* Vol. 23, No. 1, October 1930, [pp. 19-23], with the transcription of the song and all the sketches still available. [TN: a newer edition was published by Hess in the SBG, Vol. V, 1962, p. 20. This song, which is an earlier version of Op. 72, No. 2, is listed as WoO 127 in Kinsky/Halm, p. 589. Sketches for this song are found in SV45 (Grasnick 1) on folio 21v in the Beethoven-Haus, Bonn.]

137 "Schwinge dich in meinen Dom" (Swing Yourself into My Cathedral). See the following number. [TN: the title is incorrectly given by Hess as "Schwinge dich in meinen Dom" which doesn't make much sense at all. It should read, "Ich wiege dich in meinen Arm" (I Cradle You in My Arms) and the author of the text is unknown. Cooper gives this composition a "purely conjectural" date of 1795. The autograph is lost. Judging from the correct title, this was probably a lullaby. This otherwise unknown song is referred to in a price list of 1822 compiled by Beethoven in preparation for possible publication. The source for Hess's mistake in the title would appear to be Thayer. On this, Alan Tyson writes: "In an appendix to the third volume of his biography of Beethoven, Thayer cites a price list Beethoven had dawn up for a number of his unpublished (and in a couple of cases still unwritten) works. Thayer appears to have known it only from a transcript made by Otto Jahn, and his printed text contains some errors. Fortunately, it is possible to correct them, for the list is today in the SBB, catalogued as 'Mus. Ms. Autogr. Beethoven 35, 80.' The list carries no date – not surprisingly, since as a document it was probably intended for Beethoven's eyes alone. Thayer printed the list along with Beethoven's correspondence with Steiner and Haslinger from the years 1815-17, and added a somewhat enigmatic footnote to say that, according to indications in the Steiner and Streicher correspondence the document belonged to the end of 1816. (See Thayer III, pp. 487-88; reprinted unchanged in Thayer-Deiters-Riemann III, pp. 619-20. The footnote was omitted in Thayer/Krehbiel and Thayer/Forbes.) Thayer's dating was not challenged by Nottebohm. Today, however, it is plain that the list must be placed over five years later. The clearest evidence for a later date is contained in a letter that Beethoven wrote to the Leipzig publisher C. F. Peters on June 5, 1822." The letter referred to is Anderson 1079

and Brandenburg 1468. This letter contains a list of works offered to Peters for publication which included this entry, as well as entries 11 and 138, among others. This is one of several entries that Hess chose to include in the catalog without knowing for sure whether they were ever written. There are no sketches, drafts or autograph for this song. See Alan Tyson, "A Beethoven Price List of 1822," in *Beethoven Essays: Studies in Honor of Elliot Forbes*, Harvard University Press, Cambridge, Mass. 1984; see also C/C, p. 264.]

138 "Odorata - o Nice" ('Odorata' is probably a misprint; the correct word should be 'Adorata'). [TN: 'Odorata' means 'Smelled' while 'Adorata' means 'Adored.' A considerable difference indeed!] This and the previous song are found on a list of works that [records show] Beethoven offered to the publisher Steiner about 1815-1817. Nothing further is known about it. The same piece is mentioned in Thayer III, p. 619. [TN: this was not listed in a price list to Steiner of 1815-17, but in a list of works prepared by Beethoven for his own reference and later offered to C. F. Peters in 1822. See the references in the entry 137 above. The faulty misprint in the title appears to originate with Otto Jahn's transcription of the list, and was repeated by Thayer and eventually also by Hess. This work is now known today by another title, "No, non turbarti" and is listed in Kinsky/Halm as WoO 92a on p. 548. Because Hess appears to have been unaware of the true identity of this entry, he has inadvertently listed this work twice. It is identical with entry 119 above.]

139 "Minnesold von Bürger, in Tönen an Amenda ausbezahlt von Beethoven" (Bürger's Minnesold, in [musical] notes paid to Amenda by Beethoven). The autograph of a song with this title was sent in 1852 by Amenda's son to Dr. Hermann Härtel in Leipzig, who gave it to a

Professor Lobe; since then it has been missing. See also the reference in Ludwig Nohl's *Beethoven, Liszt, Wagner. Ein Buch der Kunstbewegung unseres Jahrhunderts*, W. Braunmüller, Vienna 1874, p. 94. [TN: Cooper suggests that the author of the text may have been someone named Bürger, and gives the possible composition date as c.1798. See C/C, p. 264. It turns out Cooper is correct; the poem "Minnesold" was written in the late 18th century by the poet Gottfried August Bürger (1747-1794) and was apparently the text used for this song. Also apparent is that Beethoven owed some sort of debt to Karl Amenda and paid that debt by setting this eight stanza poem to music. The first and last stanzas are given here:

Wemder Minne Dienst gelinget,	Who succeeds in love's service
O, wie hoch wird der belohnt!	Oh, how well he is rewarded!
Keinen bessern Lohn erringet,	No better wage receives,
Wer dem größten Kaiser frohnt;	Who serves the grandest emp'ror.
Den mit Scepter, Kron' und Gold,	Because with crown and gold,
Frohnt er selbst um Minnesold.	He fights for the lover's wage himself.

O, so will ich immer harren,	Oh, I will forever last,
Immerdar, mit stetem Muth,	Never failing with strong will,
Im Decemberfrost erstarren,	To freeze in December's cold,
Schmachten in des Heumonds Glut;	Starve in summer's embers.
Denn Das Alles lohnt der Sold,	This all is paid by the wage,
Den getreue Minne zollt.	Which faithful love returns.

It is not known whether Amenda requested the text to be set to music or whether it was Beethoven's idea. It was to Amenda that Beethoven sent the first version of Op. 18, No 1, and Amenda who ". . .told the story that Beethoven described in the slow movement of this quartet the farewell of two lovers, referring to Shakespeare's *Romeo and Juliet*." Certainly the concept of "faithful love" was to return again and again in Beethoven's music, culminating in his opera *Fidelio*.

See Paul Nettl's *Beethoven Handbook*, Ungar Publishing, New York 1956, p. 4.]

140 "Dimmi, ben mio, che m'ami," (Tell Me, My Dear, That You Love Me) a later setting of Op. 82, No. 1. Max Unger published and described this song in the *Zeitschrift für Musik*, Vol. 105, February 1938, pp. 153-156. The autograph is in the Paris Conservatory [TN: now the BN]. Above all else, this setting differs in the accompaniment from that printed in the GA. [TN: a newer edition was published by Hess in the SBG, Vol. V, 1962, p. 35.]

141 "Bußlied" (Song of Patience); Op. 48 No. 6. The last twelve bars [are] in another version. This is unpublished, the autograph is in the Bodmer Collection, Mh 31. [TN: this was published by Hess in the SBG, Vol. V, 1962, p. 28. The Bodmer Collection is now in the Beethoven-Haus, Bonn and this piece has been renumbered SBH 536. The autograph for song No. 6 is marked "No. 5" and song No. 5 is marked "No. 6." The order appears to have been reversed in publication. This alternate ending was written about 1803.]

142 "Wonne der Wehmut," (The Bliss of Melancholy); Op. 83, No. 1; another version. [TN: probably an earlier version.] Deviations from the printed version are found in the first autograph which is today in the possession of the Goethe and Schiller Archives in Weimar. Unpublished. [TN: this was published by Hess in the SBG, Vol. V, 1962, p. 30. William Kinderman writes of this: "The heavily revised manuscript of Beethoven's early version of *Wonne der Wehmut* (Hess 142) came into Goethe's hands, probably through Friedrich Rochlitz. A decade later, in October 1821, Goethe placed this treasure before the young Felix Mendelssohn, who delighted the ageing poet with his performance and with his clean transcription of the song, which is

housed, together with Beethoven's autograph, in Weimar." See William Kinderman's *Beethoven*, University of California Press, Berkeley 1995, p. 146.]

143 Ode "An die Freude" (To Joy); text by Friedrich Schiller. Beethoven is said to have set this poem after 1793 as a song with piano, and offered it to Simrock in Bonn together with other works in 1803. See also the reference in Kinsky/Halm to Op. 52, p. 122. [TN: probably written c.1798-9 (now lost). This early setting of Schiller's famous poem "To Joy" is referred to by Ferdinand Ries in 1803. There is also a reference in 1793 to Beethoven's intention to set the text, but there are no sketches except two brief ones that survive from 1798. The 1793 reference is from Beethoven's friend Bartolomäus Fischenich to Charlotte von Schiller, that Beethoven was already contemplating a strophe-by-strophe setting of the celebrated ode. [TN: the letter is dated 26 January 1793 and Fischenich was a professor of law at the Bonn University. Charlotte was Friedrich Schiller's wife.] It was Nottebohm who pointed out the brief sketches from 1798 in the Grasnick 1 sketchbook. There are some sketches in Robert Winter's "The sources for Beethoven's Misa Solemnis," in *Beethoven Essays: Studies in Honor of Elliot Forbes*, Harvard University Press, Cambridge, Mass. 1984, p. 233. There is no trace of the completed song. See C/C, p. 265.]

144 "Feuerfarb' " (Color of Fire), an early version. This version is found in Beethoven Autograph 11 in the Gesellschaft der Musikfreunde in Vienna. Nottebohm's statement is inappropriate that this earlier one was completed by 1792, and that this present performance-ready version differs from the printed version only by a different postlude. In fact, all of the accompaniment was newly written. The same piece is mentioned by Willy Hess in "Beethovens Lied,

Feuerfarb' " in *Musik im Unterricht,* 46/1, November 1955, pp. 338-9, where the first edition of this earlier setting is added as a musical supplement. Two working stages are clearly shown in this first setting, which means that one could speak of three settings. In the first edition [prepared by] W. Hess, both working stages are printed in their entirety. [TN: a newer edition was published by Hess in the SBG, Vol. V, 1962, p. 10. To make this perfectly clear, entry 144 is meant to represent two settings (or "working stages" one on top of the other) while Op. 52, No. 2 is meant to be the third (or final) setting.]

145 "Opferlied" (Offering Song), the text is by [Friedrich von] Matthisson; this is the very first version. The autograph was in Grasnick 8 of the Staatsbibliotek, Berlin, which is missing at the present time. [TN: the institution is now known as the SBB; however the autograph, Grasnick 8, is still lost. Sketches are found on folio 68 of the Kafka Sketchbook in the British Library, London. They are found with sketches for Op. 1, No.1, and would therefore date to about 1793-4.] See also the reference by Kurt Herbst in "Beethoven's Opferliedkompositionen," in *Neues Beethoven-Jahrbuch,* Vol. V, Henry Litolff's Verlag, Braunschweig 1933, pp. 137-153, where the first thirteen bars of this unpublished setting are printed on p. 255. [TN: this was published in full by Hess in the SBG, Vol. V, 1962, p. 10. See references to other settings of this song in entry 91.]

146 "Der freie Mann" (The Free Man), an earlier setting [of WoO 117] written about 1792-3. The important sketches appeared partially printed by Schiedermair in *Der junge Beethoven,* p. 339 and Nottebohm II, p. 562. Two completely executed settings originated in 1794 or at the beginning of 1795, from which the Gesamtausgabe used the second. [TN: to clarify, the

setting in the Gesamtausgabe is WoO 117. The two earlier settings are both listed here under the single number 146 by Hess.] A series of editions of this had already been published earlier [than the Gesamtausgabe], including Wegeler's revised edition from 1806 by Simrock with a Masonic text, "Was ist des Maurers Ziel?" (What Is the Mason's Goal?). The original setting first appeared in an edition by W. Hess in *Musica*, Vol. 10, the June issue of 1956, together with a setting that is wrongly marked in Kinsky/Halm, p. 578, as for four male voices. Contrary to Kinsky/Halm, the autographs of both settings, in addition to this setting, are all in the British Museum; the two completed settings are on folios 61v and 62r and the sketch is on page 153v of the Kafka Sketchbook, Add. Ms. 29801. [TN: all of the British Museum holdings, including the Kafka Sketchbook, are now in the BL. The Kafka Sketchbook was printed in facsimile and transcription by Joseph Kerman as *Autograph Miscellany, from ca. 1786 to 1799*, 2 Vols., British Museum, London 1970.] The sketch is also intended for a song with unison choral refrain, and was probably written in 1794. This piece is discussed by Willy Hess in "Der freie Mann: Eine ungedruckte Frühfassung von Beethovens lied," *Musica*, Vol. 10, No. 6, pp. 332-385.

147 "Der Kuss" (The Kiss), Op. 128, earlier setting (1798). This is unpublished. The same piece is mentioned in *Nottebohm II*, p. 473. Here's a question to toss up: doesn't the autograph mentioned by Max Unger (Beethoven Ms. 33 of the Paris Conservatory) represent a fragment of this first setting since it differs from the final setting? [TN: this manuscript, Ms. 33 is now in the BN.] Indeed, Unger asks inquiringly, "December 1922?" [TN: this date is a misprint and should read "1822."] This piece is listed and described by Unger in "Die Beethovenhandschriften der Pariser Konservatoriumsbibliothek," *Neues Beethoven-Jahrbuch*

VI, Henry Litolff's Verlag, Braunschweig 1935, pp. 96-97.

148 Sketches for Goethe's "Erlkönig" (The Erl-King), various drafts, between 1800 and about 1810. Principal sketches are in the archive of the Gesellschaft der Musikfreunde in Vienna [A 67 = SV 297], printed in *Nottebohm I*, pp. 100-103. [TN: other sketches are in the BN as Ms 70 (SV 223).] A completion of the draft was published by Reinhold Becker through Schuberth, Leipzig 1897, including a facsimile of Beethoven's sketches. Another completion was published by Heinrich Zöllner with Luckhardt & Belder, New York 1898, and also published by Commissionsverlag Fr. Luckhardt, Leipzig-Berlin, the same year. [TN: another edition was published in the *Neue Gesamtausgabe: Beethovens Werke*, Vol. XII, Part 1, *Lieder und Gesänge*, G. Henle, Munich 1990, p. 268. An article on the process of turning unfinished sketches into finished works and mentioning this one was written by Alexander L. Ringer, "The Art of the Third Guess: Beethoven to Becker to Bartók," *Musical Quarterly*, Vol. 52, 1966, pp.304-312.]

149 Continuity drafts [for a] song to Goethe's "Rastlose Liebe" (Restless Love) (1800-1810). [TN: sketches for this song are found beside some of the "Erlkönig" sketches of 1796]. The melody is completely drafted; the Ritornellos are sketched. A completion by Jean Chantavoine was printed in *La Revue Musicale, Publication Mensuelle*, Vol. 2, H. Welter, Paris 1902, pp. 409-414. The facsimile was published (incompletely) by Elsa Bienenfeld in the *Neue Wiener Journal*, 27 March 1927. [TN: Mark Zimmer writes of this piece: "The sketches are presently in Berlin, as part of the Fischhof Miscellany, and in Vienna at the Gesellschaft der Musikfreunde in manuscript A67. Gustav Nottebohm guessed that the sketches could have come

from anytime between 1800 and 1824; Douglas Johnson has verified that these sketches are on a paper type known to have been used by Beethoven in Prague in early 1796. The Fischhof sketches for this song were published in transcription by Douglas Johnson in *Beethoven's Early Sketches in the Fischhof Miscellany: Berlin Autograph 28*, 2 Vols., Ann Arbor, Michigan 1980, pp. 1222-5. There are, in a sense, three full continuity drafts for this song, each varying somewhat melodically, but pretty much all consistent in their general vision. I say, 'in a sense' because Beethoven wrote down one continuity draft, but of course with the usual corrections written on top of it. Douglas Johnson has nevertheless managed to decipher all the notes that were scratched out, and came to the conclusion that we have three versions written one on top of the other (or, if you want, that Beethoven worked on it on three separate occasions). Johnson has printed all three versions in his transcription, but in a way trying to preserve the layout of Beethoven's manuscript. Johnson hypothesizes that this song was written for Countess Josephine de Clary, for whom Beethoven wrote the mandolin pieces WoO 43 and 44 on the same kind of paper." If a completion by Beethoven ever existed, it is not known to have survived.]

150 Sketches to Goethe's "Heidenröslein" (Little Rose of the Moor). These sketches are in the Paris Conservatory, Beethoven Ms. 79. [TN: they are now in the BN. This sketchleaf was once owned by Alexander Wheelock Thayer, the eminent Beethoven biographer. The paper on which it was written is a type which Douglas Johnson has identified as being used between 1793 and 1796. Additional sketch material spanning many yeas may also be found in the pocket sketchbook Autograph 45, folio 31v, dating from 1818 given in Nottebohm II, p. 137), Autograph 63, pp. 2-4 from 1820 (Nottebohm II, p. 576) and the desk sketchbook

Artaria 201, pp. 77 and 115, dating between 1821 and 1823 (quoted in Nottebohm II, pp. 471 and 474 respectively). Autographs 45 and 63 are held by the Gesellschaft der Musikfreunde in Vienna while Artaria is held by the SBB.] A completion has been worked out by Henry Holden Huss, about which Henry Edward Krehbiel wrote a commentary, and published in the *New York Tribune: Illustrated Supplement* of 6 March 1898, together with a facsimile of the sketches. Beethoven worked on this song between 1796 and 1823 without finishing it.

151 "Traute Henriette" (Trusted Henriette); the author of the text is unknown. [TN: Jos van der Zanden dates these sketches to c.1792-3.] The almost completed sketches to this song may belong to the first years in Vienna, and are in the possession of the Wiener Stadtbibliothek. (catalog No. 383 of the Beethoven Centennial Exhibition of the City of Vienna, 1927.) [TN: these sketches are currently catalogued as SV 392.] Adolf Erler has worked out these continuity drafts and has published them in *Österreichische Musikzeitschrift*, Vol. 4, 1949 (part 1 of 2). See the reference by Adolf Erler in "Ein Lied aus Beethovens Frühzeit;" see also the reference on pp. 23-25. [TN: a newer edition was published by Hess in the SBG, Vol. V, 1962, p. 14.]

The continuity drafts of the songs that are listed as numbers 148-151 should be included in the edition of the new Gesamtausgabe, as well the numbers 129-131, the reason being that the works are in a state where they convey an overall artistic impression. Contrary to this, we have no longer included the sketches to the song "Wehrmannslied" by [Heinrich Joseph von] Collin, which are listed in earlier Catalogs (Hess 3)115c, for example, under No. 262. Mentioning all of Beethoven's sketches by name would go beyond the purpose of this catalog. This must be the object of a separate work.

Folksong Arrangements

(All the settings are for one or several voices, some include a small chorus, with accompaniment of piano, violin and cello.)

This chapter needs a more thorough completion, because not all the handwritten sources have yet been researched for unknown second versions, etc. For example, No. 92 of the catalog of handwritten manuscripts by Schmidt-Görg from the Beethoven-Haus (Bonn 1935) contains 43 such versions in copies reviewed by Beethoven which "in part deviate from the versions in the complete edition." My article which follows and which is part of the new complete edition should thus not be considered as final.

Thayer lists under No. 177 the incipits of thirty-one song treatments, numbered from 1-24 and 26-32, that were at that time unpublished. Of these, [there] are listed in the GA: Nos. 3 and 21 as Nos. 1 and 6 of the Twelve Scottish Songs [WoO 156], (Series 24, No. 260); No. 30 as No. 13 of the Twenty Irish Songs [WoO 153], (Series 24, No. 262), but in a one-part setting, while the original is a duet for soprano and tenor. Thayer states that this was probably a trio and that Beethoven in the beginning declared it to be for soprano, tenor, bass, and that he then, however, crossed out the bass. The duet setting still has not been published, and we have therefore included the song in this list once again by listing the piece below. Thayer's No. 13 came from A. C. Kalischer after an incomplete transcription (Deutsche Staatsbibliothek, Berlin) [TN: now the SBB] in *Die Musik*, Vol. 2, No. 6, December 1902, [p. 403], where it was printed as a youthful work of Beethoven, an error, that Schiedermair has also indiscriminately inserted into the first edition of his *Der junge Beethoven*, p. 225.

Unfortunately, Thayer nowhere declares his sources, and consequently researchers have believed many of the songs he listed to be lost. This situation changed, however, when a handwritten manuscript was discovered in the archives of the publisher Breitkopf & Härtel that contained treatments of twenty-four songs in copies revised by Beethoven. Wilhelm Lütge reported on this discovery in the annual *Der Bär*, Breitkopf & Härtel, Leipzig 1927, pp. 159-165. From the twenty-four songs, No. 8 was already identified as the twelfth piece of "Twelve Songs of Different Nationalities" [WoO 157] in the GA (Series 24, No. 259), fourteen additional songs were given among Thayer's *"Ungedruckten" (Unpublished Song List)* and the remaining nine were completely new to the research.

After different researchers, including Otto Erich Deutsch and Eusebius Mandyczewski, had worked on publication of this handwritten manuscript, Georg Schünemann put out these 23 songs (the one already published in the GA was left out) as *Neues Volksliederheft,* through the publisher Breitkopf & Härtel, in July 1940. Unfortunately, this was done without mention of the work of his predecessors and also without any attempt to find the stanzas following the first stanza of each song. A song from this publication had, incidentally, already appeared earlier, namely the "Swedish Lullaby" (No. 17 of the Schünemann edition), which Joseph Schmidt-Görg published in *Veröffentlichungen des Beethovenhauses Bonn,* Vol. 5, [Quelle & Meyer, Leipzig] 1928, where the autograph is located.

The handwritten manuscript described by Lütge (listed below as Leipzig copy) is today located in the Hessische Landesbibliothek, Darmstadt.

In the winter of 1929-30, I had worked through all the pertinent handwritten manuscripts in Berlin and with them determined a large part of those that until then were mourned as originals gone astray, together with a large number of copies of song treatments. These are mentioned by Willy Hess in "Neues zu Beethovens Volksliederbearbeitungen," in *Zeitschrift für Musik-wissenschaft*, Vol. 13, No. 6, March 1931, pp. 317-324; further was added in the addendum in the *Archiv für Musikforschung*, Vol. 1, No. 1, 1936, p. 123. Still further references can be found by Willy Hess in "52 Ungedruckte Volksliederbearbeitung Beethovens," in *Schweiz-erische Musikzeitung*, Vol. 76, 2nd April journal, 1936, pp. 236-239. [TN: a major new work on the folksongs has appeared by Barry Cooper as *Beethoven's Folksong Settings: Chronology, Sources, Style*, Clarendon Press, Oxford 1994. Subsequent references to "C/F" given in this section are to this work.]

We now give a tabular overview of the folksong arrangements, which include all the fundamental songs that should be included in the new GA. We are also including Schünemann's *Neues Volksliederheft*, although it can be considered (through his entry numbers) as a continuation of the GA (refer to p. 10, line 6 ff.). If manuscripts are without designation [in this tabulation, then] Berlin is meant, and numbers 29 I, II etc. mean Beethoven Autograph 29 I, II that are in the Staatsbibliothek, Berlin. [TN: this is now the SBB.]

Name of the songs	Number in Thayer's unpublished song list	Number in the Schünemann edition	Number in the Leipzig copy	Existing in: Autograph	Copy

152   1   -   -   Artaria 190   29 IV
Irish. Text unknown,20 bars, A major. [TN: text is "Adieu my Lov'd Harp" by Thomas Moore. WoO 158, group 2, No.1]

153   2   -   -   Artaria 190   29 IV
Irish. Text unknown. Listed by Thayer as a trio, in reality however, it is a quartet (the only quartet of this kind!), 30 bars, E-flat major. [TN: titled "Castle O'Neill" but text is still unknown. WoO 158, group 2, No. 2]

Name of the songs	Number in Thayer's unpublished song list	Number in the Schünemann edition	Number in the Leipzig copy	Existing in: Autograph	Copy
154	4	-	-	29 II	29 I, 29 V

According to Thayer, nationality unknown; Kinsky/Halm gives it as Scottish. F major, 33 bars. [WoO 158, group 2, No. 3]

| 155 | 5 | - | - | 29 II | 29 I, 29 V Ritornello also in the Bodmer Collection, Mh 36, [now SBH 596] |

Scottish, without text, E major, 15 bars. [TN: the text has been found. See C/F pp. 41, 61 and 218. Titled "Red Gleams the Sun on yon Hill Top," text by Dr. Couper. WoO 158, group 2, No. 4]

| 156 | 6 | 1 | 20 | 29 II | 29 I |

Danish, (Ritter nah'n dem Königsschloß) [TN: the Danish title is "Ridder Stigs Runer." WoO 158, group 1, No. 1]

| 157 | 7 | - | - | 29 II | 29 I, 29V Artaria 189 |

Scottish, without text, trio. G major, 39 bars. [TN: the text has been found; see C/F p.216. With two texts, titled, "Could Frosty Morning," anon. and "Erin! Oh, Erin," text by Thomas Moore. WoO 158, group 2, No. 5]

| 158 | 8 | 11 | 9 | 29 II | 29 I |

Portuguese, Cancion, "Ich traue nicht den Wogen" (I don't trust the waves). [TN: C/F gives this as Portuguese/Spanish with the title in Portuguese as "Yo no quiero embarcarme." WoO 158, group 1, No. 11]

Name of the songs	Number in Thayer's unpublished song list	Number in the Schünemann edition	Number in the Leipzig copy	Existing in: Autograph	Copy

159   9   12   10   29 II   29 I
Portuguese, duet, "Als ihre Augen kaum ich gesehen" (When I had just seen her eyes). [TN: the Portuguese title is "Seus lindos olhos." WoO 158, group 1, No. 12]

160   10   13   1   29 I   29 I
Russian, "In dem Wald, dem grünen Walde" (In the forest, the green forest). [TN: Russian title is "Vo lesochke komarochkov." WoO 158, group 1, No. 13]

161   11   14   2   29 II   29 I
Russian, "Ach, ihr Bächlein, kühlen Wasser" (Oh, you little brook with cool waters). [TN: Russian title is "Akh, rechenki, rechenki." WoO 158, group 1, No. 14]

162   12   15   3   29 II   29 I
Russian, "Uns're lieben Mädchen gingen Beeren pflücken" (Our lovely girls went berry picking). [TN: Russian title is "Kak poshi nashi podruzhki." WoO 158, group 1, No.15]

163   13   19   5   29 II   29 I
Spanish, *Bolero a solo*, "Mein Träubchen ist entflogen" (My dove has flown away). [TN: Spanish title is "Una paloma blanca." WoO 158, group 1, No. 19]

164   14   20   6   29 II   29 I
Spanish, *Bolero a due*, duet, "Die Rose lockt den Falter" (The Rose Lures the Butterfly) [TN: the Spanish is "Como la mariposa." Dorfmüller equates this entry with entry 207, while C/F asserts that 207 is a rough draft for this setting. WoO 158, group 1, No. 20]

165   15   21   7   29 II   29 I
Spanish, Tiranilla Española, "Auf, Gefährten, macht euch

Name of the songs	Number in Thayer's unpublished song list	Number in the Schünemann edition	Number in the Leipzig copy	Existing in: Autograph	Copy

bereit!" (On, companions, get yourselves ready!). [TN: the Spanish title is "La tiranna se embarca." WoO 158, group 1, No. 21]

166	16	-	-	29 II	29 I, 29 V

Nationality unknown, E minor, 33 bars. [TN: C/F, p. 218, gives the title and source for the text as "When my Hero in Courts Appears" from John Grey's *The Beggar's Opera*. WoO 158, group 3, No. 1]

167	17	-	-	29 II	29 I, 29 V

Nationality unknown, B-flat major, 51 bars. [TN: C/F, p. 218, gives the title and source for the text as "Air de Collin" ('Non, non, Colette n'est point trompeuse') from Jean-Jacques Rousseau's *Le Devin du Village*. WoO 158, group 3, No. 2]

168	18	-	-	29 II	29 I, 29 V

Air by Rousseau (Thomson), text is unknown, F major, 32 bars. [TN: this work is known as "Air Français" (author of the text is unidentified, but possibly by Rousseau?), soprano; C/F gives the composition date as early 1817 and an alternate title, "Troubadour Song." There is no equivalent WoO number.]

169	19	-	-	29 III (The ending of the Ritornello is missing)	29 I, 29 V

Nationality unknown, B-flat major, 53 bars. [TN: C/F, p. 220, gives two titles and sources for the text: "Sleep'st thou or wak'st thou" by Robert Burns and "Mark Yonder Pomp,"

Name of the songs	Number in Thayer's unpublished song list	Number in the Schüne-mann edition	Number in the Leipzig copy	Existing in: Autograph	Copy

also by Burns. One could presume this to be Scottish, since the text is by Burns. WoO 158, group 3, No. 3]

170	20	-	-	Collection L. Koch, Wildegg *	29 V Artaria 189

Scottish, without text, A minor, 26 bars. [TN: C/F, p. 216, gives the title and source for the text as "O Mary ye's be clad in Silk," anonymous.]

* It is there listed as No. 7, while No. 9 of the same collection corresponds to Thayer's "unpublished song" No. 21, i.e. No. 6 of the Twelve Scottish Folksongs (WoO 156) from the GA, and is therefore, contrary to the statement of Kinsky in, "Die Beethovenhandschriften der Sammlung Louis Koch,"*Neues Beethoven-Jahrbuch V*, Verlag des Beethovenhauses, Braunschwig 1933, p. 48 ff. [TN: the Koch col-lection in now dispersed, with some parts having gone to Hans Rahmer, Hamburg-Langenhorn, and part to the Cary Collection in the Pierpont Morgan Library, New York, and still other parts missing. See C/C, p. 224.]

171	22	18	13	29 II	-

Swiss, "An ä Bergli bin i gesässe" (I sat on a mountain) [TN: given in C/F, p. 217 as Swiss/German. WoO 158, group 1, No. 18]

172	23	2	11	29 II	-

German, "Horch auf, mein Liebchen" (Listen, oh, my dearest). [TN: given in C/F, p. 217 as Austrian/German. The text is taken from Wenzel Müller's Singspiel *Das neue Sonntagskind.* WoO 158, group 1, No. 2]

Name of the songs	Number in Thayer's unpub- lished song list	Number in the Schüne- mann edition	Number in the Leipzig copy	Existing in: Autograph	Copy

173   24   3   12   29 II   -

German, "Wegen meiner bleib d'Fräula nur da ganz allein" (For all I care, the girl may stay there quite alone). [TN: given in C/F, p. 217 as Austrian/German. The text is taken from Wenzel Müller' Singspeil *Das neue Sonntagskind*. WoO 158, group 1, No. 3]

174   26   4   4   -   -

Tyrolean, "Wann i in der Früh aufsteh" (When I Arise Early in the Morning). [WoO 158, group 1, No. 4]

175   27   -   -   -   29 V

Nationality unknown, trio, with piano only, A major, 16 bars. [TN: C/F, p. 220, gives the title and source for the text as "Bonnie Wee Thing" by Robert Burns. This setting was actually done by Haydn for Thomson with Beethoven adapting it for 3 voices. One could presume this to be Scottish, since the text is by Burns. WoO 158, group 3, No. 4]

176   28   -   -   -   29 V

Nationality unknown, trio, B-flat major, 23 bars. [TN: C/F, p. 220 gives the title and source for the text as "From Thee, Eliza, I must go" by Robert Burns. Based on the fact that the text is by Burns, one can presume nationality to be Scottish. WoO 158, group 3, No. 5]

177   29   16   19   -   29 V (only 15 bars)

Russian, "Schöne Minka, ich muß scheiden"(Beautiful Minka, I must part). [TN: given in C/F, p. 217, as Cossack/Ukrainian, and the author as Christolph August Tiedge. WoO 158, group 1, No. 16]

Name of the songs	Number in Thayer's unpublished song list	Number in the Schünemann edition	Number in the Leipzig copy	Existing in: Autograph	Copy

178   30   -   -   29 II   29 I, 29 V

Irish; the same piece is listed in Twenty Irish Folksongs [WoO153, No. 13]. Here as a duet. [TN: Cooper in C/F, p. 192, states that this duet version is the original version.]

179   31   -   -   Artaria 187   29 IV Beetho- ven- Haus, Bonn

Nationality un- known, E minor, 14 bars. Beethoven's autograph is incomplete, a new ending indicated by Vi-(de) is missing, and bars 6 and 7 (prima and seconda volta) appear to be combined into a single bar. However, the Bonn copy is complete; it is listed as piece 24 of No. 92 in the Schmidt-Görg catalog of handwritten manuscripts. Here one can also find the above-mentioned new ending. The remaining deviations of both settings are inconsequential. [TN: the nationality is given by Thomson as Scottish. Hess doubted this and thought it might be Irish and therefore left it marked here as "unknown." Cooper believes Scottish it to be correct. See C/F, p. 61. WoO 158, group 3, No. 6]

180   32   -   -   -   29 IV

Irish, without text, traditional, G minor, 23 bars. [TN: the title is given in C/F as "Lament for Owen Roe O'Neill," but still without text, p. 213. WoO 158, group 2, No.7]

181   -   23   14   Artaria 181   -

Venetian canzonetta, "Vom rosigen Munde in zärtlicher Stunde" (From Rosy Lips in Tender Hours). WoO 158, group 1, No. 23]

Name of the songs	Number in Thayer's unpublished song list	Number in the Schünemann edition	Number in the Leipzig copy	Existing in: Autograph	Copy
182	-	5	15	Artaria 188	-

Tyrolean, "Teppichkrämerlied" or "I bin a Tyroler Bua" (Carpet Sellers Song, or I am a Tyrolean Boy). [WoO 158, group 1, No. 5]

183	-	6	16	Artaria 188	-

Tyrolean, "A Madel, ja, a Madel" (A Maiden, yes, a Maiden). [WoO 158, group 1, No. 6]

184	-	9	17	Artaria 188	-

Polish, "Auf, auf, ihr Freunde" (On, On, You Friends). [TN: the Polish title is "Oj, oj upiłem sie w karczmie." WoO 158, group 1, No. 9]

185	-	10	18	Artaria 188	-

Polish, "Lenz und Liebeswonen enden"(Springtime and the Bliss of Love End). [TN: the Polish title is "Poszła baba po popiół." WoO 158, group 1, No. 10]

186	-	17	21	Beethoven-Haus, Bonn, Schmidt-Görg catalog No. 118	-

Swedish Lullaby, "Schlaf, mein Liebling, schlafe ein" (Sleep, my darling, fall asleep). [TN: the Swedish title is "Lilla Carl, sov sött I frid." WoO 158, group 1, No. 17]

187	-	7	22	Only violin and cello part in Bonn, catalog No. 118	-

Tyrolean, "Wer solche Buema afipackt" (Getting the Better of Four Lads). [WoO 158, group 1, No. 7]

Name of the songs	Number in Thayer's unpublished song list	Number in the Schünemann edition	Number in the Leipzig copy	Existing in: Autograph	Copy
188	-	22	23	29 III, only the last 5 bars, one additional sketched version in Bonn, catalog No. 118	-

Hungarian drinking song,"Nach der Heimat Rebenfluren" Vine Fields). [TN: the Hungarian title is "Ének kinos emékezet." (Home from the WoO 158, group 1, No. 22]

189	-	8	24	29 III (only as sketches)	-

Tyrolean Aria, "Ih mag di nit nehma," [TN: this song is in the Tyrolean dialect; when rendered back to standard German, it should read "Ich mag dich nicht nehmen" (I won't take you). WoO 158, group 1, No. 8]

Concerning the poets and the original texts, we refer [to those references] in Schünemann's edition, as well as to Kinsky/Halm, that bring to us all the pertinent statements. The possibility that all existing pieces are not yet listed was already mentioned in the introduction. Max Unger has mentioned the following work to me, years ago:

190 Unknown Irish song, piano version. Unfortunately, Max Unger no longer remembers where he found this (listed in Hess 3 [as] No. 250, and the piano setting as No. 65), F major, 4/4 time. [TN: Hess withdrew this entry after the publication of this catalog blaming, Unger for faulty information. He obviously could not verify the information or circumstances under which he first gathered this.

109

See, however, C/F, p. 228, where this is referred to as a ". . .two stave setting of the melody of WoO 155/21 in Anton Schindler's hand." This is in the SBB Aut. 29 I, folio 13. This was published in the SBG, Vol. 14, p. 20, but Schindler's source has not been identified.]

Hess 2, No. 66, has been found to be a draft to "No. 21 [of] 26 Welsh Folksongs," and, therefore, comes as a novelty there.

191 End of an unknown song, 9 bars, 4/4, in G minor for voice and piano. Fifteenth piece of the Berlin Beethoven autograph 29 I, found with No. 11. [TN: see also C/F, p. 228; where Cooper writes: "Abandoned setting of the melody WoO 155/19, (The Vale of Clwyd) containing just the vocal section, without the string parts. Like the piece mentioned above, it is found only in Anton Schindler's hand in autograph 29 I, folio 13 verso, and was published by Hess in SBG, Vol. 14, as No. 56," p.147.]

So far, I could further determine the following [to be] duplicate settings:

192 From 25 Irish Folksongs, No. 5. Copy: 29 I, 29 IV. [TN: this is an intended replacement (therefore a second setting, not a duplicate) for the folksong, WoO 152, No. 5, "On the Massacre of Glencoe" (text by Scott); Feb. 1813. See C/C, p. 271.]

193 From 25 Irish Folksongs, No. 20. With a different coda, Autograph Artaria 187. [TN: this is an abandoned coda for the folksong, WoO 152, No. 20, "Farewell Bliss" (text by Anne Grant and Burns), July 1810; it was published by Hess in the SBG, Vol. XIV, 1971, p. 19.]

194 From 20 Irish Folksongs, No. 5. Autograph, Paris Conservatory, Beethoven Ms. 24, No. 6 (listed in Hess 2 as No.

251, and in Hess 3 as No. 167a). Unger's statement that this piece is unknown is incorrect, just as [in] Kinsky/Halm (p. 668), who considers this to be No. 11 from "25 Irish" [Folksongs, WoO 152]. Copy: 29 IV. [TN: the autograph is now in the BN. Cooper cites this as an earlier version (first setting) of the folksong "I Dream'd I Lay" (text by Robert Burns); and that it was subsequently replaced by WoO 153, No. 5; it dates from July 1810. See C/F, p. 213. Hess, who published this in the SBG, Vol. XIV, 1971, p. 112, misidentifies the date there as 1815.]

195 From 20 Irish Folksongs, No. 11. Copy: 29 IV. [TN: see C/F, p. 215, where this is given as an alternative (second setting) to the folksong "When Far from the Home" (text by Thomson); Feb. 1813. WoO 153, No. 11. Mark Zimmer writes of this: "Beethoven composed two settings for this song at about the same time; he sent them both to Thomson with a note to the effect: 'I have composed No. 10 of the last ten airs twice. You can insert in your collection whichever of the two pleases you more.' I find this version to be just as pleasing as that which found its way into Thomson's publications and the Kinsky/Halm catalog; it certainly stood no lower in Beethoven's estimation than the other version."]

196 From 20 Irish Folksongs, No. 12; Autograph, 29 III, Copy: 29 IV. [TN: see C/F, p. 213; this is an earlier version (first setting) of "I'll Praise the Saints" (text by William Smyth); it was replaced by WoO 153, No. 12. It was written in July 1810.]

197 From 20 Irish Folksongs, No. 15; Copy: 29 IV. [TN: see C/F, p. 213. An earlier version (1st setting) of "'Tis but in Vain" (text by William Smyth); it was replaced by WoO 153, No. 15, July 1810. Hess, in his SBG, Vol.

XIV, indicates that this song is from 1815; later research has shown that, in fact, it dates from 1810.]

198 From 12 Irish Folksongs, No. 9; Autograph, Paris Conservatory, Beethoven Ms. 24, No. 2, Copy: 29 IV. [TN: now the BN. According to C/F, p. 214, this is an earlier version (first setting) of "Oh, Would I Were" (text by William Smyth); and was replaced by WoO 154, No. 9, February 1812.]

199 From 12 Irish Folksongs, No. 11. Autograph, Artaria 190. Differing only in minor things from the printed version. [TN: Cooper gives the following information: "The autograph version of WoO 154, No. 11, is essentially the same as published. Many other settings have similar kinds of variants between the autograph and the Gesamtausgabe, without having a separate Hess number." See C/F, p. 229. Hess realized that this autograph was so similar to the later published version that he subsequently withdrew it from this catalog.]

200 From 25 Scottish Folksongs, No. 4. Copy: 29 1, 29 V. [TN: this has alternative string parts for Op. 108, No. 4. There are, in fact, two earlier versions of the setting of this song. Copy: 29 I is in Anton Schindler's hand, however. Mark Zimmer wrote of this: "The second version of the string voice is even more simple than in the final version. Apparently Beethoven settled upon the third version as a happy medium. The one published by Thomson (Op. 108, No. 4) was labeled as 'best' by Beethoven."]

201 From 25 Scottish Folksongs, No. 7. Autograph, 29 V. The violin [part] deviates from the printed version [for Op. 108, No. 7]. [TN: Mark Zimmer writes: "This entry actually consists of two versions of the violin voice. The second version is more similar to the final version. When the song was collected as part of Op. 108, Bee-

thoven wrote the final string part, incorporating portions of both of the first two versions." See also C/F, pp. 29-30.]

202 From 25 Scottish Folksongs, No. 11. Autograph, 29 II, Copy: 29 I, 29 V. [TN: essentially only the key signatures differ. Cooper gives the following information: "The autograph version of Op. 108, No. 11, is essentially the same as the printed version, which transposes the music from F to E flat." Hess apparently intended the version in F major to be entry 202. See C/F, p. 229. Published in the SBG, Vol. XIV, 1971, p. 133.]

203 From 25 Scottish Folksongs, No. 20; Copy: 29 IV. [TN: according to C/F, p. 213, this is an earlier version (first setting) of, "Faithfu' Johnie" (text by Anne Grant); and was replaced by Op. 108, No. 20, July 1810.]

204 From 26 Welsh Folksongs, No. 11. Autograph, Artaria 187. Another setting with a very long coda. [TN: Hess has mistakenly attributed this coda to "Merch Megan," WoO 155, No. 11, which is sketched immediately before this coda. Hess acknowledged this error in the *Revisionsbericht* of his SBG, Vol. XIV. According to C/F, p. 229, this is an abandoned coda for WoO 155, No. 7, not WoO 155, No. 11 as stated by Hess. This was published in the SBG, Vol. XIV, 1971, p. 101.]

205 From 26 Welsh Folksongs, No. 14. I have identified this as the ending of an unknown setting of this song, from the Beethoven Ms 102 in the Paris Conservatory, where it is identified as "a fragment of an unknown movement for piano trio, B-flat major, 3/4, 14 ending bars." See the reference by Max Unger in *Neues Beethoven-Jahrbuch VI*, Henry Litolff's Verlag, Braunschweig 1935, pp. 114/5. [TN: now in the BN and according to C/F, p. 229; this is an abandoned coda for

WoO 155, No. 14. This was published by Hess in the SBG, Vol. XIV, 1971, p. 104. It is listed by Biamonti as No. 286, p.284, where it is also described as the, ". . . conclusion to an unknown trio."]

206 From 26 Welsh Folksongs, No. 20; Autograph (only the end), Artaria 187, Copy: 29 IV. [TN: according to C/F, p. 213; this is an earlier version (first setting) of "To the Blackbird" (text by David ap Gwillim or Gwilym?), July 1810; it was replaced by WoO 155, No. 20.]

207 "Bolero a due" [Italian folksong setting] (Schönemann No. 20, entry 164 of this catalog). [TN: C/C, p. 271, says: "An earlier, slightly different version of WoO 158/set one, No. 19 is also known. Hess 207 wrongly describes it as an earlier version of No. 20." Cooper reverses himself in his later work, C/F, p. 229, and describes it as a "rough draft for WoO 158/set one No. 20." See entry 164 above.] The Beethoven-Haus possesses the first half of this song, in another setting. See the reference by L. Schiedermair in *Veröffentlichungen des Beethovenhauses*, Vol. 6, Bonn 1930, pp. 17-18, where the fragment is printed. According to a letter from Samuel Geiser to me, the second part of this piece was auctioned from the Kux Collection (Chur, Switzerland) in 1953 in Luzern for 2950 [Swiss] francs and also went to Bonn, so that this autograph is completely together again after almost 100 years. Located at the end of the page, the following note is in Anton Schindler's hand, "Handschrift von L. van Beethoven. Mitgetheilt of the Frau Doctor G. Görris von A. Schindler. Aachen im Juny 1845." Therefore, Schindler was probably the sinner who cut apart the autograph copy in order to make autograph collectors happy. See also the references in the Schmidt-Görg catalog, No. 79.

Italian A Cappella Partsongs

A. W. Thayer lists under No. 264 of his *Chronologisches Verzeichniss* of Beethoven's works thirty-two Italian song compositions, some of which were supposedly composed in Bonn, and others as late as about 1814. This is inaccurate. Gustav Nottebohm, in *Beethovens Studien*, Leipzig-Winterthur, 1873, states that all the a cappella songs originated about 1793-1802 as studies in Italian song composition under the instruction of Antonio Salieri. Schubert, too, had done such studies with Salieri, partially using the same texts of [Pietro] Metastasio as Beethoven had used. See Alfred Einstein *Schubert*, Pan-Verlag, Zurich 1952, beginning on p. 60.

Thayer has further included some songs into this grouping that don't belong to it. His pieces 7-15 are not compositions by Beethoven but songs of other composers which Beethoven himself had copied as study exercises (further references under "Doubtful and Falsely Attributed Works"). Piece 23 is the scene and aria "No, non turbarti" (No. 119 of this catalog); piece 25 the duet "Nei giorri tuoi felici" (No. 120 of this catalog); piece 32 the aria "Primo amore piacer del ciel" is found in the GA Series No. 25 as No. 271.

Piece 24 would more properly be the song with piano accompaniment "O care selve antiche," that is printed as No. 279 in the GA Series 25. Based on Thayer's incipit, I had listed it as No. 69 in former editions of this catalog as a four-part a cappella song. Hans Böttcher in his *Beethoven als Liederkomponist*, Benno Filser, Augsburg 1928, expresses the supposition that the autograph of this quartet is in the British Museum, Add. Ms. 29801 folio 62b. [TN: this is now in the BL and the autograph is part of the Kafka Sketchbook, where Kerman lists it as folio 62v.] The same piece is listed in Böttcher's table III/4. This same opinion is also expressed in

Kinsky/Halm, p. 581. However, the autograph referred to from the Kafka Sketchbook in London is without any doubt identical with the piano song that appeared in the GA. It has Beethoven's indication, "Coro, solo, Coro," which Thayer's piece 24 also has, while with all of Thayer's remaining pieces the number of the voices (duet, trio, quartet) is expressly declared. So these two pieces are probably identical, although the incipit given by Thayer doesn't completely match the song. Furthermore, we will mention here the deviations of the London manuscript from the GA (which is based on a manuscript in Sketchbook 153 of the Deutsche Staatsbibliothek). During the upbeat of the voice part, the piano bass has a rest, and the voice first had a B instead of a G, which apparently was already corrected in the second copy (which the manuscript in Berlin should be regarded as). In bar 9, both chords in the piano are clearly D-A-C, and not E-A-C; the bass is somewhat unclear D instead of C. So, originally there was a seventh chord on D (without the third), instead of the sixth chord of A minor. In the third bar before the end, the chord in the left hand is G-B-D, instead of G-B. Furthermore, at the end, a "da capo" is asked for (therefore the indication, "Coro, solo, Coro"); the piece finishes with the choral part on bar 12. This is of great advantage, when seen from the point of view of a beautiful, formally rounded-off form, and it is very well possible that the indication "da capo" was simply forgotten in the Berlin manuscript, and therefore in the GA.

The piano accompaniments mentioned by Thayer for several of the pieces are not by Beethoven. We will come back to these pieces when discussing the autographs. Therefore, as true a cappella songs, the pieces numbered: 1-6, 16-22 and 26-31 remain. Additionally, there are others that Thayer did not know some of which I would find in Vienna as late as 1954. In the following list, I give an overview of all the songs known today, to which I add the dating attempted by Nottebohm. The order is done according to Thayer, with the pieces not known to him added at the end. I express great thanks to Prof. Giovanni Biamonti of Rome for his help in determining the sources of the texts not named by Thayer.

208 Song 1: Duet "Fra tutte le pene" for Tenor and Bass in F major, 24 bars and da capo. [WoO 99, No. 3a.] Text from Metastasio's opera *Zenobia,* Act 3, Scene 9 (Thayer piece 1), composed about 1796-7. [TN: published by Hess in the SBG, Vol. I, 1959, p. 11, where Hess gives this piece as existing in two versions. Giovanni Biamonti, in *Catalogo Cronologico e Thematico delle Opere di Beethoven*, ITLE, Turin 1968, pp. 154-5, numbered these two versions separately as 142 for the first version and 143 for the second version. In this catalog, Hess made no distinction.]

209 Song 2: Trio "Fra tutte le pene" for Soprano, Alto and Tenor in E-flat major, 25 bars and da capo (Thayer piece 2). [WoO 99, No. 3b.] Composed about 1796-7. [TN: published by Hess in the SBG, Vol. I, 1959, p. 15. Like entry 208 above, this piece also exists in two versions. Giovanni Biamonti, in *Catalogo Cronologico e Thematico delle Opere di Beethoven*, ITLE, Turin 1968, pp. 155-6, numbered these two versions separately as 144 for the first version and 145 for the second version. In this catalog, Hess made no distinction.]

210 Song 3: Quartet "Fra tutte le pene" for Soprano, Alto, Tenor and Bass in B-flat major, 38 bars; the da capo is written out (Thayer piece 3). [WoO 99, No. 3c.] Composed about 1796-7. [TN: published by Hess in the SBG, Vol. I, 1959, p. 21. Hess lists a revised version of this same piece as entry 224 below.]

211 Song 4: Duet "Bei labbri che amore" for Soprano and Tenor in E-flat major, 24 bars and da capo. [WoO 99, No.1.] The text is from Metastasio's cantata *La gelosia* (Thayer piece 4). Composed about 1792-4. [TN: published by Hess in the SBG, Vol. I, 1959, p. 9.]

212 Song 5: Trio "Ma tu tremi, o mio tesoro" for Soprano, Alto and Tenor in G major, 20 bars with a da capo. [WoO 99, No. 6.] The text is from Metastasio's cantata *La tempesta* (Thayer piece 5). Composed about 1792-4. [TN: published by Hess in the SBG, Vol. I, 1959, p. 13.]

213 Song 6: Quartet "Quella cetra ah pure tu sei" for Soprano, Alto, Tenor and Bass in G major, 20 bars. [WoO 99, No. 10a.] Text is from Metastasio's *Cantata Pel Giorno natalizio di Maria Terese* (Thayer piece 6). Composed about 1796-7. [TN: published by Hess in the SBG, Vol. I, 1959, p. 23.]

214 Song 7: Trio "Chi mai di questo core" for Soprano, Tenor and Bass in C major, 40 bars. [WoO 99, No. 2.] The text is from Metastasio's cantata *Il ritorno* (Thayer piece 16). Composed at the latest in 1799. [TN: published by Hess in the SBG, Vol. I, 1959, p. 17.]

215 Song 8: Duet "Scrivo in te" (not "Se vivo in te" as given by Thayer) for Soprano and Tenor in D major, 20 bars. [WoO 99, No. 11.] The text is from Metastasio's cantata *Il nome* (Thayer piece 17). Composed about 1795-6. [TN: published by Hess in the SBG, Vol. I, 1959, p. 10.]

216 Song 9: Trio "Per te d'amico aprile" for Soprano, Alto and Bass in E-flat major, 22 bars. [WoO 99, No. 9.] The text is from Metastasio's cantata *Il nome* (Thayer piece 18). Written between 1792-6. [TN: published by Hess in the SBG, Vol. I, 1959, p. 14.]

217 Song 10: Quartet "Nei campi e nelle selve" for Soprano, Alto, Tenor and Bass C major, 45 bars and da capo. [WoO 99, No. 7a.] The text is from *Cantata XXVII* in the complete edition of Pietro Metastasio's works [*Tutte le opere di Pietro Metastasio*] by Professor

Bruno Brunelli, as published by Mondadori [5 Vols., Milan 1943-54]. It is not known to me to which edition [of Metastasio's works] Thayer's designation "Cantata IX" refers, (Thayer piece 19). Composed between 1792-6. Beethoven has thickly crossed out the piece, and at its position inserted song 13. [TN: published by Hess in the SBG, Vol. I, 1959, p. 19. Also Kinsky/Halm, p. 561 lists the text source as "Cantata IX."]

218 Song 11: Trio "Quella cetra ah pur tu sei" for Soprano, Tenor and Bass in A major, 19 bars. [WoO 99 No. 10b.] For text sources see the entry [213] under song 6 (Thayer piece 20). Composed about 1796. [TN: published by Hess in the SBG, Vol. I, 1959, p. 16. Kinsky/Halm lists it as 20 bars.]

219 Song 12: Quartet "Quella cetra ah pur tu sei" for Soprano, Alto, Tenor and Bass in F major, 18 bars. [WoO 99, No. 10c.] For text sources, see the entry [213] under song 6 (Thayer piece 21). Composed about 1796. [TN: published by Hess in the SBG, Vol. I, 1959, p. 24.]

220 Song 13: Quartet "Nei campi e nelle selve" for Soprano, Alto, Tenor and Bass in C major, 36 bars and da capo. [WoO 99, No. 7b.] For text sources, see entry [217] under song 10 (Thayer piece 22). Probably composed directly after song 10. [TN: published by Hess in the SBG, Vol. I, 1959, p. 20.]

221 Song 14: Quartet "Giura il nocchier" for Soprano, Alto, Tenor and Bass in B-flat major, 23 bars. [WoO 99, No. 5a.] The text is from Metastasio's *La gelosia* (Thayer piece 26). Composed about 1801. [TN: published by Hess in the SBG, Vol. I, 1959, p. 26.]

222 Song 15: Quartet "Gia la notte s'avvicina" for Soprano, Alto, Tenor and Bass in B-flat major, 18 bars. [WoO 99, No. 4a.] The text is from Metastasio's *La pesca*

(Thayer piece 27). Nottebohm seems not to have known of this and the following piece. Both songs [i.e.,15 and 16] probably belong to the last songs [that originated from these studies], since they show no corrections in Salieri's hand and are among the most mature and beautifully developed of these pieces. [TN: published by Hess in the SBG, Vol. I, 1959, p. 27.]

223 Song 16: Trio "Gia la notte s'avvicina" for Alto, Tenor and Bass in C major, 16 bars (Thayer piece 28). [WoO 99, No. 4b.] See the reference under song 15. [TN: published by Hess in the SBG, Vol. I, 1959, p. 18.]

224 Song 17: Quartet "Fra tutte le pene" for Soprano, Alto, Tenor and Bass in B-flat major, 24 bars and da capo. [WoO 99, No. 3c.] For the text sources see the entry [208] under song 1 (Thayer piece 29). This song is a variation of song 3 and is partly identical with it. Since No. 3 in the autograph shows corrections from Salieri, we may believe No. 3 to probably be an initial stage to No. 17, and suspect that it was written out again by Beethoven before he submitted the song to Salieri [for final approval]. [TN: published by Hess in the SBG, Vol. I, 1959, p. 21.]

225 Song 18: Trio "Fra tutte le pene" for Soprano, Alto and Tenor in E-flat major, 25 bars and da capo. [WoO 99, No. 3b.] For the text sources, see the entry under song 1 (Thayer piece 30). This piece is the initial stage to song 2, since it, in contrast to song 2, contains no corrections in the hand of Salieri. [TN: published by Hess in the SBG, Vol. I, 1959, p. 15.]

226 Song 19: Quartet "Silvio, amante disperato" in A minor, 26 bars, 6/8 time. [WoO 99, No. 12.] Thayer lists this song with its incipit [of 4 bars] as piece 31 and he states the key signature and the number of bars; however, even today its finished presentation has not been

found. The text can be found in Cantata XXVII in *Tutte le opere di Pietro Metastasio* by Bruno Brunelli [5 Vols., Mondadori, Milan 1943-54], and goes:

Silvio, amante disperato,
Sfortunato cacciatore,
Infelice pastorello,
Per un core senza amore
Pur alfin cedendo al fate
Qui per sempre riposò.

Pastorelli, cacciatori,
Che passate ov' egli giace,
Gli augurate quella pace
Che la perfida sua Clori
Gli promise e gli mancò.

Thayer was unaware of the following pieces:

227 Song 20: Trio "Giura il nocchier" for Soprano, Alto and Bass in C major, 20 bars. [WoO 99, No. 5b.] For the text source see song 14 under entry 221. Composed about 1792-4. [TN: published by Hess in the SBG, Vol. I, 1959, p. 13.]

228 Song 21: Duet "Salvo tu vuoi lo sposo" for Soprano and Tenor in C major, 20 bars. Text is from Metastasio's Opera *Zenobia*, Act 2, Scene 7. Composed about 1796-7. [TN: published by Hess in the SBG, Vol. I, 1959, p. 12.]

The following pieces were unknown to Nottebohm as well:

229 Song 22: Duet "Languisco e moro per te, mio ben, ch'adoro." This piece is found on pp. 88-9 of a sketch-book of the year 1802-3, as described by Ludwig Nohl. See Nohl's *Beethoven, Liszt, Wagner. Ein Buch der Kunstbewegung unseres Jahrhunderts*, W. Braunmüller, Vienna 1874, pp. 96-101. The sketch-book named here was once the property of Mrs. Senator Wenewkinow, daughter of the Countess Wielhorski in St. Petersburg. [TN: Johnson and Dorfmüller give the spelling as Wielhorsky.] Today it is in the Leningrad [St. Petersburg] City Library. Professor Biamonti

could not find a source for the text, and a statement from Prof. Brunelli reveals that possibly it is not from Metastasio at all. [TN: R. Kramer, in "Notes to Beethoven's Education," *Journal of the American Musicological Society,* No. 28, 1975, pp. 72-101, identifies the source of the text and music as Matthisson and indicates that Beethoven has copied this canon into the Wielhorski Sketchbook. Kramer writes: "Hess 229, song version with pianoforte accompaniment, is not Beethoven's composition, but from Matthisson's *Der Vollkommene Capellmeister*. The canonic attempt is by Beethoven." I am grateful to Tadahiro Nakamoto of Osaka, Japan for this information. This same information appears to be true of entry No. 274. The Wielhorski Sketchbook was edited by Nathan Fišman and published in 3 volumes (facsimile, transcription and commentary), Muzgiz, Moscow 1962. This piece is found on p. 88, staves 1-6 of this sketchbook. A. Willem Holsbergen has commented on this piece in a communication to me that, *"Languisco e moro* is a canon and therefore doesn't seem to belong with the group of pieces written for the study of Italian vocal music under the guidance of Salieri." Hess published it in the SBG, Vol. 14, as number 54, on p. 145 (as part of the Vierte Abteilung: Nachträge zu Band 1, 2 und 5). It would appear that Hess himself recognized the inappropriateness of its inclusion with the other studies for Salieri, which were published in Vol. 1 of the SBG. This may also explain why Prof. Brunelli believes the text is not from Metastasio, which is what Salieri used almost exclusively as his text source for the Italian songs, and why Professor Biamonti couldn't locate the source for the text in Metastasio's works.]

230 Song 23: Quartet "Giura il nocchier" for Soprano, Alto, Tenor and Bass in C major, 20 bars. For the text source, see the entry [221] under song 14. This piece represents a total novelty that I found in 1954 in the

archive of the Gesellschaft der Musikfreunde in Vienna. Beethoven has it crossed out thickly, as in the case of song 10, and has, without a doubt, then inserted at this position song 14. The composition date is therefore estimated to be 1800 at the latest; the same goes for the next two pieces, which are in the same handwriting. Because of sketches to songs numbered 24 and 25, which occur together with the songs numbered 4 and 20 in the Berlin manuscript (see below), one can assume the years 1792-4. [TN: the text of this piece is the same as that used for WoO 99, No. 5a; however, the key is different. This was published by Hess in the SBG, Vol. I, 1959, p. 25.]

231 Song 24: Duet "Sei mio ben" for Soprano and Tenor in G major, 14 bars. The text is from *Cantata XXIV*, from the complete edition of Metastasio by Brunelli [*Tutte le opere di Pietro Metastasio,* 5 Vols., Mondadori, Milan 1943-54]. For the composition date, see the entry on the previous song. [TN: published by Hess in the SBG, Vol. I, 1959, p. 9. A facsimile of the autograph of this song is shown on page 124.]

232 Song 25: Melody for Tenor alone "E pur fra le tempeste" in E-flat major, 20 bars. The text is from Metastasio's cantata *La tempesta.* See the entry for Song 23 for the composition date. [TN: published by Hess in the SBG, Vol. I, 1959, p. 28, with a conjectural piano accompaniment written by Hess.]

The handwritten autographs:

By far the most important ones are contained in the autograph Artaria 166 of the Deutsche Staatsbibliothek in Berlin [TN: this is now the SBB] which is missing today; however, the Beethoven-Haus has it in a photocopy. [TN: this manuscript has been located again and is now in the SBB.] It contains, in Beethoven's own handwriting:

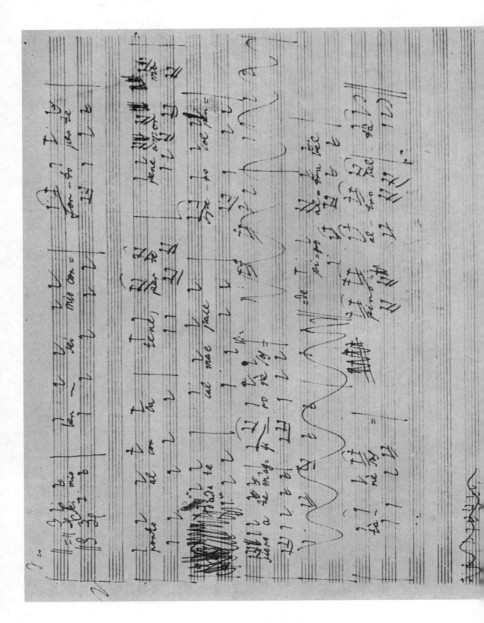

Hess 231, Song "Sei mio ben" for soprano and tenor, a cappella, facsimile of the autograph.

a) Four leaves (numbered as pages 1-8) [TN: actually it is pages 1-7; page 8 is blank], containing the songs 1-3 and a sketch to song 21.

b) Two leaves (pages 9-12) [TN: actually it is pages 9-11; page 12 is blank], containing the songs 4-5.

c) One leaf (pages 13-14), containing song 6.

d) Six leaves (pages 15-26) [TN: actually it is pages 15-25; page 26 is blank], containing songs copied from Doblhoff and Cornet (Thayer's piece nos. 7-15). [TN: the reference is about Baron Carl Doblhof-Dier (1762-1836) and Alexander Cornet, a song teacher living in Vienna about 1796. Doblhof and Cornet were classmates of Beethoven with Salieri. Beethoven copied some of their songs as study exercises.]

e) Two leaves (pages 27-30), containing song 7, as well as a sketch that Nottebohm has decided belongs to the last movement of Op. 18, No. 1 (see also the reference on page 227).

f) Four leaves (pages 31-38), containing the songs 8-10.

g) Two leaves (pages 39-42), containing the songs 11-12.

h) Two leaves (pages 43-46), containing the songs 4 and 20 as well as sketches to 21, 24 and 25.

i) Two leaves (pages 47-50), containing song 13.

Song 4 is located twice, because Beethoven wrote the song out again using the corrections from Salieri. The items under d) clearly fall from the usual framework; it gives the impression of a hasty transcription, and contains, in contrast to the other parts of the autograph, no corrections by Salieri. Therefore, we have before us, recognized through Nottebohm, the first copies of songs as such, from Salieri's student. All the pieces listed here are without piano accompaniment.

A second part has the title "Musica Del Signor Maes(tro) Luigi van Beethoven." This part gives us the following songs in copy, all provided with piano accompaniment:

Seven leaves: Songs 1-3.

Two leaves: Song 4 in the setting corrected by Salieri.
Two leaves: Song 5.
Two leaves: Song 6.
Seventeen leaves: Thayer's pieces 7-15, i.e. the copies by Doblhoff and Cornet. [TN: the reference appears to be about Baron Carl Doblhof-Dier (1762-1836) and Alexander Cornet, a song teacher living in Vienna about 1796. Doblhof and Cornet were students of Salieri and classmates of Beethoven.]
Three leaves: Song 7.
Two leaves: Song 8.
Two leaves: Song 9.
Three leaves: Song 10.
Two leaves: Song 4 in the uncorrected setting.
Three leaves: Song 13.

Here, not noticed by Thayer, are his pieces 10 and 11 with piano accompaniment. That these accompaniments don't come from Beethoven is easy to realize. First of all, he would hardly have provided an accompaniment to copies of another composer's songs. Secondly, it is no more likely that he would have provided accompaniment to song 10 that he then crossed out, than to the uncorrected version of song 4. In the remaining songs that are given in the *Verzeichnis der musikalischen Autographe im Besitze von August Artaria*, self-published, Vienna 1893, it is likely that the Kapellmeister Benedict Randhartinger, a classmate of Franz Schubert while a pupil of Salieri, has written these piano accompaniments, and that possibly these copies also come from him.

Another Berlin autograph, Mus. Ms. 1248, contains the songs 18, 17, 14, 15, 16 in this sequence and in copy. Sixteen pages, including the title page. Titled "Ludwig van Beethoven. Frünf italiensiche Gesänge für drei und vier Stimmen ohne Begleitung. Partitur." (Ludwig van Beethoven. Five Italian songs for three and four voices without accompaniment. Score.) On the second side follows the remark, "From those in A. W. Thayer's Chronol. Verz. der Werke Beethovens: presented under No. 264, The 32 Italian Song Compositions.

Present are five Nos.: 30, 29, 26, 27 & 28. The composition date is unknown." It is interesting, however, that contrary to Beethoven's handwriting in the Viennese copy mentioned below, bar 3 of song 18 is set in song 2 as well.

In the Archive of the Gesellschaft der Musikfreunde in Vienna are located the following pertinent autographs:

Autograph 79. Titled "Fra tutte le pene. Composition exercises with Italian texts." It contains:

Two pages of sketches to song 18, differing from the final form.
Two pages of a fair copy to the same song, followed by some unidentified sketches.
Two pages of a fair copy for song 17.

Autograph 69. Titled "Sketches to a Italian duet for Soprano and Tenor." Contents:

Page 1: Song 21, followed by some attempts at another setting for the soprano.
Page 2: Sketch to song 12.
Page 3: Sketch to song 11.
Page 4: Sketch to song 6.

Autograph 73. Titled "Sketches to an Italian song for quartet 'Giura il nocchier'." Contents:

Pages 1-3: Song 14.
Pages 4-7: blank.
Page 8: Two lines of sketches, probably to the above. Hereupon follow in copy the songs 14, 15 & 16.

Under the materials to the counterpoint (autograph 75) is further located a double leaf, that definitely doesn't belong here and contains the following:

Song 23, 2 pages.
Song 24, 1 page.
Song 25, 1 page.

Furthermore, under the catalog number "VI 17558," the Gesellschaft der Musikfreunde possesses another copy of the songs 14-16 that agrees in the musical text with the Berlin autograph, Mus. Ms. 1248.

In conclusion, one can say that from the twenty-five songs altogether: Nos. 1-14, 17, 18, 20, 21, 23, 24 and 25 exist in autograph; Nos. 15 and 16 we know only from copies; No. 19 is completely missing [TN: Hess writes "completely missing," however, the incipit is known; see entry 226 above.]; and No. 22 which is inaccessible for the time being.

Printed editions [TN: in addition to the specific references below, all the songs except No. 19 (which is still missing) were published by Hess in the SBG, Vol. I, 1959.]:

Song 1: Nottebohm, in *Beethovens Studien*, p. 212, the first 14 bars.
Song 2: Nottebohm, in *Beethovens Studien*, pp. 213-4, for the whole song.
Song 3: Nottebohm, in *Beethovens Studien*, pp. 215-7, for the whole song.
Song 4: Nottebohm, in *Beethovens Studien*, pp. 207-8, for the whole song.
Song 5: First edition was published by Willy Hess in *Eidgenössisches Sängerblatt*, Vol. 17, No. 12, December 1953, pp. 145-6.
Song 6: First edition was published by Willy Hess in *Schweizerische Musikpädagogische Blätter*, 1 August 1936, Vol. 25, pp. 227-8.
Song 7: Nottebohm gives two fragments from it in *Beethovens Studien*, pp. 218-9.
Song 8: Unpublished. [TN: published by Hess in the SBG, Vol. I, 1959, p. 10.]

Song 9: Nottebohm, in *Beethovens Studien*, pp. 209-10, for the whole piece.

Song 10: The first edition was published by Willy Hess in *Atlantis*, Vol. XXV, Journal 5, May 1953, p. 212.

Song 11: Unpublished. [TN: published by Hess in the SBG, Vol. I, 1959, p. 16.]

Song 12: Unpublished. [TN: published by Hess in the SBG, Vol. I, 1959, p. 23.]

Song 13: The first edition was published by Willy Hess in *Atlantis*, Vol. XXV, Journal 5, May 1953, p. 213.

Song 14: Nottebohm, in *Beethovens Studien*, pp. 220-1 for the whole piece.

Song 15: The first edition was published by Willy Hess in the yearbook of the *Accademia Nazionale di Santa Cecilia,* in Rome for 1951/2, printed in 1953, p. 349, with a separate printing on p. 51.

Song 16: The first edition was published by Willy Hess in *Die Musik*, Vol. 33, No. 2, April 1941, p. 243.

Song 17: See the entry under song 18.

Song 18: The songs 17 and 18 are found in Artaria editions of 1856 on two pages in a large portrait format. They seem to be separate printings from a larger collection, since the first and last pages are blank. (These are catalogued under the call number S A 87, A. 92 of the Österreichische Nationalbibliothek.)

Songs 19-22: Unpublished. [TN: only Song 19 remains unpublished, except for the incipit of four bars, which was published in Thayer's *Chronologisches Verzeichniss*. It is the only way by which we know of the existence of this song. Songs 20 and 21 were published by Hess in the SBG, Vol. I, 1959, pp. 13 and 12. Song 22 has appeared in Fišman's publication of the Wielhorski Sketchbook, Muzgiz, Moscow 1962, both in facsimile and in transcription.]

Song 23: The first edition was published by Willy Hess in *Schweizerische Musikpädagogische Blätter,* Vol. 42, No. 4, October 1954, p. 182. Also on p. 183 a reprint of No. 14 [appeared].

Song 24: Published by Willy Hess in facsimile in the *Neues Winterthurer Tagblatt* from 16 July 1955. (Illustration: see page 124.)

Song 25: Published by Willy Hess in facsimile in *Musica*, Vol. 8, Journal 10, October 1954, p. 451. In the December Journal of the same year, on p. 557, was published a transcription with a piano accompaniment prepared by me [that is, Hess].

I have pleaded in various publications for a complete edition of these songs. This will not appear, because the publisher (Universal-Edition, Vienna) only wants to publish a selection. They are not yet able to state when it will be issued. Due to this, the new Beethoven Gesamtausgabe will have to publish these complete choral songs in a Critical Beethoven Edition. Possibly this can include the other a cappella songs, canons and musical jokes already printed in the old Gesamtausgabe, since they too are a cappella music. Maybe all of Beethoven's original choral tunes will be presented in the belief that all the a cappella compositions also represent [interesting] music.

Contrapuntal Studies

It goes without saying that the new complete edition should collect not only the song studies executed under the instruction of Salieri, but must also take into account those written during Beethoven's studies with Franz Josef Haydn and Johann Georg Albrechtsberger, which give an extremely interesting insight into the workings of this genius. Especially in this area, there still remains very much to do, however, because for the most important things, we are still dependent today on the examinations of Gustav Nottebohm relating to these works. Unfortunately, from his extensive work, only a first volume of his *Beethoven Studien* has appeared, and that deals only with the autographs of Beethoven studies in Bonn as well as those with Haydn, Albrechtsberger and Salieri. This work was published by J. Rieter-Biedermann, Leipzig and Winterthur, in 1873.

In I[gnaz] R[itter] von Seyfried's book, *Ludwig van Beethovens Studien im Generalbasse, Contrapunkte'* etc., and Gustav Nottebohm, in his essay, "Generalbaß und Compositionslehre betreffende Handschriften Beethovens" published in *Beethoveniana,* Leipzig and Winterthur, 1872, pp. 154-203, examine what is known today as "Beethoven Autograph 75" in the archive of the Gesellschaft der Musikfreunde in Vienna, and simultaneously undertake an identification of the catalogued manuscripts of Beethoven that are stored there. Seyfried's book, which is now exposed as a clumsy forgery, appeared from the publisher Tobias Haslinger, Vienna in 1832. In that book, not only did Seyfried unsystematically mix up all the existing materials, but indiscriminately mixed the real and the false, so that use of his book should take place with all the greatest precaution.

To not digress too much, we will now list the works as grouped by Nottebohm. Those mentioned by Seyfried are only mentioned if they were not included by Nottebohm.

233 Approximately 300 exercises in simple counterpoint, based on six *Cantus Firmi*, which are in the six authentic church-modes. From these are found 245 surviving exercises. They are listed in Nottebohm as follows: pp. 25-26, four two-part exercises; pp. 26-30, twelve three-part exercises; and on pp. 30-41, thirty-two four-part exercises; therefore, in the whole, forty-eight exercises. To this, Seyfried adds: sixteen three-part exercises (p. 107, the first and third examples; p. 108, four more examples; from the bottom of p. 111 until the top of p. 113, three examples; from the middle of p. 116 until the top of p. 118, four examples; pp. 120-1, three examples); and fifteen four-part exercises (p. 124, there are three examples; p. 125 top, one example; p. 127, three examples; p. 128, one example; pp. 132-134, four examples; p. 138, three examples). [TN: Hess is correct that there are sixteen three-part exercises in Seyfried; however, according to Mark Zimmer, of the sixteen given, No. 13 is identical to No. 15 from Nottebohm's *Beethoven Studien*; therefore Seyfried only offers fifteen additional ones, not sixteen as given above.] Therefore, seventy-nine [actually seventy-eight unquestionable] examples have appeared in print; however, the text of Seyfried has to be compared with the autographs, since Seyfried arbitrarily alters [these] on occasion. These pieces, written with Haydn, fall into the year 1793 (or the end of 1792) up to Haydn's departure for England in January 1794. All of the following are written under Albrechtsberger's instruction:

234 Approximately 125 exercises in strict counterpoint, based on two *Cantus Firmi* in F major and D minor. Nottebohm lists on pp. 48-50: eight two-part exercises;

on pp. 50-54: nine three-part exercises; and on pp. 54-57: six four-part examples. The rest are unpublished.

235 Twenty-six exercises in free style. Nottebohm presents on p. 58: five two-part exercises; on pp. 59-61: six three-part exercises; and on pp. 61-62: five four-part examples. From Seyfried we have twenty examples, on pp. 146-154: included in those there are five two-part and two three-part examples [for a total of seven], which are not listed by Nottebohm. Therefore twenty-three pieces are printed, and three are still unpublished. On page 155, Seyfried lists another four-part example of mixed type, for which no handwritten autograph exists.

236 Eighteen two-part simple fugues in strict counterpoint. Nottebohm lists eleven on pp. 73-88; another in G major published by Seyfried is found on pp. 187-8, while the remaining six are unpublished. [TN: the sources for the thematic material used in the twelve published exercises are all from Albrechtsberger's list as follows: No. 1 is based on the second theme; No. 2 is based on theme 4; No. 3 is based on theme 5; No. 4 is based on theme 8; No. 5 is based on theme 10; No. 6 is based on theme 11; No. 7 is based on theme 12; No. 8 is based on theme 15; No. 9 is based on theme 16; No. 10 is based on theme 18; No. 11 is based on theme 19; No. 12 is based on theme 13. The key signatures for the published ones are: No. 1 in D minor; No. 2 in E Phrygian (also called "E plagal" by Albrechtsberger); No. 3 in F major; No. 5 in D minor; No. 6 in E minor; No. 7 in F major; No. 8 in B-flat major; No. 9 in C major; No. 10 in E minor; No. 11 in F major; and No. 12 (from Seyfried) is in G major.]

237 Seven three-part simple fugues in strict counterpoint. Nottebohm lists three on pp. 89-94; Seyfried lists two further ones, in D minor and B-flat major, on pp. 192-

6. Two [more] are still unpublished. Another fugue in free form written in E minor for two violins and cello has been listed in this catalog under No. 29. [TN: this fugue in E minor, which Hess lists as No. 29, is combined with a *Nachahmungssätz* (imitation movement) also in E minor to form a prelude and fugue. The *Nachahmungssätz* is published by Nottebohm on p. 63. The sources for the thematic material used in the five published exercises are all from Albrechtsberger's list as follows: No. 1 is based on theme 27; No. 2 is based on theme 26; No. 3 is based on theme 11; No. 4 is based on theme 24; No. 5 is based on theme 29. Hess does not give the thematic sources for the two unpublished fugues. The keys for the three published by Nottebohm are: No. 1 in F major, No. 2 in G major and No. 3 in E minor.]

238 Nine four-part simple fugues in strict counterpoint. From Nottebohm, we are given five on pp. 95-111; another in A minor is in Seyfried on pp. 206-210; and the last three are unpublished. [TN: the sources for the thematic material used in the six published exercises are from Albrechtsberger's list as follows: No. 1 is based on theme11; No. 2 is based on theme 10; No. 3 is based on theme 16; No. 4 is based on theme 21; No. 5 is based on theme 22; and No. 6 is based on theme 28. The keys for the five fugues published by Nottebohm are: No. 1 in E minor, No. 2 in D minor, No. 3 in C major, No. 4 in A minor and No. 5 in B-flat major. The one published by Seyfried, No. 6, is in A minor.]

239 Three choral fugues. No. 1 in F major. The first transcript (fragment) from Nottebohm is on pp. 113-4; a second transcript beginning at bar 23 is on pp. 115-119; the whole fugue in a second setting is on pp. 239-245 of Seyfried. No. 2 in D minor is in Nottebohm on pp. 120-124. While No. 3 in G-major is found only with Seyfried on pp. 233-239. [TN: No. 1 of this set is de-

rived from a choral theme from Albrechtsberger. No. 3 is a four-part choral fugue.]

240 Four two-part exercises in double counterpoint of the octave. They are found on pp. 128-131 of Nottebohm. [One of] the fugues belonging here has been listed under No. 30 of this catalog. [TN: there is a fifth exercise in this group which Hess chose to list separately as No. 30 of this catalog, because it was arranged for string quartet with a *Nachahmungssätz* (imitation movement) added at the beginning to form a "prelude and fugue."]

241 Twenty-four exercises in double counterpoint of the decime (octave and a third). From them, eight two-through four-part examples are found on pp. 143-147 of Nottebohm; the remaining 16 are unpublished.

242 Six exercises in the double counterpoint of the duodecime (octave and a fifth). Four of them are found with Nottebohm on pp. 149-151; another is found with Seyfried on pp. 278-282. One is unpublished.

243 Five four-part double fugues in double counterpoint. Four of them are given in Nottebohm: C major on pp. 152-154; F major on pp. 155-157; C major on pp. 167-170, and one in D minor on pp. 172-175. The last has remained unpublished. The larger fugue for strings in C major, we have already listed here as No. 31 of this catalog. [TN: Nottebohm actually lists five four-part double fugues in double counterpoint, not four. Again Hess has made this catalog confusing by listing one of those as entry 31. Apparently, he did this because it is the only one of the five where Beethoven indicated the instrumentation. The one given in this catalog as entry 31 is the third one listed in Nottebohm, on pp. 158-166. A sixth fugue of this type, which Hess has indicated "remained unpublished," is not given a source

reference or location. The largest number of Beethoven's autographs of the counterpoint studies are found in Autograph 75 in the Gesellschaft der Musikfreunde in Vienna. Hess examined this autograph before writing this catalog and we can presume it is found there. The reader should note that Nottebohm did number the fugues in this set, No. 1, No. 2, etc., but without, of course, using a Hess number to precede the individual numbers. Hess gave them a general entry number "243," but did not individually number them. For the sake of clarity, I will use Nottebohm's individual numbering. The sources for the themes used in these fugues are as follows: No. 1, consisting of two themes: the first is No. 1 in Albrechtsberger's list and the second is by Beethoven; No. 2: the first theme is from No. 12 in Albrechtsberger's list and the second is from Beethoven; No. 3 (the one for string quartet): both themes may be by Beethoven, but probably by Albrechtsberger, but not from his list; No. 4: the first theme is a variation on No. 1 from Albrechtsberger's list, while the second is from Beethoven; No. 5: the first theme is No. 24 from Albrechtsberger's list, and the second theme is by Beethoven, but modified by Albrechtsberger. The sources are not known for No. 6, the unpublished fugue.]

244 Two four-part triple fugues. Both are in Nottebohm: one on pp. 178-184 in D minor, and one on pp. 185-190 in F major. [TN: the second of these two fugues uses for its first theme No. 14 from Albrechtsberger, while the second and third themes are from Beethoven and Albrechtsberger together.]

For information concerning the *Studien Kanons* (canon studies), see the following section. The three *Nachahmungssätze* (imitation movements) used as preludes to the free – style fugues for strings in E minor, F major and C major

[TN: listed in this catalog as entries 29, 30 and 31] also belong to these studies.

Generally, these are the results of Nottebohm's studies. Of course, all this material would have to be examined again while making use of the pertinent manuscripts located outside of Vienna. The Deutsche Staatsbibliothek, Berlin [TN: now the SBB], for example, owns a handwritten autograph (Artaria 153) of about 100 pages that includes a series of interval and instrumental studies, drafts of counterpoint works, drafts of fugues, etc., which is quite certainly connected with the Autograph 75 in Vienna. There are further examples next to sketches to the song "Adelaide" that are presented by Unger in his catalog under Mh 62 of the Bodmer Collection, *Eine Schweizer Beethovensammlung Katalog*, Verlag der Corona, Zurich 1939 [TN: the manuscript Mh 62 is now renumbered SBH 614 in the Beethoven-Haus, Bonn.]:

245 Fragment of a String Quartet Fugue in D minor, "probably worked on by Beethoven during the lessons with Albrechtsberger." Grouped under Mh 46 are another 18 pages with transcriptions by Beethoven from the works of Albrechtsberger, Marpurg, and others. [TN: the manuscript Mh 46 is now renumbered SBH 597 in the Beethoven-Haus, Bonn. This fragmentary fugue is written on the back of a sheet containing sketches for the song "Adelaide" (Op.46) and therefore dates from 1794 or 1795. As Nottebohm points out in his *Beethoven Studien*, p. 70: "We have in Beethoven's handwriting only the last page of the fugue, which contains 17 bars. So, the fugue was completed by Beethoven, but the preceding pages have been lost. The fugue, written in free style, ends on the dominant chord instead of the tonic, which suggests that another movement was to follow the fugue." This leads to speculation as to whether this fugue may have belonged to the same group as the Prelude and Fugue in E minor, entry 29, because Beethoven, at some stage, apparently in-

tended the entry 29 fugue to be followed by another movement, since he wrote on the fair copy of it "mit einem presto endigen" (to end with a presto).] The question is whether those pages may have previously belonged to the Vienna Autograph 75, which in Seyfried's time was considered to be more complete. One page of those fragments that is mentioned here, "Seyfried gave as a present to the Music Director Weber of Rostock; the letter, which he sent to his friend Friedrich Schwaan in which he asks him to pass it on, is also included (Br 380)." This information is from Max Unger. Furthermore, Unger lists [this fragmentary fugue] under Mh 61 of the same collection [TN: the manuscript Mh 61 is now renumbered SBH 697 (SV 108) in the Beethoven-Haus, Bonn. As mentioned in the paragraph above, Mh 62, now cataloged SBH 614 (SV 109), also contains sketches for this fugue. Johnson writes, "The quartet score on SBH 614 is probably the end of a prelude to a fugue in D minor (not the fugue itself, as Hess suggests)." See Johnson: *Beethoven's Early Sketches in the 'Fischhof Miscellany': Berlin Autograph 28,* Doctoral Dissertation, University of California, Berkeley 1978, p. 234.]

246 Double fugue in F major for four parts as for a choir (theme: Kyrie eleison, contrast: Christe eleison). This may be on themes of Albrechtsberger, and is fragmentary and unfinished (two pages). [TN: I have the following information from A. Willem Holsbergen: "Hess seems to link the sketch for this double fugue to the other fugues Beethoven wrote for Albrechtsberger, it should therefore date from about 1794-95. Hess also suggests that the themes of this fugue may be by Albrechtsberger. This seems less likely. In the case of the other double fugues Beethoven wrote at this time, one theme was always derived from the list of themes which Albrechtsberger gave to his pupils, the second being by Beethoven himself or Albrechtsberger. In the

case of Hess 246, neither theme is from this list. More importantly, as Jan Templiner has pointed out, there are striking similarities between the two themes of Hess 246, and the 'Kyrie Eleison'–double fugue from Mozart's 'Requiem.' If anything, Beethoven has modeled the present sketch on Mozart's illustrious example."]

Canons

First, we give the pieces [in the same order] as listed by Kinsky/Halm, then followed by those that are missing from that list.

247 Three-part canon without text in G major, 24 bars. After the melody of the song "O care selve antiche" (GA Series 25, No. 279), written at the end of the period of Beethoven's studies with Albrechtsberger. It is found in the Beethoven Autograph 75, located in the Gesellschaft der Musikfreunde in Vienna. First published by Seyfried (see above), pp. 327-9, and by Nottebohm (see above), p. 192. [TN: this is listed in Kinsky/Halm as WoO 160a, p. 669, and was also published by Hess in the SBG, Vol. V, 1962, p. 78.]

248 Four-part canon without text in C major, 16 bars. It has the same origin as No. 247 above. Published by Seyfried on pp. 331-3, and by Nottebohm on p. 193. [This is] the third of the study canons listed in the GA, Series 23, No. 256/1. See the section "Doubtful and Falsely Attributed Works," Nos. A 60-A 62, for more information about this type of canon. [TN: this is listed in Kinsky/Halm as WoO 160b, p. 669. This was published by Hess in the SBG, Vol. V, 1962, p. 78. This canon was presented by Seyfried in 1832 without a text. The Seyfried edition was published by Haslinger, Vienna, in 1832; later, in 1844, Haslinger also published a version of this same canon as "Singen ist des Lebens Freude" in a work, *Der Liederbote*, edited by J. H. Fischer with a text presumably added by Fischer. That canon is listed in this catalog as entry 312.]

249 Four-part canon, "Brauchle-Linke" in C major, 8 bars. Presumably written about 1815. The autograph is in the Staatsbibliothek, Berlin [TN: now known as the SBB]. The first edition was included by Thayer on p. 196 as an addendum to No. 263, reprinted in Nohl II [as] No. 119. Printed in score as No. 159, p. 147, of the work by MacArdle/Misch. The same source is mentioned in No. 257 of this catalog. [TN: this is listed in Kinsky/Halm as WoO 167, p. 674. This was published by Hess in the SBG, Vol. V, 1962, p. 80. The text of this canon consists of only two words, "Brauchle" and "Linke." It appears to have been written for Joseph Xavier Braucle, who was tutor to the children of Countess Erdödy, and for Joseph Linke, cellist in the private quartet of Prince Razumovsky. After the Razumovsky palace burnt down on New Year's Eve 1814, Linke went to Croatia in 1815 in the service of the Erdödys.]

250 Canon "Ich küsse Sie, drücke Sie an mein Herz!" (I Kiss You, [and] Press You to My Heart!), puzzle canon (or only a musical joke?) in C major, 6 bars [written] as a postscript to a letter dated 6 January 1816, to Anna Milder-Hauptmann. The autograph is in the Staatsbibliothek, Berlin [TN: now known as the SBB], in the *Varnhagen-Sammlung of the Handschriften-Abteilung,* "Konvolut Beethoven." The first edition was in "Eine Reliquie von Beethoven," in *Die Jahreszeiten,* Vol. 12, No. 3, 13 January 1853, pp. 89-92. Further, [it is] given in Thayer as No. 201; again by Kalischer in *Neue Zeitschrift für Musik,* 12 April 1905; also in Thayer III, pp. 536-7, and in Nohl I, No. 125. This same piece is [also] mentioned in Kalischer III, 2nd edition, No. 503. Ludwig Misch in "Pseudokanons und Rätselkanons von Beethoven," in *Die Musikforschung,* Vol. 3, Journal 3/4, 1950, beginning on p. 253, rejects Riemann's solution as a three-part canon and concedes that at most a two-part solu-

tion is possible; see pp. 256-8. He believes, however, that it may not be a canon at all.*) In contrast to this Kinsky/Halm [as] WoO 169, [p. 676,] gives the piece as a two-part puzzle-canon in the upper-fifth. [TN: A. Willem Holsbergen writes of this canon: "The first riddle about this riddle canon is whether it is a canon, or not. The notes are in two separate chunks (1. Ich küsse Sie, and 2. Ich der Hauptmann!) and it is not clear whether they should be sung simultaneously. Ludwig Misch (in the reference cited above, pp. 256-8) discusses the apparent impossibility to solve this canon. However, Hess in the *Revisionsbericht* of the SBG, Vol. V, indicates two solutions: 1) entry of the second voice after one bar a fourth higher, and 2) entry of the second after one bar as mirror image in the prime. The second chunk ('Ich der Hauptmann) can in both solutions be inserted as free counterpoint starting in the second bar." He also writes that, ". . .in the case of both solutions suggested by Hess, it appears that the first chunk can also be inserted starting in the first bar, a fourth lower, thus turning both solutions into double canons. The fact that these solutions as double canons seem possible, does not, in itself, prove that Beethoven had either solution actually in mind when he wrote down his two chunks."]

*) In the article by Ludwig Misch mentioned [above], which is emphatically recommended to the reader, Misch brings not only an exhaustive list of all the literature on the canons of Beethoven, but prints the following pieces of our list in their entirety, often with several attempts at solutions to the puzzle canons: Nos. 250, 255, 280, 302, 294, 282, 261, 272, 265, 253, 271. Furthermore, he tries solutions to the puzzle canon "Si non per portas" (GA, Series 23, No. 256/17) [WoO 194], and then explores the possibilities of a real canon based on the bass part of the little piece

"Glaube und hoffe!" (GA, Series 25, No. 285/3) [WoO 174].

251 Two-part canon, "Ars longa, vita brevis" (Art Lasts, Life Is Short), first [version of this] composition, C major, 12 bars. A two-part canon, written at the beginning of April 1816 for Johann Nepomuk Hummel. The autograph is in Hummel's family autograph album, which is now missing. The first edition was in Nohl II as No. 133, also published in Thayer III, p. 550. [TN: this autograph album is no longer missing. It is now in the Goethe-Museum, Düsseldorf. Another copy of this canon can also be found in the Harvard Music Library, Cambridge, Massachusetts. See Craig Wright, "Rare Music Manuscripts at Harvard," in *Current Musicology*, No.10, New York 1970, pp. 25-33. A facsimile was published by Karl Benyovsky in *J. N. Hummel*, Bratislava 1934. This, the first of three settings of this text, is listed in Kinsky/Halm p. 677. This was published by Hess in the SBG, Vol. V, 1962, p. 80.]

252 Four-part canon, "Glück fehlt dir vor allem!" (You Lack Happiness above All!) in G major, 4 bars. [TN: Hess gives the second word as 'fehlt;' it should read 'fehl',' which is a contraction for 'fehle,' which is grammatically correct.] For "Nanni" [Anna] Giannatasio Del Rio for her birthday in 1817. [TN: because the title of this work is derived from the first part of the rather short text, it starts out sounding like a curse rather than a friendly birthday greeting. When the full text is given it reads, "Glück fehl' dir vor allem, Gesundheit auch niemalen!" It translates, "Above all, may you never ever lack happiness nor good health."] The autograph is now missing. First printed in Frimmel's *Neue Beethoveniana*, Carl Gerold's Sohn, Vienna 1888, p. 100; reprinted in Thayer IV, p. 521. This canon has also been included in Fritz Jöde's *Praktischen Zwecken dienende Kanonsammlung*, Kallmeyer,

Wolfenbüttel 1926, p. 207. It appeared, as well, without a year date in my small collection, *Acht Singkanons von Ludwig van Beethoven*, Hug & Co., Zürich & Leipzig 1949. Also in MacArdle/Misch as No. 204, p. 199. [TN: this is listed in Kinsky/Halm as WoO 171, p. 677. This was published by Hess in the SBG, Vol. V, 1962, p. 81. This may be by Michael Haydn; see the reference by Dorfmüller in *Beiträge zur Beethoven Bibliographie*, G. Henle, Munich 1978, p. 78. Mark Zimmer has supplied me with the following updated information: "The exact same canon appears in Charles H. Sherman and T. Donley Thomas' *Johann Michael Haydn (1737-1806): a Chronological Thematic Catalog of His Works*, Pendragon Press, Stuyvesant, NY 1993. It is listed there as composed in Arnsdorf in 1795?; it was published as part of *Six Deutsche Canons zu 4 und 5 Singstimmen ohne Begleitung*, Mayrische Buchhandlung, Salzburg 1800. Obviously, this is well before the supposed composition by Beethoven." More information on the identification of this canon can be found in Dorfmüller, pp. 384-5.]

253 Four-part puzzle canon, "Hol euch der Teufel? B'hüt euch Gott!" (Devil take you? God protect you!) in B-flat major, 4 bars. Composed in the summer of 1819 for the publisher S. A. Steiner. The location of the autograph is unknown. [TN: this canon can be found in the Conversation Book No.10, which began in March 1820, where it was written out by Carl Czerny. This was published by Georg Schünemann in *Ludwig van Beethovens Konversationshefte*, Max Hesses Verlag, Berlin 1941, Vol.1, pp. 384-5. A second edition was published in *Ludwig van Beethovens Konversationshefte*, edited by Karl-Heinz Köhler and Grita Herre, VEB Deutscher Verlag für Musik, Leipzig 1972, Vol.1, pp. 390-1, where the writer of the canon is given as August Friedrich Kanne, not Carl Czerny as is given

in Dorfmüller. The Conversation Book is in the SBB.] The first edition was done by Thayer as No. 220, [in his *Verzeischniss*, and reprinted] in Thayer IV, p. 176. This two-part solution is what Kinsky/Halm also accepts (WoO 173) [p. 678]; Misch, in "Pseudokanons und Rätselkanons von Beethoven," in *Die Musikforschung*, Vol. 3, Journal 3/4, 1950, on pp. 273-4, puts forward two pretty four-part solutions. See MacArdle/Misch, their entry No. 267, p. 288. [TN: what Hess doesn't make clear is that since this is a puzzle canon, it is capable of both two- and four-part solutions. Thayer and Kinsky/Halm have presented only two-part solutions and Misch has presented four-part ones. This was published by Hess in the SBG, Vol. V, 1962, p. 81.]

254 Canon-fragment, "Hol dich der Teufel" (The Devil Take You) in G major, 2½ bars. From the year 1801, it [was intended for Ignaz] Schuppanzigh. Written down at the top of the last page of the autograph of the Sonata Op. 28 in the Beethoven-Haus, Bonn. A facsimile and transcription was published by L. Schiedermair in *Veröffentlichungen des Beethovenhauses*, VI, Bonn 1930, Table VII, particularly p. 20; also in MacArdle/Misch as No. 25, p. 28. [TN: this canon-fragment is described in Kinsky/Halm under WoO 173, p. 679, but not cataloged as such. It was published by Hess in the *Revisionsbericht* section of the SBG, Vol. V, 1962, p. 93.]

255 Two Canons:
No. 1 "Sankt Petrus war ein Fels" (Saint Peter Was a Rock) in A major, 2 bars.
No. 2 "Bernardus war ein Sankt?" (Was Bernard a Saint?), in A minor, 4 bars.
Written towards the end of 1819, according to Kinsky/Halm, WoO 175, [p. 680,] in an undated letter to Councilor Carl Peters. The letter finally came into

the possession of John Ella in London, where Thayer copied it. [TN: the autograph is now in the Royal College of Organists, London. The letter is Anderson 1067 and Brandenburg 1368.] Reprinted in Thayer IV, p. 189 (Thayer No. 225), and in Nohl II as No. 231. These are obviously two canons. Kinsky/Halm writes: "Puzzle-canon (Two voices. The lower voice on the words *'Bernardus war ein Sankt'* brings the theme of the upper 'per augmentation,' i.e. with doubling of the note values, a third lower)." In contrast, Misch states in "Pseudokanons und Rätselkanons von Beethoven," in *Die Musikforschung*, Vol. 3, Journal 3/4,1950, pp. 258-9, that these are only the incipits of two lost canons, although one could execute them in canonical style [as one canon]: the first in the lower sub-third after two fourths, and that of the second in the upper third after two halves. [TN: these were published by Hess in the SBG, Vol. V, 1962, p. 81.]

256 Fragment similar to a three-part canon, "Sankt Petrus ist der Fels" (Saint Peter is the Rock), in A major, 8 bars in score-form. [TN: Hess gives the fourth word of the title as "der" while it should actually be "ein," which would translate as "a Rock," not "the Rock." In the sketchbook, the word is given as "ein;" however, in a conversation book of that period, the text only is given, with the word as "kein."] The two upper parts go together and mimic the motif of the canon for [Councilor Carl] Peters (entry 255, No. 1), while the third voice is led in free imitation. The autograph is, as described by J. Schmidt-Görg, from *Ein Skizzenbuch aus den Jahren 1819/20*, [the *Missa Solemnis*], p. 32 [in the facsimile]; and p. 45 of the transcription, [Beethoven-Haus] Bonn, 1952. Riemann's printing of it in Thayer IV, p. 191, is not quite correct. Contrary to Riemann's and Schmidt-Görg's view, Misch holds that the piece is not a separate canon, but a sketch to the canon [entry] 255, No. 1 (see his "Pseudokanons und

Rätselkanons von Beethoven," in *Die Musikforschung*, Vol. 3, Journal 3/4, 1950, p. 259). [TN: A. Willem Holsbergen writes: "From a musical point of view, I would disagree to call this a canon. True it is based on the same motif as Entry 255, but here it is not handled as a canon. Apparently later on, Hess realized the same too, because when he published this piece in the *Supplemente* he calls it a 'Musikalischer Scherz (Musical Joke) auf Hofrat Carl Peters' and not a canon. Furthermore, it seems complete, and not a fragment." While mentioned in Kinsky/Halm under WoO 175, this entry is not the same. This is cataloged as SBH 665 and SV 81. This was published by Hess in the SBG, Vol. V, 1962, p. 81.]

257 "Bester Magistrat, ihr friert" (Good Magistrate, You Freeze) in E major, 8 bars. According to Unger, [it is] for four bass voices with accompaniment of cello or contrabass. Written in 1819 or 1820; the autograph is in the Bodmer Collection, Mh. 38. [TN: this collection is now in the Beethoven-Haus, Bonn, and the autograph has been renumbered SBH 594.] A facsimile was used as background of the title to Auction Catalog CXXXII (27-28 April 1928) from K. E. Henrici, Berlin; the first edition of the musical notation was in *New Beethoven Letters*, translated and annotated by Donald W. MacArdle and Ludwig Misch, University of Oklahoma Press, Norman, Oklahoma 1957, p. 303, as No. 280. [TN: this is listed in Kinsky/Halm as WoO 177, p. 682. This should not be confused with entry 299 of this catalog which uses the same text, but is a different setting. This was published by Hess in the SBG, Vol. V, 1962, p. 81.]

258 "Gehabt euch wohl" (Have a Good Time, or, Enjoy Yourself), 4 bars, C major. The autograph is in the Deutsche Staatsbibliothek, Berlin, and located in the sketchbooks for the *Missa Solemnis*. [TN: this is now

the SBB.] Therefore, it was written about 1819/20. Schünemann gives us a three-part solution with the first edition in the *Festschrift zum 60. Geburtstag Arnold Scherings*, A. Glass, Berlin 1937, pp. 208-9. MacArdle/Misch suggests it to be a four-part canon; see [their] entry No. 340 mentioned on p. 393. Both seem possible. [TN: this is listed in Kinsky/Halm as WoO 181b, p. 685. This was published by Hess in the SBG, Vol. V, 1962, p. 82.]

259 "Tugend ist kein leerer Name" (Virtue Is No Empty Word), three-part canon, C major, 6 bars. The information on this entry is the same as with entry 258 above. The first edition was by Schünemann; see p. 209 of the book mentioned above; and a later edition was published by MacArdle/Misch, on p. 394 as No. 341. [TN: this is listed in Kinsky/Halm as WoO 181c, p. 669. This was published by Hess in the SBG, Vol. V, 1962, p. 82.]

260 "Fettlümmerl, Bankert haben triumphiert" (The Fat Lout, [and] the Bastard have Triumphed). [TN: my thanks to Mark S. Zimmer and the <*www.unheardbeethoven.org*> website for the translation of this rather idiosyncratic title! The reference is supposedly to Beethoven's sister-in-law, Therese and her illegitimate daughter, Amalie Waldmann (1807-1831). Therese van Beethoven née Obermayer actually had two illegitimate daughters; the first, Amalie was given her maternal grandmother's maiden name "Waldmann." The second child was Magdalena Obermayer who was born 23 April 1808 and died on 26 May 1809. Johann van Beethoven was not the father of either child although he did latter adopt Amalie Waldmann.] The sketches to a three-part canon on this text are found on Beethoven's Haus- und Jahreskalender (household calendar) from the year 1823. It is not known if the piece was completed.

Schünemann printed the sketches (probably not with complete correctness) in the [Arnold] Schering *Festschrift*, pp. 210-12, [which is] also referred to in entry 258 of this catalog. [TN: in his transcription, Schünemann first gives two rhythmical drafts, followed by six bars for a single voice (in F, 3/4, bass clef). He says that there are more "musical notations" for the canon, but that they are so badly faded that he can't decipher them with certainty. A canon on just the six bars as given by Schünemann doesn't seem possible. This canon is mentioned under WoO 181 in Kinsky/Halm, p. 685, but not cataloged there.]

261 "Bester Herr Graf, Sie sind ein Schaf" (Dear Count, You Are a Sheep). A four-part canon in F major, 8 bars. Composed on 20 February 1823, to Count Moritz Lichnowsky. The autograph is in the Berliner Staatsbibliothek, Folder I, No. 35, of the Schindler-Nachlass. [TN: now in the SBB.] A facsimile was printed in Journal 10 of Hirschbach's *Musik. krit. Repertoriums aller neuen Erscheinungen im Gebiete der Tonkunst*, Leipzig 1844, supplement to p. 468. Also printed in Kalischer IV, as No. 874, and in score by Misch, see p. 264 in "Pseudokanons und Rätselkanons von Beethoven," in *Die Musikforschung*, Vol. 3, Journal 3/4,1950, and again by MacArdle/Misch, where it is given on p. 402 as No. 349. The canon is inadvertently named twice in the third edition of Hess's earlier catalog, under Nos. 199 and 244. It is furthermore printed in Thayer IV, p. 389, but, not quite correctly, like the others [meaning, other editions or printings] besides Misch. [TN: this is listed in Kinsky/Halm as WoO 183, p. 686. It was also published by Rudolf Klein in *Sämtliche Kanons*, Verlag Doblinger, Vienna 1970, p. 31. This was published by Hess in the SBG, Vol. V, 1962, p. 82.]

262 "Falstafferel, laß dich sehen!" (Falstaff, Show Yourself!).
Five-part canon, in G major, 31 bars, written on 26
April 1823 to the greeting and invitation [by Beetho-
ven] to violinist Ignaz Schuppanzigh at the time he
came back from Russia. The autograph is in the collection of K. Geigy-Hagenbach, Basel, Switzerland. [TN:
according to Dorfmüller, p. 386, this is now in the
Kunstmuseum, Basel.] A copy [facsimile] and the first
edition were in *Die Musik*, Vol. II, Journal 13, 1 April
1903, as well as a copy in Paul Bekker's *Beethoven*,
[Schuster & Loeffler], Berlin 1911, p. 22 of the illustrations. Reduced copies, p. 80 in the Auction Catalog
CXXVII, from K. E. Henrici in Berlin, 1928; Entry XI in
the Autograph Catalog of K. Geigy-Hagenbach, Basel
1929. This canon is also entered with that of No. 252
in Fritz Jöde's previously mentioned work *Praktischen
Zwecken dienende Kanonsammlung*, Kallmeyer,
Wolfenbüttel 1926, p. 203. [TN: this is listed in
Kinsky/Halm as WoO 184, p. 727. This was published
by Hess in the SBG, Vol. V, 1962, p. 82.]

263 "Te solo adoro," two-part canon, in E-flat major, 8 bars,
unpublished. See the following number. [TN: C/C, p.
261, says that this was possibly written for Carlo
Evasio Soliva in 1824, and that it is similar to, or an
earlier version of, WoO 186. It was published by Hess
in the SBG, Vol. V, 1962, p. 83.]

264 "Te solo adoro," two-part canon, in E-flat major, 8 bars,
unpublished. Both pieces [this entry and entry 263
above] are found drafted on page eight of the trombone parts to the 9th Symphony written by Beethoven
himself. This is in the Bodmer Collection, Mh 28 of
Unger's catalog. [TN: the manuscript, Mh 28, now renumbered SBH 570, is in the Beethoven-Haus, Bonn.]
Max Unger, in a letter to Donald W. MacArdle, remarks: "I only recognize my deciphering of the one in
E-flat major (NB: Both are in E-flat major! W. H.),

which is some sort of preliminary study made before of the presently known version before the known setting. (GA Series 25, No. 285/1.) Another attempt by Beethoven to set the same words to music is simply not decipherable. The music which was written with a lead pencil has blurred and faded considerably. However, the attempt also seems to me to fail, because Beethoven doesn't seem to have found the right rhythm for the words here. . ." It should be added that during a visit with me in March 1957, Unger recognized the two aforementioned canons and said that he must have thought of another as a fourth draft, or rather as a third one in the Bodmer Collection, Beethoven-Haus, Bonn. The matter, therefore, still needs clarification. [TN: this is similar to, or perhaps an earlier version of, WoO 186. As clarification, there are at least three similar, but nevertheless different, settings of the text "Te solo adoro," which are labeled as WoO 186, Hess 263 and Hess 264. It is unclear which one of the three, or perhaps even an unknown fourth one, Unger meant in his letter to MacArdle. This one (Hess 264) was published by Hess in the SBG, Vol. V, 1962, p. 83. A. Willem Holsbergen wrote to me, "To add to the confusion, Deutsche Grammophon, in their *Complete Beethoven Edition* of 1997, included a canon 'Te solo adoro,' which they refer to as WoO 186, but which is, in fact, Hess 264."]

265 Canon "Gott ist eine feste Burg" (God Is a Mighty Fortress) is in E-flat major, 4 bars. [TN: Hess gives "E-flat major," but it is in fact in B-flat major.] A puzzle canon composed on 12 January 1825 for Colonel von Düsterlohe of Kurland. [TN: Kurland is an historic state in the territory of today's Latvia. It ceased to exist as a political district in 1940.] Today the autograph is missing. A facsimile is in catalog 36 of *Autographenversteigerung* (beginning 17 November 1906) as No. 1049, p. 142, from the antiquarian Leo

Liepmannssohn in Berlin; furthermore, in [Hans Volkmann's "Beethoven als Epigrammatiker,"] in *Die Musik*, Vol. 7, No. 13, April 1908, [p. 26]; and in the illustrations of [Paul] Bekker's *Beethoven*, p. 131. Furthermore, it was published full size on p. 3 (illustration No. 7) in the Auction Catalog CIV (14th and 15th of May 1925) from K. E. Henrici, Berlin. Printed in musical transcription as No. 1175 in F. Prelinger's *Ludwig van Beethoven: sämtliche Briefe und Aufzeichnung* (Beethoven's collected letters and notes), Vol. 4, 1909, p. 177. See also a reference on p. 205 by Jöde, who printed the piece as a three-part canon, probably in agreement with Thayer V, p. 170; Kinsky /Halm presents it as a two-part canon as WoO 188, which Misch also indicates in fact with some two-part solutions; see his "Pseudokanons und Rätselkanons von Beethoven," in *Die Musikforschung*, Vol. 3, Journal 3/4,1950, pp. 271-3; however, Frimmel's opinion inclines to believe it is unsolvable. [TN: this was published by Hess in the SBG, Vol. V, 1962, p. 82. In the *Revisionsbericht* section, p. 94, where Hess remarks that Riemann's three-part solution is "not very convincing."]

266 "Doktor, sperrt das Tor dem Tod" (Doctor, Close the Gate unto Death). Four-part canon, C major, 16 bars, written on 11 May 1825 by Beethoven for his physician, Dr. Anton Braunhofer. The autograph is the property of the Gesellschaft der Musikfreunde in Vienna. A facsimile was printed as a supplement to the *Wiener Telegraph*, No. 2, 1838. [TN: another facsimile appeared by Joseph Schmidt-Görg in *Ludwig van Beethoven*, Georg Westermann Verlag, Braunschweig 1969, p. 30.] Printed by Nottebohm in the *Allgemeine Musikalische Zeitung*, No. 9, 1870, as well as by Kalischer in *Neue Beethoven-Briefe,* p. 187. It is cited in Nohl I, No. 335; Thayer V, p. 196; and in Kalischer V, No. 1069, where the first edition is declared to be in the *Leipziger Allgemeine Musikalische Zeitung* of 2

March 1870, p. 67 and the following page. [TN: this is listed in Kinsky/Halm as WoO 189, p. 691. It was published by Hess in the SBG, Vol. V, 1962, p. 83.]

267 "Ich war hier, Doktor, ich war hier" (I Was Here, Doctor, I Was Here). Two-part puzzle-canon (in the lower fifth, entry of the 2nd voice occurs in the 2nd bar), C major, 8 bars. Composed on 4 June 1825 for Dr. A[nton] Braunhofer. The autograph is in the possession of Mrs. Agathe von Philipp in Leipzig. [TN: tragically, this autograph was destroyed in 1944 during World War II.] A facsimile is on p. 36 (item No. 424), in Catalog 21 of the Autographs' Auction of the 29th and 30th of April 1912, of the antiquarian M. Breslauer in Berlin; a further facsimile appeared on the title page to the brochure *Berühmte Musikerhandschriften*, published by Drei-Masken Verlag, Berlin 1920, as well as in Auction Catalog XLIII, item No. 17 of Karl Ernst Henrici. It has been published in *Neues Winterthurer Tagblatt*, of 21 July 1952; and by Stephan Ley in *Aus Beethovens Erdentagen*, [Glöcker,] Bonn 1948, p. 192. Printed in transcription as No. 406 by MacArdle/Misch; see p. 469. [TN: this is listed in Kinsky/Halm as WoO 190, p. 693. The letter is Anderson No. 1385 and Brandenburg No. 1981. It was published by Hess in the SBG, Vol. V, 1962, p. 83. Hess, in the *Revisionsbericht* of Vol. V, p. 95, also gives a solution for four voices: second voice in the lower fifth in the second bar, third voice in the upper second in the seventh bar, and fourth voice in the lower fourth in the eighth bar. This solution can also be found on the website: <www.unheardbeethoven.org>.]

268 "Ars longa, vita brevis" (Art lasts, Life is short). Second version. Four-part puzzle canon, F major, 4 bars. Written on 16 September 1825 for Sir George Smart. The autograph cannot be located today. [TN: a facsimile was published by H. Bertram Cox and C. L. E. Cox in

Leaves from the Journals of Sir George Smart, Longmans, Green & Co., London & New York 1907, as an insert after p. 124.] First mentioned in Thayer as No. 254 (there the wrong date is given: 6 instead of 16 September), mentioned again in Thayer V, pp. 247-8. [TN: this is listed in Kinsky/Halm as WoO 192, p. 694. It was published by Hess in the SBG, Vol. V, 1962, p. 83. The autograph of this little souvenir piece was inscribed by Beethoven with: "Geschrieben am 16. September 1825 in Baden, als mich ein lieber talentvoller Musikkünstler u. Freund Smart (aus England) allheir besuchte. Ludwig van Beethoven." (Written on the 16th September 1825 in Baden, for a dear talented musical artist and friend, Smart (of England), who visited me here. Ludwig van Beethoven.)]

269 "Ars longa, vita brevis" (Art lasts, Life is short). Third version. Puzzle canon, C major, 5 bars. Not yet solved, and the composition date remains unknown. [TN: Albert Willem Holsbergen writes: "No doubt Beethoven jotted down this canon with tongue-in-cheek, because he's cheating here: all the notes of the melody belong to the tonic triad, which means it can be combined in any way you want without ever creating any harmonic roughness. It can be worked out for 5 voices, or even more. However, by going beyond 5 voices the solution will sound more and more like just one big triad. It's better to just smile at Beethoven's chaff. The words 'Ars longa, vita brevis' are depicted in the music, 'Ars longa' has long notes, and 'vita brevis' has short notes."] Kinsky/Halm lists the piece as WoO 193 [p. 727], and based on reason of the handwriting asserts the year 1825 as the composition year. A facsimile appeared on the title page (item No. 511) to the Auction Catalog CXX (27th and 28th of May, 1927) from Karl Ernst Henrici, Berlin. The autograph is owned by the Heinemann Foundation, New York. [TN: according to a database compiled by Patricia Stroh, this piece is

was deposited in 1962 on loan by the Heinemann Foundation to the Pierpont Morgan Library, New York and in 1977 it was made a permanent part of their collection. This was published by Hess in the SBG, Vol. V, 1962, p. 83.]

270 "Es muß sein!" (It must Be!). A four-part canon, 16 bars, in F major, written in April 1826; see the anecdote given in Kinsky/Halm, WoO 196, p. 697. The autograph is missing, a facsimile appeared in Gassner's *Zeitschrift für Deutschlands Musikvereine und Dilettanten*, Vol. 3, Karlsruhe 1844, in the leaflet before p. 133. Mentioned in Thayer V, p. 302; and in Fritz Jöde's *Praktischen Zwecken dienende Kanonsammlung*, Kallmeyer, Wolfenbüttel 1926, p. 202; and lastly by MacArdle/Misch, No. 446, p. 512. [TN: this was published by Hess in the SBG, Vol. V, 1962, p. 84. There are sketches for another setting of this canon found on the heading of the autograph for the finale of Op. 135. A facsimile of the sketches, together with a lengthy discussion of the meaning and circumstances of both the finished canon and these sketches can be found in Lewis Lockwood's Beethoven: The Music and the Life, W. W. Norton New York 2003, pp. 479-82.]

271 "Da ist das Werk, sorgt um das Geld!" (Here is the Work, Get Me the Money!) Five-part canon, C major, 10 bars. Written early in September 1826, as a joking invitation to Carl Holz to call on the publisher M. Artaria to receive a royalty payment of twelve ducats for Op. 134 (piano arrangement of the Quartet Op. 133). The autograph is in the Library of Peabody College of Music in Baltimore. The first facsimile was published by Otto B. Albrecht in *The Musical Quarterly*, October 1945, Vol. XXXI, pp. 492-503, as part of an article, "Adventures and Discoveries of a Manuscript Hunter." The German reprint of the article appeared in *Musica*, Vol. II, 1948,

pp. 128-139, with what followed as an unsuccessful reprinting of the canon. Further editions are a facsimile in the *Neues Winterthurer Tagblatt* of 21 May 1949 (Willy Hess), and again on p. 280 of *Beethoven*, a biography by Willy Hess, Büchergilde Gutenberg, Zürich 1956, p. 281. The canon is also found along with my entry No. 252 [from this catalog] as the last piece in Fritz Jöde's previously mentioned *Praktischen Zwecken dienende Kanonsammlung*, Kallmeyer, Wolfenbüttel 1926, p. 207. A copy in the handwriting of Carl Holz is located in the Wiener Stadtbibliothek, Signatur MH 9635 c, one page, large [portrait] format (it is not mentioned in Kinsky/Halm); and is in MacArdle/Misch, No. 461, p. 524. [TN: it is the "large portrait format" autograph that is not mentioned in Kinsky/Halm; this piece is, however, listed there as WoO 197, p. 698. It was published by Hess in the SBG, Vol. V, 1962, p. 84.]

272 "Das Schöne zu dem Guten" (The Beautiful to the Good), 2 bars in A major. A composition written in the family autograph album of Ludwig Rellstab, 3 May 1825. Misch writes that there are two possible solutions as a four-part canon, see his "Pseudokanons und Rätselkanons von Beethoven," in *Die Musikforschung*, Vol. 3, Journal 3/4,1950, p. 270, so that we are permitted to add this to the [list of] canons. The first edition was in Rellstab's *Garden und Wald*, Vol. 4, Leipzig 1854, p. 109. Later in Nohl I, No. 329; again in *Neue Wiener Musikzeitung* of 11 March 1855, it is cataloged by Thayer as No. 249, and mentioned in Thayer V, p. 209. [TN: this is listed in Kinsky/Halm as WoO 203, p. 704. This is, according to Emily Anderson, not from a "family autograph album" as described above but from a now lost letter of the same date. See notes on Anderson letter 1366b, Vol. 3, pp. 1190-1. It was published by Hess in the SBG, Vol. V, 1962, p. 83.]

273 Instrumental canon, in A major, 8 bars. [TN: actually it is written in 9 bars, the last being identical to the first.] Presumably for two violins. Written on 3 August 1825 for Otto de Boer. It is located in the autograph collection of Paul Warburg, New York. The first edition was in Nohl II, No. 290, reprinted in Thayer V, p. 226. Kinsky/Halm, [p. 476,] places the canon under the chamber music works for string instruments as WoO 35. [TN: recent scholarship identifies this work as having been written for two cellos, not two violins, and intended for the Dutchman, Samson Moses de Boer, not Otto de Boer. See Jos van der Zanden's *Beethoven: Nieuwe onthullingen*, Uitgevermaatschappij Holland, Haarlem 1993, pp. 128-140, where he identifies the recipient as Samson Moses de Boer, an amateur cellist; see also van der Zanden's revised and expanded article on the same subject "A Dutch Visitor to Beethoven," in the *Beethoven Journal*, Vol. 14, No. 2, The American Beethoven Society, San Jose, California, Winter 1999, p. 50. The autograph is now in the Houghton Library of Harvard University, Cambridge, Massachusetts.]

274 Two-part canon, G major, 4/4 [time], unpublished. It is located on p. 89 of the Wielhorski Sketchbook (see an additional reference in entry No. 229 of this catalog) and is, according to Nohl, completely executed. It was composed in 1801. [TN: this untexted canon (SV 343) was published by Hess in the SBG, Vol. IX, 1965, p. 23. The Wielhorski Sketchbook was edited by Nathan Fišman and published in 3 Volumes, (facsimile, transcription and commentary), Muzgiz, Moscow 1962. This work may not be by Beethoven, but a copy in Beethoven's own hand of a canon by [Friedrich von] Matthisson. See Richard Kramer's "Notes to Beethoven's Education," *Journal of the American Musicological Society*, No. 28, 1975 pp. 72-101.]

275 Two-part canon, A-flat major, 8 bars, [c.1803]. Determined by me to be from page 118 of the Beethoven note book E 90 (SV 60) of the Deutsche Staatsbibliothek. [TN: this is now the SBB. However, this "note book" E 90 (more commonly known as the "Eroica Sketchbook" or "Landsberg 6") is presently held by the Biblioteka Jagiellońska, Cracow, Poland.] The piece is completely executed and seems to have been set for piano. Unpublished. [TN: this entry is identical to a later entry, No. 328. It appears that Hess discovered this work on his own while examining the sketchbook and accordingly entered it here as No. 275, while the inclusion of entry No. 328 rests entirely on information from Nottebohm without ever comparing the two, and thus results in a duplication. See entry No. 328 below. It was published by Hess in the SBG, Vol. IX, 1965, p. 23.]

276 "Herr Graf, ich komme zu fragen, wie Sie sich befinden" (Dear Count, I Come to Ask How You Are). A three-part canon in C major, 24 bars. Completely executed, only the text is not fully deciphered. Max Unger writes that the piece is written for Nikolaus Zmeskall von Domanovecz and was composed about 1797. It is a quite delightful and graceful piece; hopefully it can appear in print soon. The autograph is in the Bodmer Collection now in the Beethoven-Haus, Bonn, but not named in the catalog, since according to a verbal communication from Unger, it is a later Bodmer acquisition. [TN: it was not given an "Mh" number because it was a later addition to the Bodmer Collection, but it is presently cataloged as SBH 632 and SV 167. It was published by Hess in the SBG, Vol. V, 1962, p. 78. The entire text has been worked out by Rudolf Klein and published in his *Beethoven Sämtliche Kanons*, Verlag Doblinger, Vienna 1970, p. 7.]

277 "Esel aller Esel" (Donkey of All Donkeys!) [TN: the German word "Esel" normally translates as "ass" or the more polite "donkey;" however, like its English equivalent, it can also be translated as "fool," thus "Fool of All Fools!" is an equally satisfactory translation.] Two-part canon with a third voice that sings "he-haw" as ostinato. Eight, as well as 12 bars in F major. [TN: Hess appears to have been confused about the key signature. See the references just below.] This is unpublished. Found by Fritz Kaiser (Darmstadt) in Mus. Ms. Beethoven Autograph 24, folio 51, in Berlin and currently stored in Tübingen. [TN: it was published by Hess in the SBG, Vol. V, 1962, p. 79, where Hess gives the correct key signature as D major. It was also published by Rudolf Klein in *Sämtliche Kanons*, Verlag Doblinger, Vienna 1970, p. 8, where the key is also given as D major. The autograph of this work is now back in the SBB.]

Altogether, from these thirty-one canons, five numbers are without text (247, 248, 273-275); the text to 251, 268 and 269 is probably taken from Seneca's *De brevitate vitae*. Numbers 263 and 264 are quoted from Metastasio's spiritual opera *La Betulia liberata*, while 272 is from the last stanza of [Friedrich von] Matthisson's *Opferlied*, and all the remaining texts are from Beethoven himself.

Humorous Musical Greetings, Jokes in Letters, Diaries etc.

278 Musical Joke "Lob auf den Dicken" (In Praise of the Fat One) for three solo voices (tenor and two bass voices) and four-part choir, in G major, 16 bars. Written in 1801 for the violinist Schuppanzigh. Autograph [is] on the last page of the original manuscript of the Sonata Op. 28, Beethoven-Haus, Bonn [SBH 527]. First published in 1890 in Grove's *Dictionary of Music and Musicians*, article on Schuppanzigh, Vol. III, p. 424. Facsimile in *Beethovens Handschrift aus dem Beethoven-Haus*, 1928, illustration 3, as well as in *Veröffentlichungen des Beethovenhauses VI*, Bonn 1930 (facsimile and transcription by L. Schiedermair). Also a transcription by MacArdle/Misch, p. 27, as No. 25 (with English text). [TN: this is listed in Kinsky/Halm as WoO 100, p. 563. It was published by Hess in the SBG, Vol. V, 1962, p. 79.]

279 Musical Joke "Graf, Graf, liebster Graf" (Count, Count, Dearest Count), for three voices, 18 bars, in E-flat major. Written in the autumn of 1802 for Nicholas Zmeskall von Domanovecz. The autograph is in the Nationalbibliothek in Vienna; a copy was reproduced in the Viennese magazine *Moderne Welt*, Journal 9, 1920, p. 17. First listed by Thayer as No. 98; afterwards mentioned in Thayer II p. 337. Listed in Nohl I as No. 112, where he believes the relevant letter is directed to Count Moritz Lichnowsky. The pieces 278 and 279 would have to be printed in score with the remaining a cappella songs in a special volume of the new GA. [TN: this is Anderson No. 65 and Brandenburg No. 115. A facsimile is in "Pis'ma Betchovena 1787-1811," edited by Nathan Fišman,

Moscow 1970, Fig. XVI. This is listed in Kinsky/Halm as WoO 101, p. 564. It was published by Hess in the SBG, Vol. V, 1962, p. 79.]

280 "Wir irren allesamt, nur jeder irret anders" (We All Err, Only Everyone Errs Differently). A whimsical setting in four bars [noted in the] (bass clef). Written for Carl Holz in the beginning of December 1826. The autograph has not been traced; mentioned in Nohl I as No. 385, and in Kalischer V as No. 1196. [TN: the letter is Anderson No. 1541 and Brandenburg No. 2234. Anderson writes, in footnote No. 4, p. 1320, "According to Nohl, who transcribed the letter which was then in private ownership, it was written by another hand, but all the words from 'Finally' and the musical setting are in Beethoven's handwriting." The word "Finally" begins the last phrase of the letter followed by the musical setting.] – A setting somewhat deviant from it in the treble clef [with the] (text, "Wir irren allesamt, ein jeder irret anders") can be found on a scrap paper in the Österreichische Nationalbibliothek, which according to Misch in "Pseudokanons und Rätselkanons von Beethoven," in *Die Musikforschung*, Vol. 3, Journal 3/4,1950, p, 259, is not written in Beethoven's hand. [TN: A. Willem Holsbergen believes that this somewhat deviant copy may be in the handwriting of Carl Holz, to whom it was written and who was a violinist, thus accounting for the transposition to the treble clef. Holz frequently acted as copyist for Beethoven.] Entered by Thayer as No. 277, and in Kalischer V as No. 1180. Beethoven probably has taken the text from the title vignette of [Johann Philipp] Kirnberger's *Die Kunst des reinen Satzes in der Musik*, Berlin, 1771. [TN: this is listed in Kinsky/Halm as WoO 198, p. 699. It was published by Hess in the SBG, Vol. V, 1962, p. 84.]

281 "Ich bin der Herr von zu" (I Am the Master of You), 8 bars in D major, it is written on p. 3 of the large

sketchbook that Beethoven used in the autumn of 1814 to compose the Cantata Op. 136, which is in the Deutsche Staatsbibliothek. [TN: this is now the SBB. However, this piece is found in the Mendelssohn 6 Sketchbook, which has been in the Biblioteka Jagiellońska, Cracow, Poland since the end of World War II. Also, it is found on page 5, not 3, as given by Hess. Hess's numbering would be correct if one counts by folios.] It is Nohl's assumption that this was written as a remark of displeasure over an uncomfortable or unreasonable demand of the Archduke Rudolph. Mentioned in Nohl II, No. 108. [TN: this is listed in Kinsky/Halm as WoO 199, p. 700. It was published by Nohl in *Neue Briefe Beethovens*, p. 84, in a footnote to No. 107.]

282 "Ich bin bereit" (I Am Ready), four bars in C major, as the start of a double fugue on the text, "Ich bin bereit. Amen." A transcription is found in a letter, dating from June 1818, to Vincenz Hauschka, expressing Beethoven's willingness to do the composition of an oratorio, "Der Sieg des Kreuzes" (The Victory of the Cross) by [Josef] Karl Bernard. (NB: The oratorio was never written!) The autograph is in the property of the Gesellschaft der Musikfreunde, Vienna. [TN: Dorfmüller, p. 389, asserts that it is not a double fugue, but two musical jokes separated by several lines of text in the letter.] It was first listed as a musical joke by Thayer as No. 298. The whole letter was given by Nottebohm in the *Leipziger Allgemeine Musikalische Zeitung* IV, 1870, p. 68; and in Thayer IV, pp. 99-100. Misch shows canonical possibilities; see his "Pseudokanons und Rätselkanons von Beethoven," in *Die Musikforschung*, Vol. 3, Journal 3/4, 1950, p. 262. [TN: this is listed in Kinsky/Halm as WoO 201, p. 702.]

283 "Das Schöne zum Guten" (The Beautiful to the Good), 2 bars in F major. Written on 27 September 1823 on a

page in a family autograph album for Mrs. Marie Pachler-Koschak. The autograph is in the collection of the Gesellschaft der Musikfreunde, Vienna. Listed by Thayer as No. 242, and again in Thayer IV, p. 467; also in Nohl II as No. 266 (in a footnote). A facsimile was printed by A. Göllerich in *Beethoven,* Berlin 1904, p. 49. The text is the final line of Matthisson's *Opferlied.* [TN: this is listed in Kinsky/Halm as WoO 202, p. 703. It was published by Hess in the *Revisionsbericht* of the SBG, Vol. V, 1962, p. 94.]

284 "Holz geigt die Quartette so, als ob sie Kraut eintreten," (Holz Plays the Quartet as If He Were Stomping on Cabbage), in D minor, 6 bars. A musical joke on Carl Holz' violin playing, written at the end of September 1825. A transcription is in a conversation book in the Deutsche Staatsbibliothek. [TN: this is now the SBB. This is from Conversation Book 97 which was in use from 11 to 26 September 1825. The entry is found on 57r and was transcribed by Karl-Heinz Köhler and Grita Herre in *Ludwig van Beethovens Konversationshefte*, Vol. 8, VEB Deutscher Verlag für Musik, Leipzig 1981, p. 172.] Listed in Thayer V on p. 250. [TN: this is listed in Kinsky/Halm as WoO 204, p. 704. Hess calls this a "musical joke," but it can be worked out as a canon for two or even four voices. See: <*www.unheardbeethoven.org*> for the four- part version. This is a fine example of Beethoven's love of word play and homely expressions. It was a practice in Beethoven's time to make sauerkraut by cutting the heads of cabbage into quarters, placing them into a barrel and then stomping on them in bare feet to release the juices in order to speed the fermentation process. This creates quite an image, if indeed Holz did play the violin that way.]

285 Musical joke on "Tobias," 11 bars (the twelfth and final bar is illegible), a song in E-flat major. This is unpub-

lished. [TN: Hess says that "the twelfth and final bar is illegible;" in fact, the entire piece is practically unreadable.] This is from the collection of H. C. Bodmer. Unger has written that this piece was "written after 1814;" see "Von ungedruckter Musik Beethovens," *Zeitschrift für Musik*, Vol. 102, Journal 1, November 1935, bottom of p. 1194). However, Unger counter dates it under number Mh 99 of the Bodmer catalog, where he writes that this joke is likely from the end of 1824. [TN: the catalog number Mh 99 of the Bodmer Collection has been changed, and it is now listed as SBH 677 (SV 148) in the catalog of the Beethoven-Haus, Bonn.] The autograph of this piece is located together with sketches of the String Quartets Op. 127 and Op. 132, so that this later dating is probably more likely to be correct. [TN: this is not listed in Kinsky/Halm with a separate WoO number, however, it is mentioned under WoO 182, p. 686, where it is suggested that it is perhaps a "draft"to WoO 182 or WoO 205 g-k. Dorfmüller also lists it as a "draft" for a musical joke; see p. 397. On this piece, A. Willem Holsbergen writes to me: "I don't think this is a draft for any of WoO 205 g-k, since it's musically not related. Because WoO 182 dates from 1821, it's not likely that Hess 285 is a draft for that either. Hess 285 seems in character close to the first theme of the finale of Op. 127. The music suggests canonic possibilities, but a solution has eluded me."]

The following ten pieces are united in Kinsky/Halm as WoO 205 a-k ("Musical Jokes in Letters"). [TN: there is no piece marked "j." Kinsky/Halm has followed an old-fashioned practice and omitted the use of this letter since there is no "j" in the Latin alphabet.] We continue by using that numbering here. Although these are about the smallest of musical structures, often only two bars, they are, however, typical of our master's working manner and peculiarity. [TN: none of these were printed by Hess in his SBG.]

286 "Baron, Baron, Baron," in C major, 4 bars. [This is used as the salutation] in a letter addressed to Nicholas Zmeskall, 1798 or 1799. The autograph is in the Nationalbibliothek, Vienna. First printed in Nohl I, as No. 10; and in Thayer II, p. 117, where in the second bar there is an alto-[clef] instead of a tenor-clef. This mistake has found its way into many other editions. [TN: this is listed in Kinsky/Halm as WoO 205a, p. 705. The letter is listed in Anderson, Vol. 1, p. 31 as No. 29, and in Brandenburg, Vol.1, p. 46 as No. 39. The incorrect printing of the key signatures has been corrected in Kinsky/Halm, Anderson and Brandenburg.]

287 "Allein, allein, allein, jedoch Silentium," (But, But, But, However Silence), in A minor, 2 bars. Found near the end of a letter of 21 September 1814 to Count Moritz Lichnowsky, on the sentence, ". . .Nothing can be done with the Court, I made an offer – but. . ." The autograph is unknown. The first edition was published by A. B. Marx in *Beethoven*, 2nd edition, Otto Janke, Berlin 1863, p. 121; also mentioned in Thayer III, p. 445. [TN: this is listed in Kinsky/Halm as WoO 205b, p. 705. The usual translation of "allein" is "alone;" however in this instance Beethoven means "but," which is commented on by Anderson in a footnote to her translation of this letter. The letter is given in Anderson, Vol. 1, p. 471 as No. 498, and in Brandenburg, Vol. 3, p. 56 as No. 740.]

288 "O Adjutant," written without a bar line at the end of an undated letter to Tobias Haslinger, in January 1817. The autograph is missing. [TN: the autograph is no longer missing. The letter is in the Beethoven-Haus, Bonn, cataloged as SBH 223.] The first edition was on p. 33 of the appendix to Seyfried's *Beethovens Studien*, Haslinger, Vienna 1832. [TN: on p. 31 in the 1852 edition.] Listed in Nohl I, as No. 168; and also in Thayer III, p. 631. [TN: this is listed in Kinsky/Halm as

WoO 205c, p. 705. The letter is given in Anderson, Vol. 2, p. 693 as No. 742 and in Brandenburg, Vol. 4, p. 11 as No. 1065.]

289 "Wo, wo?" (Where, Where?), 2 bars, from the end of the inside of a letter to Frau Nannette Streicher from 20 July 1817; after the question, "Where are my blankets?" The autograph is missing. [TN: the autograph is no longer missing; it is in the Beethoven-Haus, Bonn, where it is cataloged as NE 204.] The first edition was in Nohl II, as No. 172. Printed in Thayer IV, p. 489. Nohl I, No. 202, mentions this joke in context with another letter. [TN: this oblique reference is made clear by two footnotes in Anderson. The first footnote, on p. 692, reads: "The 'enclosed letter' is obviously Letter 789, written on July 20th, which in 1817 fell on a Sunday." The phrase "enclosed letter" is from Anderson's Letter 792, written on July 27, which Nohl and Thayer assumed contained this musical joke, and which Hess presumed was lost. The second footnote, p. 693, which refers to Letter 792, reads: "The autograph lacks the musical addition quoted in all the printed versions of this letter. The owner of the autograph (Vice Counsel Fritz Hunziker at that time) suggests that the missing portion was added to the "enclosed letter', i.e. Letter 789." It is clear that Hess was aware of the association of the two letters, but not aware that the musical quip could be from letter 789, not 792 as had been generally accepted. Letter 789 is given in Anderson, Vol. 2, p. 690, and Letter 792 is on p. 693. The two letters are given in Brandenburg, Vol. 4, pp. 83 and 86, and numbered 1142 and 1145. This is listed in Kinsky/Halm as WoO 205d, p. 706.]

290 "Erfüllung, Erfüllung" (Fulfilment, Fulfilment), 2 bars for four-part chorus in D major, with the [tempo] designation. [It is] contained in a letter of congratulations of June 1819 to the Archduke Rudolph on his appoint-

ment as the Prince-Archbishop of Olmütz. The autograph is missing. [TN: this autograph is no longer missing. The first part of this letter with the musical notation is in the Institut Russkoj Literatury (Institute for Russian Literature), St. Petersburg (Pushkin House, Collection of A. F. Onegin, Signatur 28659). The remainder of the letter is in the Gesellschaft der Musikfreunde in Vienna.] The first edition was published by Theodor Frimmel in *Montags-Revue*, Vienna, 12 November 1900, and reprinted by MacArdle/Misch; see their entry No. 244, p. 246. [TN: the letter is given in Anderson, Vol. 2, p. 813 as No. 948, and in Brandenburg, Vol. 4, p. 245 as No. 1292. Nathan Fišman dates the letter from February 1819, not June. Facsimile is in *Sovetskaja Muzyka* No. 12, 1960, p. 62. This is listed in Kinsky/Halm as WoO 205e, p. 706.]

291 "Scheut euch nicht" (Don't Shy Away), 2 bars in F major. Written in an undated letter to [Georg] Friedrich Treitschke after the words, "Wir sind euch wo möglich allzeit zu Diensten." (We are, as far as possible, ever at your service.) The autograph is unknown. [TN: the autograph is in the Beethoven-Haus, Bonn, cataloged as SBH 453.] Printed in Kalischer V, No. 595, and in [Emerich] Kastner's *Ludwig van Beethovens sämtliche Briefe*, Hesse, Berlin and Leipzig 1910, p. 436 as No. 663. Contrary to Kastner and Kalischer, Kinsky/Halm doesn't attribute the letter to the year 1816, but to about 1820. This was first published in the *Allgemeine Deutsche Musikzeitung*, Berlin-Charlottenburg, 6 April 1888, Vol. XV, No. 14, p. 140, with the wrong text, "Schreit auch nicht." About this, Donald W. MacArdle writes to me: "According to my records, the Erstdruck of the letter was in *Signale* [*für die Musikalische Welt*] Vol. 14 (1856), [p.] 282. I don't know whether the music was also given." [TN: the musical notation was not given in the 1856 printing of the letter. The letter with the musical

notation is given in Anderson, Vol. 2, p. 937 as No. 1068, and in Brandenburg, Vol. 4, p. 194 as No. 1216. This is listed in Kinsky/Halm as WoO 205f, p. 706.]

292 "Tobias! Paternostergäßler" (Tobias! Paternoster Street), 7 bars in E major, as addressed in an undated letter written to Tobias Haslinger, but probably from the end of September 1824. [TN: this title really doesn't make much sense until one reads the rest of the text of the letter, in which Beethoven calls Haslinger an "alehouse musical Philistine of Paternoster Street."] The autograph is in the collection of Louis Koch, Wildegg (Switzerland). [TN: the Koch Collection is now dispersed, with some parts with Hans Rahmer, Hamburg-Langenhorn, and part in the Cary Collection in the Pierpont Morgan Library, New York, and still other parts missing. See C/C, p. 224.] The same piece is mentioned in Georg Kinsky's catalog of the Koch Collection, No. 108, p. 121. First printed by A. C. Kalischer in "Vierzehn Ungedruckte Briefe Beethovens," in *Die Musik*, Vol. V, No. 18, June 1906, p. 371. Mentioned as well in Unger's *Briefausgabe*, Berlin 1921, as No. 87, p. 70. [TN: the letter is given in Anderson, Vol. 3, p. 1144 as No. 1312, and in Brandenburg, Vol. 5, p. 357 as No. 1887. This is listed in Kinsky/Halm as WoO 205g, p. 707.]

293 "Tobias," in D major, 4 bars. In another undated letter to Tobias Haslinger, probably written in the Spring of 1825. The autograph is in the collection of L. Koch, Wildegg (Switzerland). [TN: the Koch Collection is now dispersed with some parts with Hans Rahmer, Hamburg-Langenhorn and part in the Cary Collection in the Pierpont Morgan Library, New York and still other parts missing. See C/C, p. 224.] The same piece is mentioned in Kinsky's catalog of that Collection as No. 109, p. 122. First published in the *Allgemeine Musikalische Zeitung*, 15 September 1869 (New Series

IV, No. 37). Nottebohm I, p. 104, gives 1816 as the date. [TN: the letter is given in Anderson, Vol. 3, p. 1189 as No. 1365 and in Brandenburg, Vol. 6, p. 50 as No. 1955. This is listed in Kinsky/Halm as WoO 205h, p. 707.]

294 "Bester To(bias)" (Good Tobias), in C major, 2 bars. From another undated letter written in Gneixendorf to Tobias Haslinger, probably at the start of October 1826. [TN: this lost letter was listed in a catalog of the Antiquarian Joseph Baer of Frankfurt in 1888 as having been dated "2 October 1826."] Published in Kalischer V, No. 1191; Nohl I, No. 383, p. 329; and in Unger's *Briefsausgabe* as No. 99. According to Misch, see his "Pseudokanons und Rätselkanons von Beethoven," in *Die Musikforschung*, Vol. 3, Journal 3/4,1950, p. 262, it is possible to imitate the little phrase in the spacing of a bar in unison. [TN: the letter is given in Anderson, Vol. 3, p. 1314 as No. 1534, and in Brandenburg, Vol. 6, p. 297 as No. 2219. This is listed in Kinsky/Halm as WoO 205i, p. 707.]

295 "Erster aller Tobiasse" (First of all Tobiases), in C major, 12 bars, with part in two voices and part in three voices. In a letter addressed to Tobias Haslinger of 13 October 1826 and sent from Gneixendorf. [TN: the musical phrase actually forms the salutation of the letter to Haslinger.] The autograph, according to Thayer's *Chronologisches Verzeichniss*, is in the Gosudarstvennoja Publičnaja Biblioteka, Leningrad [now St. Petersburg]. The first edition of this musical joke is in Thayer V, p. 393; and in Nohl I, No. 384, p. 330. [TN: while the letter is given in Nohl, the musical notation is not, only an indication where the notes should be, and Nohl indicates only eight bars at that. A facsimile of the autograph was published by Nathan Fišman in *Sovetskaja Muzyka*, No. 8, 1958. Fišman also presented an accurate transcription in *Musical*

Quarterly, Vol. 47, 1961, p. 20. The letter is given in Anderson, Vol. 3, p. 1316 as No. 1536, and in Brandenburg, Vol. 6, p. 298 as No. 2221. This is listed in Kinsky/Halm as WoO 205k, p. 708.]

Sketches, Continuity Drafts, Unclear Notations, Miscellaneous

296 A Small Cadenza for Léon de Saint-Lubin. This is unpublished. The manuscript is the property of the Österreichische Nationalbibliothek (Sm 3154). Two lines of music in Beethoven's hand with lead pencil. Below them, Saint-Lubin wrote: "Beethovens Notenschrift. – Cadenz, die er mir aufschrieb, als ich am 3. Oktober 1822 bey Eröffnung des k. k. privaten Theaters in der Josephstadt ein Violinsolo von ihm vortung." (Beethoven's musical notation. – A cadenza, that he wrote down for me when I played at the opening of the private Imperial and Royal Theater in the Josephstadt on 3 October 1822.) Unfortunately, on the occasion of my visit to Vienna in 1954, this piece could no longer be found, so that no further statements are possible. [TN: I am grateful for the following information from Thomas Leibnitz of the Österreichische Nationalbibliothek: "This manuscript was discovered missing when an inventory was conducted in 1948 and it still has not been located."]

297 Adagio for Three Horns in E-flat major, 10 bars. [TN: this probably dates from 1815.] This is unpublished and found on page 7 of the Berlin Artaria Autograph 153. Although obviously thought to be an instrumental study, the little piece is complete in itself and could be printed without further annotation in a score for hunting horn. [TN: this was published by Hess in the SBG, Vol. VII, 1963, pp. 274-5.]

298 Sketches for a Symphony movement in C minor. [TN: the theme corresponds to the first movement theme of WoO 36, No. 1, written about 1791-3.] The autograph

is in the British Museum [TN: now the BL, in the "Kafka Sketchbook" (SV 185)], and Fritz Stein published it completely in the *Sammelbände der Internationalen Musikgesellschaft*, Vol. XIII, 1912, p. 131. [TN: an even more complete transcription was published by Joseph Kerman in *Autograph Miscellany, from ca. 1786 to 1799*, British Museum, London1970.] The extensive 111 bar draft is continuous. [TN: there are some additional fragments that accompany this draft.] This piece is so important as a landmark in Beethoven's development that it deserves a place in the new GA. [TN: Jos van der Zanden gives the probable composition dates as 1786-90. See his reference in the program notes to a Compact Disc 389.02.88 produced by Raptus Records in 1989. An even more detailed description together with a completion by A. Willem Holsbergen is found in the website: <*www.unheardbeethoven.org*>.]

299 Draft of a Canon, "Bester Magistrat" (My Dear Magistrate). This is unpublished, in A major, 7 bars. Along with entry No. 277, this piece is found in the Berlin Beethoven Autographs [TN: Autograph 24 (SV 30) on folio 35r. No doubt this canon was intended for the same Viennese magistrate for whom the canon "Bester Magistrat, ihr friert," WoO 177 (entry 257 in this catalog) was written, and who had taken the side of Beethoven's sister-in-law in the court case over his nephew Carl. Probably written about the same time, 1820.] We mention this and the following canon draft here, because one can always expect that one or another piece will appear somewhere in its complete version, or one can take leave to complete them from the drafts. [TN: this was published by Hess in the SBG, Vol. V, 1962, p. 93. While the recipient and the text may have been the same as for WoO 177, this is not the same setting. As Hess has suggested, "one can take leave to complete them," so A. Willem Holsbergen has worked out a

solution for this canon draft. He writes on this: "A solution for this canon is the second voice entering on the first beat of the 3rd bar, in the octave. In bar 6, on the 4th beat, Beethoven writes, next to the melody, one extra note on top of the stave. This G sharp coincides exactly with the note the second voice has in the proposed solution. It seems likely, therefore that Beethoven was at least looking at this solution. Having said that, the solution still has some problems, which can be partly resolved by changing a few notes in bar 7. The melody has a modulation (to the dominant, in bar 5), therefore one can say that this is a skillful canon."]

300 Draft of a Canon for [Aloys] Weißenbach. "Liebe mich, werter Weißenbach" (Love Me, Dear Weißenbach). [TN: according to C/C, p. 261, "This 2-part? canon was written about Jan. 1820." Johnson gives the title as, "Liebe mich, werther Freund" (Love Me, Dear Friend). See *The Beethoven Sketchbooks*, University of California Press, Berkeley 1985, p. 367. From A. Willem Holsbergen, I have the following information: "When you look at the actual sketch, it is clearly for 3 voices. This canon is scattered over four different places in the pocket sketchbook BH 107 (SBH 665 and SV 81) in the Beethoven-Haus, Bonn. This sketchbook *Skizzenbuch aus den Jahren 1819/20* was published [in transcription] by Joseph Schmidt-Görg, through the Beethoven-Haus, Bonn 1952 and in facsimile in 1968. First we have, on p. 40, a single line with the first 4 bars of the melody, and the word 'Canon' written above the stave. Several pages later, on p. 43, we find three attempts by Beethoven to work out the canon. The first of these is very sketchy, giving few clues. The last two attempts on the other hand are, more or less, fully worked out, but differ from one another in detail. Three staves joined together in one system makes clear that Beethoven was working on a

3 part canon (or actually a round, to be more accurate)."] See the following number:

301 Draft of a Canon for Wähner. "Es ist kein Wahn" (It is no Mania); written about January 1820 for Friedrich Wähner. [TN: this is a pun on Wähner's name which can be translated either "mania" or "delusion."] These two canons are found on pp. 43 [for No. 300 above] and 45 [for No. 301] (manuscript pp. 28-9 and 33) from *Skizzenbuch aus den Jahren 1819/20*, published by Joseph Schmidt-Görg, through the Beethoven-Haus, Bonn 1952, and in facsimile in 1968. The Wähner Canon seems completely executed; the other one [i.e., Hess 300] can in a pinch be turned into a canon from the sketches. [TN: A. Willem Holsbergen holds that the opposite is true: "For the Wähner Canon we have only a single melodic line, 20 bars long. There are no clefs and no key signature, therefore interpreting the draft itself is problematic. On the other hand Hess 300 is more or less fully worked out." Like entry 300 this is cataloged SBH 665 and SV 81.]

302 "Uns geht es kannibalisch wohl als wie fünfhundert Säuen." [It probably goes,] (We are as pleasantly cannibalistic as five hundred sows), 4 bars. Sketched among work (SV 26) on the Fugue Op. 133, (given in Nottebohm II, p. 11, where the supposition is put forward that it could perhaps be a two-part canon). Frimmel notes in *Neue Beethoveniana*, edition of 1890, p. 341, that in approximately 1825, Beethoven drafted a canon to a mutilated verse from *"Faust"* (followed by the title above). [TN: the correct line from *Faust* is, "Uns ist ganz kannibalish wohl, / als wie fünfhundert Säuen."] The same piece is also mentioned in Misch; see his "Pseudokanons und Rätselkanons von Beethoven," in *Die Musikforschung*, Vol. 3, Journal 3/4, 1950, pp. 259-60. A completed compo-

sition is not known. [TN: Misch rejects the two-part solution. He finds it too primitive and that it is, therefore, better not to regard it as a canon at all. However, Misch might have changed his opinion if he had noticed the sketch could also be worked out as a four-part canon, which was discovered by A. Willem Holsbergen. "The second voice enters after half a bar, a fifth lower; the third voice after 2 bars in unison; and the last voice after 2½ bars, again a fifth lower. The fact that this solution is possible does not mean that Beethoven actually had it in mind. However, the odd way in which he notes the rhythm does suggest that he was looking at more than just the two-part solution."]

303 "Großen Dank für solche Gnade" (Many Thanks for Such a Favor). See the reference in Thayer IV, pp. 441-3, and Thayer V, p. 21, where it is stated that the canon "Großen Dank," mentioned by Beethoven in a letter from July 1823, is located together with the sketches to the Adagio of the Ninth Symphony. It is, however, only sketched and was printed in Nottebohm II on p. 177. [TN: the letter referred to is Anderson No.1214, or Brandenburg No. 1713, written to the Archduke Rudolph in July 1823. In the letter, Beethoven does indeed mention a canon; however, that canon is not given in the letter and no trace of it can be found. What Hess does not make clear is that Thayer (i.e., Riemann) believes that the "canon" is found among the sketches to the Ninth Symphony, when it is actually only the sketches for the canon that are there, not the canon itself. Nottebohm printed only the sketches for this canon. The Beethoven literature (Nottebohm, Unger and Kinsky/Halm) generally refer to this as a "two-part canon." It has, however, been worked out as a four- and eight-part canon by A. Willem Holsbergen. See the website: <www.unheardbeethoven.org> for more information. Mr. Holsbergen writes: "To me it seems likely that Beethoven did have the four-part

solution (second voice enters after one bar, a second lower, third voice after 2 bars, a third lower, and a fourth voice after 3 bars, a fourth lower) in mind, rather than just the dull two-part solution. That the two-part solution can be superimposed on the four-part solution, thus creating the eight-part solution, is a remarkable fact. Whether Beethoven did see, or indeed, could have seen the eight-part solution without first writing down the four-part solution in full (which he didn't do), may be doubtful."]

304 "Ich blase das Fagott" (I Blow the Bassoon). This three-bar draft in G major is printed by [Georg] Schünemann on p. 210 of his *Festschrift zum 60. Geburtstag Arnold Scherings*, A. Glass, Berlin 1937. He tells us that it is uncertain whether this is for a canon. [TN: Schünemann says that this may have been part of a larger comical canon, the rest of which is, however, so badly faded that it has become indecipherable. The date of the draft is unknown. A. Willem Holsbergen also says the key is clearly in C, not G, major as given by Hess.] See also the reference in No. 258 of this catalog.

305 "Geschlagen ist der Feind" (The Enemy Has Been Beaten). An eight-bar draft in D major [SV 135]. It is found with the sketches to the "Battle of Vittoria" (Mh 87 of the Bodmer Collection). [TN: the Bodmer Collection is now in the Beethoven-Haus, Bonn and this has been renumbered SBH 638.] Max Unger told me that it is, "A canon by Beethoven on Germany's uprising." However, Unger later wrote to Donald W. MacArdle: "After completion of the catalog, I have determined that only a small part of the (likely) canon 'Geschlagen ist der Feind' has been written down. Beethoven apparently had wanted to write a canon about it, however, he has not gotten past the start." [TN: the catalog to which Unger refers is his *Eine Schweizer*

Beethovensammlung, Verlag der Corona, Zurich 1939, which is a catalog of the H. C. Bodmer Collection, now in Bonn. A. Willem Holsbergen puts forth this interesting supposition: "Given the text of the canon (The Enemy Has Been Beaten) and the fact that the canon is in the same key as the final movement of the Battle Symphony, it seems plausible that at one stage Beethoven was thinking of giving the Battle Symphony a choral ending. If so, then this would constitute a link between the Choral Fantasy, Op. 80 and the Ninth Symphony, Op. 125." That is to say, a symphonic work with a choral finale. The fact that the setting of these words is in canonical form seems to be an example of Beethoven's notorious love of puns and word play, a canon in a Battle Symphony.]

The existence of the following four canons is debatable:

306 "Wie Silber [ist] die Rede, doch zu rechter Zeit schweigenist lautres Gold" (Speech Is like Silver, However Being Silent at the Right Time is Pure Gold). Beethoven would have written down this canon for the family of Giannatasio Del Rio; see the reference in [Albert] Leitzmann's *Beethovens Persönalichkeit*, Insel-Verlag, Leipzig 1914, p. 222. See also the reference in [Ludwig] Misch's "Pseudokanons und Rätselkanons von Beethoven," in *Die Musikforschung*, Vol. 3, Journal 3/4, 1950, p. 225, which points out that it is likely that Beethoven wrote the canon (GA, Series 23, No. 256/5) at this incident. It would have been incorrectly quoted from memory by Fanny Del Rio. [TN: this is probably the same as WoO 168, with this different text being the result of Fanny Del Rio's faulty memory.] Anyway, until today another canon has not come to light.

307 "Ewig Dein" (Forever Yours). Max Unger in *Zeitschrift für Musik*, November 1935, p. 1199, reports of a canon,

"Ewig Dein," that Beethoven would have written for Toni von Arneth, about which nothing else is known. Is this not a [possible] mix-up with GA Series 23, No. 256/14? And if not – where has this canon gone? [TN: the canon, No. 256/14 from the GA is listed in Kinsky/Halm as WoO 161, p. 670. This may be an example of Hess creating a redundant entry in this catalog, since this is very probably the same canon as that already printed in the Gesamtausgabe. WoO 161 was written for Antonia Adamberger, and the autograph is in the Beethoven-Haus, Bonn and cataloged as SBH 592. It is part of the Bodmer Collection, and was cataloged by Unger as Mh 40; see *Eine Schweizer Beethovensammlung Katalog*, Verlag der Corona, Zurich, 1939, pp. 138-9.]

308/9 Two unknown canons for Friedrich Kuhlau. Lenz repeats in Vol. 5 of his *Beethoven: eine Kunststudie*, [Ernst Balde], Hamburg 1860, pp. 364-6, that somewhat doubtful history from the *Humorist*, No. 83, 1837, according to which Beethoven would have written for Kuhlau two additional canons besides the known one, "Kühl, nicht lau" (GA Series 23, No. 256/12, [WoO 191 in Kinsky/Halm, p. 693]).

The following three numbers were pointed out to me by Fritz Kaiser. However, he could not supply further details [TN: after an extensive three-year search in twenty-seven libraries in North America and Europe, no trace of the references for entries 310 and 312 could be found until a reply to an inquiry was received from Irmgard Broening, acting as secretary for Fritz Kaiser. In her letter to me, she said that Kaiser did not possess copies of the two publications, but mentioned that Kaiser thought he had found them in Berlin while doing research there. A second attempt was made to locate them at the Staatsbibliothek zu Berlin-Preussischer Kulturbesitz; this time they were found by Helmut Hell, who kindly supplied me with copies of the Beethoven entries from each of these books. It is now possible to identify all three of these entries. See below.]:

310 Prelude for organ in C major. A piece listed as such is said to be published in a volume called "*87 kleine Praeludien*," edited by Paul Honegger. [TN: a copy of this work was located in the SBB. The edition in which this is found was prepared by Paul Homeyer [1853-1908], not "Honegger" as given by Hess. The prelude is not a new work by Beethoven, but rather a slightly edited version of the last 9 bars of the first prelude from Op. 39. It was listed as "No. 1" in the index of the Homeyer work, but without the Opus number. It was published c.1900 by Steingräber Verlag, Leipzig with additional publication or distribution by Bowerman in London and Schuberth in New York.]

311 Song, "Grasmücke" (Song of the Warbler). This can be found in Carl Reinecke's *Jungbrunnen*. [TN: this song was later identified by Hess as "musically identical to 'Blümchen Wunderhold,' Op. 52, No. 8," obviously with a different text. See Dorfmüller, p. 78. Reinecke [1824-1910] was a rather prolific arranger and editor of other composers' works. He showed a particular interest in song arrangements, especially those for children. Reinecke's work, *Jungbrunnen,* was published by Breitkopf & Härtel, Leipzig; it is undated but was probably issued in the 1890s.]

312 "Singen ist des Lebens Freude" (To Sing is Life's Delight), four-part canon. Found in J. H. Fischer's *[Der] Liederbote*, [part] 3, entry 22. [TN: a copy of Fischer's book was found in the SBB. It was published by Schwartz in Brieg about 1844. It is undated, but was listed in Hoffmeister's music catalog of 1844 as "A collection of songs, chorales, hymns, motets choruses, etc. in 4 parts (issued in 8 sections)." The Beethoven

Hess 312, "Singen ist des Lebens Freude," a four-part canon, facsimile of J.H. Fischer's first edition from *Der Liederbote*, as published by Schwartz in Brieg about 1844.

canon is from part III, section 3. A careful examination of Fischer's publication reveals that this is WoO 160, No. 2 (Hess entry 248) with a text added. The full text runs:

Singen is des Lebens Freude,	To sing is life's delight,
singen is der Jugend Lust;	to sing is the joy of youth;
darum singen wir auch heute,	therefore we sing today,
freudevoll aus froher Brust.	joyful with a happy heart.

The original canon, which was written without a text, was first published in 1832 by Iganz Ritter von Seyfried in his *Beethovens Studien*, Haslinger, Vienna, p. 331. One can assume that this new text was written by Fischer, but there is no indication of that in Fischer's publication. It is reprinted here for the first time since 1844. See illustration on page 180. See also entry 248 of this catalog.]

Also, all of the following numbers still need clarification:

313 Vocal piece with Italian text for [Carlo Evasio] Soliva, from 1824. Thayer mentions this [in his *Verzeichniss*] under No. 243. Max Unger suspects that this is the canon, "Te solo adoro" in one of the settings from the GA Series 25, No. 285/1, or our numbers 263 and 264 [in this catalog]. Kinsky/Halm in WoO 186, [p. 689,] takes this as fact, so that our number 313 is possibly unnecessary. [TN: Dorfmüller also accepts this view, that this is probably one of the known settings and that this entry is redundant. See Dorfmüller, p. 387.]

314 "A Mourning Cantata for Cressener." This work was supposedly composed about 1781 on the death of the English emissary [to the Electoral Court at Bonn], George Cressener. The same piece is mentioned in Thayer I, p. 141. Until now, no trace of the work has been found.

315 Unknown fugue. See the following number! [TN: the letter from Franz Joseph Haydn to the Elector and the Elector's reply are given in full in Thayer/Forbes, pp. 144-6.]

316 Unknown quintet. This and the previous work were sent by Haydn, as Beethoven's teacher, to the Elector Maximilian Franz in Bonn on 23 November 1793, together with the Oboe Concerto (No. 12 in this list) and two additional works, that Reinöhl suggests are Op. 103 and one of the then existing sets of variations. Whereas the Oboe Concerto is known from the sketches [and incipits], no one knows a thing at all about the quintet and the fugue; not even their instrumentation is known. The question would be solved if the works that were sent to the Elector would surface again. These were discussed by Fritz von Reinöhl in "Neues zu Beethovens Lehrjahren bei Haydn," *Neues Beethoven-Jahrbuch,* Vol. VI, Verlag des Beethovenhauses, Braunschweig 1935, pp. 36-47, particularly pp. 38-9. [TN: Hess speculated that this entry may be the same as, or part of, several entries, including numbers 318, 319 and 320. Entries 316, 318, 319 and 320 are only known by description or references. They may, in fact, all be the same work. Until autographs or sketches are found, no one can tell exactly what they are from the surviving descriptions. See Dorfmüller, p. 79.]

317 "Europens Befreyungsstunde." A cantata with this name (the poet is unknown) was begun in 1814. [TN: the writer of the text is now known. It was written by Josef Karl Bernard. See the article, "Der Wiener Kongreß im Spiegel der Musik," written by Michael Landenburger in *Beethoven Zwischen Revolution und Restauration*, Beethoven-Haus, Bonn 1989, beginning on p. 293.] The completed autograph of the work remains unknown, and we also don't know if it was ever actually

completed. Sketches for it are located in the Deutsche Staatsbibliothek, Berlin, Musical Manuscript: Beethoven Autograph, Grasnick 20b; the Paris Conservatory, Beethoven MS 93; and the Bodmer Collection, Mh 89, in the Beethoven-Haus, Bonn. [TN: the Deutsche Staatsbibliothek is now the SBB; and the Paris Conservatory has transferred its holdings to the BN; while the Bodmer manuscript in Bonn has been renumbered as SBH 625 (SV 137).] Two further sketch leaves were located in the former Heyer Collection in Cologne; the same piece is mentioned by G. Kinsky in *Musik-historisches Museum of Wilhelm Heyer in Köln*, catalog Vol. 4, Music Autographs No. 223, 1916, p. 182. The entire text [of the Cantata] was printed for the first time in the *Festschrift zum 60. Geburtstag von Joseph Schmidt-Görg*, Bonn 1957, pp. 363-366. The same piece is mentioned by Wilhelm Virneisel in *Kleine Beethoveniana*; see the reference beginning on p. 361. [TN: a copy of the text and a page of the sketches were published in facsimile in *Beethoven Zwischen Revolution und Restauration*, Beethoven-Haus, Bonn 1989, pp. 296 and 297.]

The following three chamber music works are found in references from W. W. Cobbett, [whose work is] previously mentioned under [entry] No. 49/50 [TN: this reference is to Cobbett's *Cyclopedic Survey of Chamber Music I*, London 1929.]:

318 "Unfinished string quintet (otherwise unidentified)" p. 85. [TN: see the reference to Cobbett above. Also see comments in entry 316 above.] Probably composed before Op. 1.

319 String Quintet, mentioned by Beethoven in a letter of 1 June 1805 to Artaria. [TN: the letter referred to is Anderson No. 117, Vol. 1, p. 137, and Brandenburg No. 224, Vol. 1, p. 258.] The fate of this quintet is not

described by Cobbett, p. 283: "A matter of complete uncertainty; it certainly never arrived at publication." [TN: Anderson comments in a footnote on p. 137 that "it was probably never written."] Question: perhaps [one of] our Nos. 39, 316, 318 and 319 may be identical to it. [TN: Hess's rhetorical question is really more of an ambiguous statement. All four of these entry numbers describe four string quintets and all four are taken from different sources or references. What Hess is really saying is that without further identifying or corroborating evidence, these four entries may, in fact, all refer to only one piece, or parts of the same piece. See comments on entry 316 above.]

320 Andante in G for a string quartet. Quoted from p. 99 [of Cobbett], "taken from the sketches of an unfinished quintet," later than 1815. I owe the information about the numbers 49, 50, 318-320 to Donald W. MacArdle, Dallas, Texas, USA. [TN: since Hess wrote this catalog in 1957, numbers 49 and 50 have been identified as WoO 38 and WoO 39. The remaining numbers are still unclarified. See comments on entry 316 above.]

Nottebohm II prints a few lovely, and in themselves complete, melodies:

321 A small instrumental melody in B-flat major, 12 bars with *da capo*. Written before 1800; p. 576.

322 "Gott allein ist unser Herr, er allein" (God Alone Is Our Lord, He Alone). Written in 1818, in E-flat major, 4 bars, p. 137. [TN: found in Autograph A 45, (SV 275) held by the Gesellschaft der Musikfreunde, Vienna. Facsimiles of folios 20v and 21r, containing entries 322 and 323, were published by Johnson, Tyson and Winter in *The Beethoven Sketchbooks: History, Reconstruction, Inventory*, University of California Press, Berkeley 1985, p. 352.]

323 "Leb wohl, schöne Abendsonne" (Farewell, Beautiful Sunset). Written in 1818, C major, 2 bars, p. 137. [TN: contained in Autograph A45 (SV 275), held by the Gesellschaft der Musikfreunde, Vienna. Facsimiles of folios 20v and 21r, containing entries 322 and 323, were published by Johnson, Tyson and Winter in: *The Beethoven Sketchbooks: History, Reconstruction, Inventory*, University of California Press, Berkeley 1985, p. 352.]

The following three entries are found in the Wielhorski Sketchbook [which was] mentioned with No. 229 [TN: the Wielhorski Sketchbook was published by Nathan Fišman, 3 Vols. (transcription, facsimile & commentary), Muzgiz, Moscow 1962]:

324 Melody in C minor with piano accompaniment, 2/4, 8 bars (on p. 24 or shortly after). [TN: Nathan Fišman gives the page as 28; see Dorfmüller, p. 64. However, it is actually on page 24. The melody is in the piano right-hand, the accompaniment in the left-hand.]

325 Piece in D major, 3/4, 17 bars. (Following the above [entry in its source].)

326 Little piece in four-part fugue style in C major, p. 109. [TN: this piece is incomplete; we have in Beethoven's hand the exposition of the fugue (seventeen bars), followed by the word "Schluss" (ending) and twelve more bars. The middle seems to be missing.]

From Nottebohm's *Ein Skizzenbuch von Beethoven aus dem Jahre 1803*, Breitkopf & Härtel, Leipzig 1880 [TN: the following four entries are all taken from the *Eroica* (or *Landsberg 6) Sketchbook* [SV 60], which has been in the Biblioteka Jagiellońska, Cracow, Poland, since the end of World War II.]:

327 Two small, pretty melodies, A minor, C major, p. 97 of the sketchbook. These are mentioned on p. 57 of Nottebohm. [TN: these melodies are not only mentioned by Nottebohm on p. 57, they are transcribed in full. However, they are both in A minor, not A minor and C major as Hess states.]

328 Two-part canon, p. 118. Mentioned on p. 57 of Nottebohm. [TN: Hess took this to be an uncatalogued canon without realizing that it is actually identical to entry 275, which he found in a different source.]

329 The beginning of a polyphonic composition, "Tibi gratulor," p. 119. Mentioned on p. 57 of Nottebohm. [TN: this is only a sketch of 5 bars in C major.]

330 A march-like piece, almost completed in draft, p. 155. Mentioned on p. 70 of Nottebohm. [TN: this march is in C minor and is 19 bars in length. The notation "Graffin" [sic] is contained in the margin before the first bar. A. Willem Holsbergen writes: "I read Beethoven's sketch (p.155 of the Eroica Sketchbook) as two attempts at the same piece; the second time he stops at the same point as the first time. Both attempts have the same structure: a phrase of 4 bars followed by an incomplete one of 6 bars. In the second attempt he tries out an alternate for the first four bars. The second phrase is almost identical in both attempts, only he uses different inversions of the chords. Comparing the two versions gives a pretty clear idea of the intended harmonies." The marginal notation is of interest; why would Beethoven have written "Gräffin" in the margin, and to whom does it refer? The misspelling is Beethoven's.]

According to information from Fritz Kaiser, there are four little one-part pieces (playable on a violin), partially belonging to the Quartet Op. 18, No. 5, located in a sketchbook from

1801. [TN: this sketchbook is "Grasnick 2" and is now in the SBB. Douglas Johnson, in *Beethoven Sketchbooks: History, Reconstruction, Inventory*, University of California Press, Berkeley 1985, gives the date of the Grasnick 2 sketchbook as "February/March to late summer 1799."] Furthermore, this sketchbook contains drafts to the first four of the Quartets, Op. 18. These four pieces are printed on p. 125 of the *Beethoven-Album* which was published in 1846. [TN: the *Beethoven-Album* was published as a 312-page commemorative book following the unveiling of the Beethoven Monument in Bonn in 1845. It consisted of numerous articles and features dealing with Beethoven, and was published by Hallberger'sche Verlagshandlung in Stuttgart. These pieces are listed as being on "page 123" by Dorfmüller; see p. 398. Dorfmüller is partly correct; entry 331 is on p. 123, and entries 332, 334 and 333 (in that order) are on p. 124. None of these are on p. 125, as given by Hess.]:

331 Minuet in B-flat major, 16 bars, p. 61 of the sketchbook. [TN: according to Mark Zimmer, upon examination of the sketchbook, this minuet may continue beyond the point published in the *Beethoven-Album*, p. 123, cited above.]

332 Pastorella in D major, 16 bars, p. 67 of the sketchbook. [TN: this was published in the *Beethoven-Album*, p. 124. This was a 312-page commemorative book published in 1846, following the unveiling of the Beethoven Monument in Bonn in 1845.]

333 Minuet-Scherzo in A major, 10 bars, p. 67 of the sketchbook. [TN: Mark Zimmer gives this as an 11-bar phrase. This was published in the *Beethoven-Album*, p. 124. This was a 312-page commemorative book published in 1846, following the unveiling of the Beethoven Monument in Bonn in 1845.]

334 Allegro in A major, 16 bars, p. 64 of the sketchbook. [TN: this is given as a "Presto" in the *Beethoven-Album*, cited above, although the tempo marking is "allegro" and Hess gives it here as "Allegro." Zimmer also says, ". . .that the sketch appears to continue for a few more measures." This was published in the *Beethoven-Album*, p. 124. This was a 312-page commemorative book published in 1846, following the unveiling of the Beethoven Monument in Bonn in 1845.]

335 Second task for Archduke Rudolph. The music catalog of the Archduke contains the following entry: "Aufgabe für S. K. Hoheit den Erzh. Rudolph vor der Abreise. Mödling, 11ten Sept. 1820." (Task for His Royal Highness the Archduke Rudolph before his departure. Mödling, 11th September 1820.) Thayer lists this under No. 216 of his *Chronologische Verzeichniss,* and states that he suspects, under the assumption of a mistake in the date, that it is our number 75, while Carl Czerny says the song, "Gedenke mein" [WoO 130] (GA Series 25, No. 281) was the tune selected for it, and that it subsequently was printed in the GA with the statement, "Apparently this was composed in Mödling on the 11th September 1820." Actually, however, it belongs to the year 1804, so that it still remains to be determined what was Beethoven's task for the Archduke from the year 1820. [TN: Cooper in C/C, p. 267, asserts that "Gedenke mein" was drafted in 1804-5?, but not completed until 1819-20. Gerhard Croll in "Die Musiksammlung des Erzherzogs Rudolph," in *Beethoven-Studien: Festgabe der Österreichischen Akademie der Wissenschaften*, Hermann Böhlaus, Vienna 1970, pp. 52-3, states that there are "no justifiable doubts" that this is the task put to the Archduke Rudolph in Mödling in 1820, based on entries in the catalog of the Music Collection of the Archduke.]   The same piece is mentioned in Kinsky/Halm on pp. 592-3.

I believe that this may conclude this enumeration. Undoubtedly, other completed pieces will emerge, once all the sketchbooks have been thoroughly reviewed. Without doubt, other handwritten manuscripts will surface in the future, which are not yet known and which will surprise us. A work like the present one can only be considered a milestone on the way to the goal of completeness.

Doubtful and Falsely Attributed Works

Of course, a critical complete edition does not need to include works whose authenticity is disproven beyond doubt; however, doubtful pieces should be grouped together in a separate section where their genuineness can be discussed. This is all the easier, because the number of such works is relatively small with Beethoven, in contrast to the complete works of Haydn and Mozart.

If the following is as complete a catalog as possible of these falsely attributed works, it is written with the awareness of the lack of such a complete catalog. Nottebohm's work, relating to this approach, in his thematic catalog of the works which has appeared in print (2nd Edition, [Breitkopf & Härtel,] Leipzig 1868, and in annotated reprints in 1913 and 1925), is far from complete; Kinsky/Halm offers only a selection, and my own compilation in the December issue of the *Schweizerische Musikzeitung*, Vol. 94, 1954, pp. 452-457, is also surpassed today [with this publication.] The research constantly remains in a state of flux; however, it is important for the researcher to know the information which lies behind everything that has appeared under Beethoven's name.

Instrumental Works
(Numbered as "A" meaning "Appendix" 1, 2 etc.)

A 1 Symphony in C major. Found by Fritz Stein in 1908 or 1909 in parts among the scores of the Jena "Akademischen Konzertes" founded in 1769. Two parts carried the notations, "Par Louis van Beethoven" and "Symphonie von Beethoven" respectively. The same piece is discussed by Fritz Stein in "Eine unbekannte Jugendsymphonie Beethovens?" in *Sammelbände der Internationalen Musikgesellschaft*, Vol.

13, Journal 1, October 1911, pp. 127-172. In 1911, Stein published the symphony through Breitkopf & Härtel in score and parts. But approximately fifty years later, namely in our time, the American researcher H. C. Robbins Landon, [while] living in Vienna, found in the music library of the Göttweig Foundation in lower Austria, a handwritten copy of this symphony under the name Friedrich Witt (1770-1837), and it must now be determined whether it is among the nine printed symphonies of Witt, which would remove every doubt as to the authorship. See H. C. Robbins Landon, "The 'Jena' Symphony" in *The Music Review*, Vol. 18, 1957, p. 109ff. The same piece is discussed by Otto Erich Deutsch in "Fünfzig Jahre 'Jenaer Sinfonie.' Das Ende einer Legende," *Nationalzeitung,* Basel, 20 March 1957, No. 131. [TN: listed in Kinsky/Halm as Anh. 1, p. 713. This work has now been clearly established to be by Witt and all doubt removed.]

A 2 Marsch für das Yorck'sche Korps (March for the York Corps). This appeared about 1818-19 as No. 37 in a collection of quick marches arranged by [Moritz Adolph?] Schlesinger. This march is a setting, by an unknown hand, of Beethoven's "Marsch für die Böhmische Landwehr." Therefore, the music is authentic, the instrumental arrangement notwithstanding. [TN: the original version by Beethoven is listed in Kinsky/Halm as WoO 18, p. 456. This version should not be confused with it.] The same piece is mentioned under No. 6 [of this catalog].

A 3 Unknown arrangement of the "Marsch zur großen Wachtparade." This march appeared in its original form in the Gesamtausgabe (Series 2, No. 15). [TN: it is listed as March in D for Military Band, WoO 24 in Kinsky/Halm, p. 462.] The former Preußische Staatsbibliothek possesses a transcription of this march in the following orchestration (from the top and then downward): first and second violins, violas, two oboes, piccolo, two flutes, two clarinets in C, two bassoons, two horns in D, two horns in low B, four trumpets in D, kettledrums, three trombones, triangle, cymbals, bass drum, cellos and double basses. From whom did this arrangement come? On the first page enclosed in brackets is "Artaria 223." The manuscript seems to have shifted owners several times, because on the left stands "Mus. ms. 1261" (or 1201?), in the middle "Mus. ms. 1901. 406." All these statements are obviously later pencil additions; in the handwriting of the copyist only stands "Marcia di Beethoven." If Beethoven himself did not make this arrangement, then who has orchestrated the march? [TN: the answer to Hess's question seems to have been found by Clemens Brenneis in "An Orchestral Version of Beethoven's *Marsch zur großen Wachtparade*," in *Haydn, Mozart and Beethoven, Studies in the Music of the Classical Period: Essays in Honour of Alan Tyson*, Clarendon Press, Oxford 1998, beginning on p. 213. In this essay, Brenneis names Baron Eduard von Lannoy as the arranger of the March for a special charity concert given in Vienna in April 1844.]

A 4 "Marsch in geschwindem Tempo," (March in Quick Time) in D major for wind instruments. Thayer No. 284. It was found in Beethoven's estate in a copy [in an unidentified hand]; its genuineness cannot be confirmed. The handwritten manuscript came from the Artaria Publishing House Archive into the possession of the Wiener Stadtbibliothek in 1936, (Signature MH 91 85c). I published a piano transcription in the *Schweizerische Blasmusikzeitung* of 15 June 1954, Vol. 43, pp. 270 to 272. [TN: Hess published a second edition of the piano version along with an analysis and history of the work in his *Beethoven Studien*, Beethoven-Haus, Bonn, G. Henle, Munich-Duisburg 1972, pp. 86-90.]

A 5 Twelve Ecossaises and Twelve Waltzes for orchestra. In the year 1807 [in the Wiener Zeitung] (on 21 March), there appeared an advertisement by J. Traeg for Twelve Ecossaises and Twelve Waltzes by Beethoven for two violins and bass, two flutes and two horns ad libitum, arranged after other works. These editions are untraceable today; however, there are located Twelve Waltzes, in Volume 15a of the Haslinger Rudolfinischen Sammlung, that I mentioned at the beginning, which mainly go back to known music of Beethoven. The first two pieces given there are quite naive simplifications; the first is from the scherzi of the Second Symphony and the second is from the minuet of the First Symphony. It seems unlikely that Beethoven should have planned this simplification of his own works himself. On the other hand, Beethoven confirms, with his signature in the beginning of the first volume, that all of the works of the Haslinger-Rudolfinischen Sammlung are original creations by him. One is faced with a puzzle. Contrary to Kinsky/Halm's entry for WoO 16, I would on no account identify the Ecossaises listed under No. 3 of this catalog with those twelve missing pieces that appeared from Traeg. We know about no ecossaises at all that the master would have composed before 1810. [TN: it was a common practice in Beethoven's time for some publishers to act as distributors and retailers of other publishers' work. While the advertisement may have said "available from J. Traeg" there is no guarantee that he actually published these pieces. An edition of Twelve Ecossaises for piano was published by Rudolph Werckmeister in Berlin in 1806. It was discovered in the Netherlands by W. M. Duits in Oudewater. This edition is now in the Beethoven-Haus, Bonn. Martin Staehelin, in "'Beethovens' Eccossaisen WoO 16 wiedergefunden," *Beethoven-Jahrbuch*, Vol. 10, Verlag des Beethovenhauses, Bonn 1983, pp. 313-318, has identified most of the sources for themes of the

Ecossaises as coming from known works of Beethoven; the first two pieces are, in fact, adaptions of thematic material from the First and Second Symphonies. He also repeats Shin A. Kojima's opinion that "we are dealing here not with publications by Traeg's own company in Vienna, but rather with the products of. . . Rudolph Werckmeister from Berlin." Hess's statement that "we know about no ecossaises that Beethoven would have composed before 1810" may be true; but we now know about ecossaises that appeared under Beethoven's name before 1810. Whether Beethoven actually wrote them remains a mystery.]

A 6 Piano Concerto Movement in D major. This entry was included by Guido Adler in 1890 as No. 311 in the Gesamtausgabe. He still associated this piece with Beethoven at this late date for the reason that Joseph Bezecny (Prague) had in the 1830s prepared a transcription of the solo part and the orchestral parts. The same piece is also mentioned by Guido Adler in "Ein Satz eines unbekannten Klavierkonzertes von Beethoven," *Vierteljahresschrift für Musikwissenschaft*, Vol. 4, 1888, pp. 451-470. Only in 1925, Hans Engel identified the movement as the first movement of a piano concerto, Op. 15 by Johann Joseph Rösler, published by J. André in Offenbach. According to Kinsky/Halm, p. 721, this was written in 1809. See also Hans Engel, "Der angeblich Beethovensche Klavierkonzertsatz," *Neues Beethoven-Jahrbuch*, Vol. II, Benno Filser, Augsburg 1925, pp. 167-182. [TN: this work is listed in Kinsky/Halm as Anh. 7, p. 721.]

A 7 Six String Quartets (C major, G major, E-flat major, F minor, D major, B-flat major). They are in handwritten parts in the Musical Manuscripts 15439/15 of the Deutsche Staatsbibliothek, Berlin [TN: now the SBB], and are unpublished. [Listed] by the old Artaria Number 92i, and formerly attributed to Mozart, as early works

(Köchel-Einstein appendix 291a, pp. 903-5, and 1049); the French Mozart researcher G. de Saint-Foix, who acquired the first four of these quartets in score in 1913 from the property of Professor Koester, suspected these works to be compositions of the young Beethoven. See the reference in his article, "Nouvelle contribution à l'étude des oeuvres inconnues de la jeunesse de Beethoven," *Rivista Musicale Italiana*, Vol. 30, 1923, pp. 177, and those following, as well as in *Revue de Musicologie*, February 1927. He only discusses the first four of these quartets; he doesn't seem to have known [about either of] the last ones. [TN: these works are listed in Kinsky/Halm as Anh. 2, p. 715.]

A 8 Quintet for Flute, Violin, two Violas and Violoncello after the Violin Sonata Op. 30, No. 3. This arrangement appeared in 1811 by I. P. Speer [sic, should read Spehr] in Braunschweig as Op. 85; Franz Aubell in "Die Flöte in der Kammermusik," in a supplement from the *Obersteirische Volkszeitung*, Leoben, No. 26 of 5 March 1925, p. 4, believes that it can be attributed to Beethoven himself. Kinsky/Halm vigorously rejects this assumption. The late Georg Kinsky had stated the same opinion in a letter to me, however, without quoting any justifying reasons. [TN: Hess fails to mention that Frimmel, in his *Beethoven Handbuch*, Vol. II, Breitkopf & Härtel, Leipzig 1926, pp. 47-8, goes to great lengths to show that this arrangement might be by Beethoven. He has suggested that one of Beethoven's brothers may have sent it to Spehr with, or without, Beethoven's knowledge or blessing. However, other possibilities for the arranger are Spehr's house arranger, J. H. C. Bornhardt, or more likely, Franz Anton Hoffmeister, who was a very prolific arranger and also did other work for Spehr.]

A 9 *Sonata a tre*, in six movements, edited and provided with an explanatory preface by A. Pochon for 2 Violins and

Violoncello, Carl Fischer Publisher, New York 1926. Pochon has taken the content of this work [mainly] from Seyfried's notorious *Studien* (the first identification of the pieces was done by Professor Giovanni Biamonti, Rome). [TN: Dorfmüller presents the order of the six movements differently than Hess; I and II are from P. E. Bach; III and IV are the two from entry 29; V and VI are from Handel.]:

I. Andante and Maestoso, B-flat major. Seyfried, pp. 348-352. Both pieces are taken from the overture to Handel's oratorio *Esther*, with the order reversed; thus the Andante leading to G minor, is suddenly followed by the B-flat major Maestoso, which Seyfried labels Allegro.
II. Adagio in G minor. Seyfried, pp. 160-163. It is the second movement of the fourth sonata from Ph. E. Bach's *Sei sonate per Cembalo*, Op. 2.
III. Fugato in B-flat major. Seyfried, pp. 302-307. This corresponds to the allegro part from Handel's overture to the oratorio *Esther*.
IV. Andante in E-flat minor. Seyfried, pp. 163-167. It is the second movement of the fifth sonata of the work named under II above.
V. *Nachahmungssätz* (imitation movement) in E minor. [TN: this is the same as the first part of entry 29.]
VI. Fugue in E minor. [TN: this is the same as the second part of entry 29.]

Only these last two pieces are from Beethoven; they are identical with No. 29 of this catalog. To list [all] the other pieces that Seyfried falsely ascribed to Beethoven in his *Studien* is unnecessary, since his book played out its role as a reference work long ago. [TN: while Seyfried made many mistakes in his *Studien*, he may not have been quite so cavalier, as Hess implies, with the sources for the first and third parts of this entry, Handel's overture to *Esther*. Beethoven did copy out Handel's overture in his own hand, and it is found in A 75 in the Gesellschaft der Musikfreunde in Vienna. Seyfried had access to this autograph and since it was in Beethoven's handwriting; Seyfried may not have realized it was Handel's work instead of Beethoven's.] Whoever is interested in thorough examinations of it is referred to Nottebohm's *Beethoveniana I*, beginning on p. 154. Concerning the second edition of Pochon, the same piece is mentioned in No. 31 of this catalog.

A 10 "Andante favori" (GA Series 18, No. 192) [WoO 57] as a string quartet. This appeared about 1806 with F. A. Hoffmeister in Vienna, and has been reprinted many times. Because it gives the impression of a primitively crafted arrangement, this treatment can hardly come from Beethoven. The arrangers are possibly F. Ries or Hoffmeister himself. [TN: if this is indeed, "primitively crafted" it could hardly be by Ries. The piano version is given in Kinsky/Halm as WoO 57, p. 502. The quartet version is described on p. 503, but given a separate catalog number. Gustav Nottebohm notes in his 1851 catalog of Beethoven's works that both Carl Czerny and Wilhelm von Lenz erroneously assume that the string quartet version is the original form and that the piano version is the transcription. See Kinsky/Halm, p. 504.]

A 11 Sonata for Piano and Flute, B-flat major. Thayer No. 21. The work was found in a transcription in Beethoven's estate. Hugo Riemann in Thayer I, pp. 321-2, questions its genuineness for stylistic reasons. It was published by Ary van Leeuwen as a composition of Beethoven though Zimmerman Verlag, Leipzig and Berlin, 1906, however, with small shortenings in the first movement and changes in the musical text, which makes this edition unsuitable for scholarly purposes. In Volume VI of *Neues Beethoven-Jahrbuch,* 1935, I subjected Leeuwen's edition to a critical examination.

At the end of 1951, my edition, which minutely follows the manuscript (Artaria 130, Deutsche Staatsbibliothek, Berlin), was published through Bruckner-Verlag, Leipzig, now Breitkopf & Härtel, Leipzig. [TN: later editions were published by Breitkopf & Härtel in 1961 and 1966. This is listed in Kinsky/Halm as Anh. 4, p. 718, where the date of composition is suggested as 1790 and where it is also suggested that it might be related to WoO 26 (a piece for two flutes, entry 17 of this catalog), which was written in 1792 for Beethoven's friend J. M. Degenhart.] The question of the authorship must remain open. However, let me give you here what I wrote in the foreword to my edition of it:

"Above the sonata, hastily written with pencil, stands, 'I Sonata. . .di Bethoe -,' the end of the name is shortened, the word after Sonata is illegible. This heading has obviously been written very early; and on no account is it an addition after Beethoven's death, that would have the effect of increasing the value of the work through adoption of Beethoven's authorship. Also, we find from time to time in the youth of the composer, Beethoven's name written with only one 'e' [instead of two in the beginning]. If the heading mentioned had already been written, however, then the genuineness of the work would probably, at the very least, have to be conceded as valid, because Beethoven hardly would have had someone else's composition, that obviously came from a still unfinished masterpiece, and kept it for the rest of his life, even less so with his name on it." [TN: while Beethoven did occasionally misspell his name by leaving out one of the first two "e"s, it is not likely that he left out the "v" between "o" and the last "e" as well as the final "n." Hess's statement that Beethoven would not write his name on an unfinished work of another composer and then keep it for the rest of his life seems to be the most valid reason for asserting that this is indeed an authentic work of Beethoven.]

A 12 Serenade Op. 41 for piano and flute, a transcription of the Trio Op. 25. The first edition was published in 1803 by Hoffmeister; reprinted in 1858 by C. F. Peters, and later also by Steingräber. Regarding the question of the genuineness of this work, see the comments about Op. 42 under A 13, below. [TN: this piece was published by Hess in the SBG, Vol. IX, 1965, p. 65. In his comments under entry A 13, Hess indicates that this may have been arranged by Ferdinand Ries and corrected by Beethoven. Peter Clive in, *Beethoven and his World: A Biographical Dictionary*, Oxford University Press, Oxford 2001, p.187, cites a statement made by Beethoven in a letter to Hoffmeister & Kühnel (Anderson No. 82 and Brandenburg No. 157), that "these arrangements were not made by me, but I have looked them over and have completely changed some passages." In a letter written to Breitkopf & Härtel a little earlier (21 May 1803), Beethoven's brother Karl offers some arrangements for piano with accompaniment of certain instrumental works, all of which had been made by Franz Xavier Kleinheinz "under my brothers direction." See Brandenburg. No. 138. These references are clearly about Op. 41 and Op. 42 and Hess's assertion that Ries was the arranger would appear to be incorrect.]

A 13 Notturno Op. 42 for viola and piano. A transcription of the Trio Op. 8. The first edition was done by Hoffmeister in 1804, reprinted by C. F. Peters in 1858 and in the complete edition by Holle-Liszt in Wolfenbüttel. These two arrangements of Op. 41 and Op. 42 were probably done by F. Ries; however, they have been looked over by Beethoven and improved here and there. For comparisons, see Thayer II, p. 207. The newest editions of Op. 41 and Op. 42 that I could locate have partially significantly altered settings and are therefore arrangements of arrangements. There is one revised edition by William Primrose of Op. 42 (Breitkopf Edition No. 10091), which, in a footnote, comments on the original edition of 1804 and also mentions an unauthorized reprint with Artaria that is said to have angered Beethoven. [TN: this piece was published by Hess in the SBG, Vol. IX, 1965, p. 84. Peter Clive in, *Beethoven and his World: A Biographical Dictionary*, Oxford University Press, Oxford 2001, p.187, cites a statement made by Beethoven in a letter to Hoffmeister & Kühnel (Anderson No. 82 and Brandenburg No. 157), that "these arrangements were not made by me, but I have looked them over and have completely changed some passages." In a letter written to Breitkopf & Härtel a little earlier (21 May 1803), Beethoven's brother Karl offers some arrangements for piano with accompaniment of certain instrumental works, all of which had been made by Franz Xavier Kleinheinz "under my brothers direction." See Brandenburg. No. 138. These references are clearly about Op. 41 and Op. 42 and Hess's assertion that Ries was the arranger would appear to be incorrect.]

A 14 Trio for Piano, Violin and Violoncello, E-flat major, Op. 63, after the String Quintet Op. 4. This work appeared in [July] 1806 with Artaria in Vienna. Beethoven had no part in this arrangement. [TN: Kinsky/Halm, p. 152, suggests that the arranger could be Franz Xavier Kleinheinz. Peter Clive also suggests Kleinheinz as the arranger, see the reference to his statement in entries A 12 and A 13 above.]

A 15 Sonata for Piano and Violoncello, E-flat major, Op. 64, after the String Trio Op. 3. This work appeared in 1807 with Artaria in Vienna. Beethoven also had no participation in this arrangement. [TN: Hess's emphatic statement that Beethoven "had no participation in this arrangement" seems to run counter to statements by Kurt Dorfmüller that the announcement in the Weiner Zeitung of 27 March 1807 says that the work was prepared "under Beethoven's eyes, so to speak" (sozusagen unter Beethovens Augen), and that Beethoven enjoyed not only a commercial but a personal relationship with the publisher, Artaria, whose offices were then located only a few steps from Beethoven's apartment, and finally that it has an assigned Opus number. All this would seem to support the supposition that not only did Beethoven approve of its publication, but supervised it as well. See Dorfmüller's "Eine wiederentdeckte Cellosonate Beethovens?" in *Münchener Beethoven-Studien*, Musikverlag Emil Katzbichler, Munich & Salzburg 1992, pp. 128-30. Peter Clive suggests Franz Xavier Kleinheinz as the arranger, however he had moved to St. Petersburg in 1804 and may not have been in Vienna when this was arranged and published. He could have done the arrangement before leaving, but three years before its publication seems unlikely. See the reference to Clive's statement in entries A 12 and A 13 above.]

We have mentioned the four arrangements (Op. 41, 42, 63 and 64) here however, because these opus numbers have not been covered in a listing of other works like for example; Op. 60 (Fourth Symphony) and Op. 61 (Violin Concerto), which Simrock used for Ries' arrangements of Op. 18 and Op. 9 as piano trios; otherwise we may give up taking into account those old, and today completely forgotten, arrangements by others.

A 16 Trio for Piano, Violin and Violoncello, D major. Two movements, preserved in the British Museum, Add. Mss. 31.748. [TN: now the BL. This work is listed in Kinsky/Halm as Anh. 3, p. 717.] In the first movement, there is a gap of two pages. The piece was regarded until 1910 as a work of Mozart (Köchel, 2nd Edition, appendix 52a), and in 1926 was published by G. de Saint-Foix as a work of Beethoven in "Oeuvres inédites de Beethoven," Vol. 2 of the *Publications de la Société française de Musicologie*, Paris, E. Droz. Since three pieces published in this volume are associated with the same handwriting and have turned out to be the works of L. A. Kozeluch (see below), it has also reinforced the doubts that this trio is genuine. [TN: Otto Erich Deutsch gives the date of Saint-Foix's discovery as 1919, not 1910, in "Kozeluch ritrovato," in *Music and Letters*, Vol. 26, No. 1, January 1945, pp.47-50. Another edition was done by Jack Werner as a work of Beethoven, *Rondo in D. Trio for Violin, Cello and Pianoforte*, Chappell, London 1962. An article by Stanley Sadie and Jack Werner appeared in *Musical Times*, Vol. 104, 1963, pp. 572, 637 and 798. See also references to this in entry 2 of this catalog.]

A 17 Two Pieces for Violin and Piano, also for String Quartet. They are listed as No. 12½ and No. 14 (originally number 14 as 14½) in the edition of the ballet piece, *Die Geschöpfe des Prometheus*, provided by C. Zulehner for piano and violin, as well as for string quartet. (N. Simrock, Bonn 1831.) So far no score has been found for these pieces and no one knows from whom they came. Yet the introduction of the inserted number 14 seems to be a transposition of the original number in G major.

A 18 Three Pieces for Piano Four-Hands: a Gavotte in F major, an Allegro in B-flat major, and a *Marzia lugubre* (fragment) in C minor. This is in the same handwriting as A 16, and was published together with that trio. All three of these pieces are the works of Leopold Anton Kozeluch, and can be found in his ballet, *La ritrovata figlia di Ottone II*, performed in Vienna in 1794. The same pieces are mentioned by Otto Erich Deutsch in "Eine merkwürdige Notenhandschrift," in

Schweizerische Musikzeitung, January 1952, Vol. 92, pp. 14-15; Kinsky/Halm, p. 722, also states that these works are by the same author. [TN: these three pieces are listed in Kinsky/Halm as Anh. 8. See reference to these pieces in entry 2 of this catalog. There is also another article by Deutsch on this subject, "Kozeluch ritrovato," in *Music and Letters*, Vol. 26, No. 1, January 1945, pp. 47-50.]

A 19 Nine German Dances for Piano Four-Hands. They are found anonymously in the music book of a collector c. 1815, Mus. Ms. 38033 in the Deutsche Staats-bibliothek, Berlin. [TN: now the SBB.] They were published by Carl Bittner through C. F. Peters, Leipzig 1939, as possibly coming or derived from Beethoven. The assumption of this authorship is amply bold, and Kinsky/Halm mentions on p. 724, "That Beethoven's life-data is declared there to be 1772-1828 (corrected in the second edition! W. Hess) is a further mark of the [lack of] diligence of the publication." [TN: this is listed in Kinsky/Halm as Anh. 9, p. 723.]

A 20 Rondo B-flat major for Piano Two-Hands. This belongs to the same handwriting and to the same publication as A 16 and A 18. [TN: this Rondo in B-flat major is now believed to be by Leopold Anton Kozeluch; see the references in entries A 16 and A 18 above.] Nevertheless, it was included by Otto von Irmer in his Urtext edition of Beethoven's bagatelles (see the reference under entry No. 51), where he very freely gives the composition date as 1791! [TN: this edition is Beethoven's *Klavierstücke*, published by G. Henle, Munich-Duisburg 1950, and there are numerous later editions.] In the same year that Irmer published it, Jack Werner also brought out what had until now been an unpublished work, and Louis Kentner from Columbia Records played this fascinating, wide-ranging piece as a work of Beethoven, indeed! [TN: this is listed in

Kinsky/Halm as Anh. 6, p. 720. This piece was published by Hess in the SBG, Vol. IX, 1965, p. 107. See reference to this work in entry 2 of this catalog.]

A 21 Bagatelle Op. 119, No. 12. This piano arrangement of the song, "An Laura" can hardly have come from Beethoven (the same piece is mentioned in No. 128), by reason of the printer's plate number; it probably appeared in 1826 in the second edition of Op. 119 with Diabelli & Co. in Vienna. A photocopy was reprinted through Willy Hess in *Schweizerische Musikpädagogische Blätter*, No. 16, July 1953, p. 39. The same piece is mentioned by Willy Hess, "Beethovens Bagatelle Op. 119, No. 12," on pp. 37-40; and in the Heyer-Katalog IV, p. 162. [TN: this piece was published by Hess in the SBG, Vol. IX, 1965, p. 114.]

A 22 "Trauermarsch" (Funeral March), in C minor, 16 bars. The autograph is found in the album of Mozart's student, Babette Ployer, Salzburg, Mozarteum. The same piece is mentioned in Roland Tenschert's "Eine unbekannte Komposition Mozarts?" in *Die Musik,* Vol. 22, No. 1, October 1929, pp. 16-22. Tenschert believes that this piece with the title, "Marche funèbre des Sig. Maestro Contrapunti," would much better be attributed to Mozart than Beethoven, which was viewed as Mozart's work for a long time. [TN: this is listed in Köchel's *Mozart Verzeichnis*, sixth edition, 453a, where it is described as, "doubtless from Mozart and just as doubtless, not very seriously thought."] The facsimile was printed as a supplement.

A 23 Introduction and Waltz. Revised and edited by Jack Werner, Bosworth, London. The foreword is dated March 1951. This large work in F major represents, without a doubt, an example of those forgeries of which Nottebohm has already pointed out quite a few. Incidentally, it already appeared in January 1835 in

The New Hess Catalog of Beethoven's Works — *Errata:*

Entry A 24, page 205, should read:

A 24 "Alexandermarsch" (Alexander's March). It seems to come from [Louis Antoine] Duport's ballet, "Der blöde Ritter" (The Foolish Knight), whose premiere was in Vienna, 11 April 1812. The piano transcription [of the ballet] appeared in May 1812. The music [for the ballet] is a colorful composite of works by different masters; the overture, for example, is a composition by [Daniel] Steibelt. The march is very probably by [Louis Luc Loiseau de] Persius (1769-1839); it was later put into the music for [Georg Friedrich] Treitschke's "Ehrenpforten," and together with Beethoven's closing chorus [WoO 97] again performed on 15 July 1815. The march appeared as the work of Beethoven in a piano setting in 1829, published by Bachmann in Hanover. [TN: Paul Nettl in *Beethoven Handbook*, Ungar Publishing, New York 1967, p. 249 says, "Friedrich Starke was . . . the arranger (for piano) of the Alexander March, falsely attributed to Beethoven." This is listed in Kinsky/Halm as Anh.11, p. 725, where it is asserted that the piano arrangement by Starke, his Op. 78, was published by Steiner in Vienna during the Congress of Vienna and gained wide popularity. It was published as "Alexander's Favorite March;" presumably this is a reference to Emperor Alexander I of Russia who attended the Congress. Another march related to Duport, this one actually by Beethoven, is listed by Biamonti in his catalog as No. 839, p. 1030. Mark Zimmer has given me the following information on this march: "This brief march of 16 bars is sketched in autograph 9, bundle 1, dating from about 1825, held by the Preußischer Staatsbibliothek Kulturbesitz in Berlin and is found among sketches for the Tenth Symphony, the BACH Overture and the Grosse Fugue. There is a notation, "Duport Marsch" at the top of the sketches in Beethoven's hand. According to Schindler, this may refer to the choreographer Louis Antoine Duport (1781-1853). In 1824 Duport was the manager of the Kärntnertor Theatre, where the Ninth Symphony was premiered, when Beethoven attempted to repeat the success of the first concert a week later, the house was only half-filled and Duport had to bear the loss on the concert. The little march was presumably sketched out as a token of appreciation to Duport, although Schindler suggests it was a joke of some kind (Beethoven scholar Gustav Nottebohm wryly notes that if it is a joke, it is not understandable to us)." The surviving sketches are apparently for an orchestral force of some kind, since the low first note is indicated as being for horns, but the orchestration of the melody line is not indicated. The Biamonti march is not known to have been completed by Beethoven; if it was, his orchestration has been lost. The incipit for the *Alexandermarsch* published in Kinsky/Halm also in no way matches the sketches for Biamonti 839. What the existence of another march for Duport (whether completed, or not) tells us is that since Beethoven was willing to do a march for Duport in 1825 then he may very well have been willing to do one earlier, in 1812. The attribution of this march (A 24) to Beethoven would appear to be much stronger than Hess or Kinsky/Halm suspected. The Biamonti catalog was not published until 1968, that's 13 years after Kinsky/Halm and 11 years after Hess. Although nothing survives to definitely link Beethoven to A 24, its authenticity can't be completely ruled out.]

Entry Hess A 24, page 235, should read:

Hess A 24: *Alexandermarsch* was used in a ballet, "Der blöde Ritter," by Louis Antoine Duport, which is a pastiche of musical pieces from several composers. Hess says it is probably by Louis Luc Loiseau de Persius (1769-1839). It was later put into the music for Georg Friedrich Treitschke's "Ehrenpforten," and together with Beethoven's closing chorus (WoO 97), performed in 1815. This is its first public association with Beethoven. It circulated widely during the Congress of Vienna in a version for piano by Friedrich Starke as "Alexander's Favorite March" and the march appeared as the work of Beethoven in a piano setting in 1829. Because this march achieved fame in piano versions by others, doubt has been cast on its authenticity; however there are sketches in Berlin for another march for Duport dating from about 1824-5. Since it appears that Beethoven was willing to write a later march for Duport, then he may very well have been willing to also write the earlier one for Duport even though no sketches or autographs have survived.

Musical Magazine with the addition, "composed by Beethoven, but never published before." Here too, therefore, Jack Werner's "first edition" is also a reprint, like most of his first editions. [TN: this is listed in Kinsky/Halm as Anh.17, p. 729.]

Nottebohm has already listed the following fourteen pieces on pp. 189-191 of his thematic catalog. [*Thematisches Verzeichniss der im Druck Erschienenen Werke Ludwig van Beethovens*, Leipzig, 1868.] Concerning all details, I refer the reader to his elaborations, as well as to the Kinsky/Halm Anh. (Appendix), Nos. 11-16:

A 24 "Alexandermarsch" (Alexander's March). It seems to come from [Louis Antoine] Duport's ballet, "Der blöde Ritter" (The Foolish Knight), whose premiere was in Vienna, 11 April 1812. The piano transcription [of the ballet] appeared in May 1812. The music [for the ballet] is a colorful composite of works by different masters; the overture, for example, is a composition by [Daniel] Steibelt. The march is very probably by [Louis Luc Loiseau de] Persius (1769-1839); it was later put into the music for [Georg Friedrich] Treitschke's "Ehrenpforten," and together with Beethoven's closing chorus [WoO 97] again performed on 15 July 1815. The march appeared as the work of Beethoven in a piano setting in 1829, published by Bachmann in Hanover. [TN: Paul Nettl in *Beethoven Handbook*, Ungar Publishing, New York 1967, p. 249 says, "Friedrich Starke was . . . the arranger (for piano) of the Alexander March, falsely attributed to Beethoven." Kinsky/ Halm asserts that the piano arrangement by Starke, his Op. 78, was published by Steiner in Vienna during the Congress of Vienna and gained wide popularity. It was published as "Alexander's Favorite March;" presumably this is a reference to Emperor Alexander I of Russia who attended the Congress. This is listed in Kinsky/Halm as Anh.11, p. 725.

This work is also listed by Biamonti in his catalog as No. 839, p. 1030. Mark Zimmer has given me the following information on this march: "This brief march of 16 bars is sketched in autograph 9, bundle 1 held by the Preußischer Staatsbibliothek Kulturbesitz in Berlin and is found among sketches for the Tenth Symphony, the BACH overture and the Grosse Fugue. There is a notation, "Duport Marsch" at the top of the sketches in Beethoven's hand. According to Schindler, this may refer to the choreographer Louis Antoine Duport (1781-1853). In 1824 Duport was the manager of the Kärntnertor Theatre, where the Ninth Symphony was premiered . . . when Beethoven attempted to repeat the success of the first concert a week later, the house was only half-filled and Duport had to bear the loss on the concert. The little march was presumably sketched out as a token of appreciation to Duport, although Schindler suggests it was a joke of some kind (Beethoven scholar Gustav Nottebohm wryly notes that if it is a joke, in is not understandable to us)." The surviving sketches are apparently for an orchestral force of some kind, since the low fist note is indicated as being for horns, but the orchestration of the melody line is not indicated. The march is not known to have been completed by Beethoven; if it was, his orchestration has been lost, but it was used in an orchestral form in Duport's ballet. The attribution of this march to Beethoven would appear to be much stronger than Hess or Kinsky/Halm suspected. Although the completed orchestral version may be lost; it does survive in the piano versions by Starke and others and should now be considered authentic.]

A 25 "Pariser Einzugsmarsch" (Parisian Entrance March). It appeared anonymously about 1822 with [Adolph Martin] Schlesinger in Berlin, and as a work of Beethoven after 1859 with Schuberth in Leipzig. [TN: this is listed in Kinsky/Halm as Anh. 12, p. 726. Hess appears to have taken information about its first publication from Nottebohm, who gives it as 1822. This is contradicted by Kinsky/Halm, which gives the first appearance as "1818-19," and the full title as "Pariser Einzugsmarsch 1814." Kinsky/Halm goes on to say that the Schuberth edition is from 1860, not 1859, and is a two-hand piano version. In Mendel-Reißmann's *Musikalischem Conversations-Lexikon*, Vol.11, 1879, p. 249, Johann Heinrich Walch is given as the composer of this March and the Trauermarsch listed below as entry A 26.]

A 26 "Trauermarsch" (Funeral March). This supposedly appeared as a work of Beethoven about 1830 with Kaiser in Graz, and later (after 1844) with [Joseph] Aibl in Munich. According to Nottebohm, the composer is J[ohann] H[einrich] Walch, [b. 1776,] who died in 1855 in Gotha. [TN: according to Dorffmüller, p. 392, this funeral march was published in 1829 by J. L. Greiner in Graz, not "1830 with Kaiser" as given by Hess. A copy made between 1820-30 of this piece in C minor is titled "Funeral March for Carl, Prince von Schwartzenberg." Prince von Schwartzenberg died on 15 October 1820 in Leipzig.] Through Fritz Kaiser (Darmstadt), I was made aware of a [Pietro] Mechetti edition of this Funeral March. It is given there as No. 14 of a collection of marches and is in B-flat minor, while it is otherwise printed in F [minor]. [TN: Jean Witold says that the arranger of the Mechetti two-hand piano version was Ph. Röth. See *Beethoven: Das Genie und seine Welt*, Verlag Kurt Desch, Vienna 1963, p. LXXI. Witold also suggests that Walch may have been the composer of entry A 25, Parisian Entrance March; see above.] It is found in B-flat minor, even if this is a somewhat different arrangement, at the end of Series II of the complete edition of Beethoven's works begun by Haslinger, which appeared about 1845. The same piece is mentioned by Otto Erich Deutsch in "Beethovens gesammelte Werke. Des Meisters Plan und Haslingers Ausgabe," *Zeitschrift für Musikwissenschaft*, Vol. 13, No. 11, 1930, pp. 60-79, especially the pages above 75 and in footnote 6 below. Deutsch speaks here of a "Funeral March" in B-flat major, and it has escaped him that the piece is identical with that identified by Nottebohm. [TN: this is listed in Kinsky/Halm as Anh. 13, p. 726. See also the article by George Kiorpes, "Lost Treasures in a Bookstore With a March Possibly by Beethoven," *Clavier,* April 2002, p. 6, where the complex history of this march is discussed and a facsimile of the Haslinger edition of the march appears on pp. 10-11.]

A 27 "Sehnsuchtswalzer" (Longing Waltz), in A-flat major. This is a compilation of Franz Schubert's "Sehnsuchtswalzer" and Fr. H. Himmel's "Favoritwalzer" (Favorite Waltz), which was dedicated to the Queen of Prussia. As a work of Beethoven, the piece appeared for the first time in 1826 with Schott, later with Bachmann in Hanover. [TN: the first sixteen bars of this conflation are taken from No. 2 of 36 Tänze, Op. 9, by Franz Schubert (nicknamed "Trauerwalzer" - Hess seems mistaken in calling Schubert's waltz "Sehnsuchtswalzer" in this entry); the last sixteen bars are from the "Favoritwalzer." Himmel's waltz was something of a top hit around 1815-17. The identity of the arranger is still not known. The title of the 1826 edition by Schott reads, "Souvenir à Beethoven: Six valses et une Marche funèbre pour le piano," which suggests that it was dedicated to Beethoven (or his memory) rather than ascribed to him. A handwritten copy, not by Beethoven, of this waltz titled "Ländler" can be found in the Bentheimschen Bibliothek (Leihgabe Universitätsbibliothek, Münster), and another handwritten copy dating from c.1830 is in Schloß Harburg. Waltzes number A 27-A 29 were published by Heckel in Mannheim, plate number 247. This is listed in Kinsky/Halm as Anh.14, No.1, p. 727.]

The following five entries (A 28 - A 32) all appeared in 1828 with Schott as works of Beethoven. For a closer examination, see Nottebohm [*Verzeichniss*, Breitkopf & Härtel, Leipzig 1851, p. 151] and Kinsky/Halm, [pp. 727-8]:

A 28 "Schmerzenswalzer" (Aching Waltz), in F minor. [TN: this is listed in Kinsky/Halm as Anh.14, No. 2, p. 727. A handwritten copy, not by Beethoven, of this waltz can be found in the Bentheimschen Bibliothek (Leihgabe Universitätsbibliothek, Münster). A printed copy as "Walze Favorite" was done by Schott with the plate number 742, which would date it much earlier than the 1828 edition. A copy of this early printed edition is in King's College, Cambridge. The waltzes numbered A 27-A 29 were published by Heckel in Mannheim, plate number 247.]

A 29 "Hoffnungswalzer" (Hopeful Waltz), in E-flat major. [TN: this is listed in Kinsky/Halm as Anh.14, No. 3, p. 727. The waltzes numbered A 27-A 29 were published by Heckel in Mannheim, plate number 247.]

A 30 "Geisterwalzer" (Ghost Waltz), in A major. [TN: this is listed in Kinsky/Halm as Anh.14, No. 4, p. 727.]

A 31 Waltz in F major. [TN: this is listed in Kinsky/Halm as Anh.14, No. 5, p. 727.]

A 32 Waltz in D-flat major. [TN: this is listed in Kinsky/Halm as Anh.14, No. 6, p. 727.]

A 33 "Jubelwalzer" (Jubilation Waltz), C-sharp major. Appeared after 1847 with Heckel in Mannheim. [TN: this is listed in Kinsky/Halm as Anh.16, No. 1, p. 728.]

A 34 "Gertruds Traumwalzer" (Gertrude's Dream Waltz), B-flat major. Appeared after 1852 with Schuberth,

Leipzig. [TN: this is listed in Kinsky/Halm as Anh.16, No. 2, p. 728.]

A 35 "Sonnenscheinwalzer" (Sunshine Waltz), in E-flat major. Printed sometime after 1852 by Kahnt in Leipzig. [TN: this is listed in Kinsky/Halm as Anh.16, No. 3, p. 728.]

A 36 "Mondscheinwalzer" (Moonlight Waltz), in A-flat major. Printed sometime after 1852 by Kahnt in Leipzig. [TN: this is listed in Kinsky/Halm as Anh.16, No. 4, p. 728.]

A 37 "Glaube, Liebe und Hoffnung," (Faith, Love and Hope); waltz in F major. Printed about 1838 with G. Crantz in Berlin, and later under the title, *Beethoven's Adieu to the Piano, Being His Last Composition*, by Boosey in London. [TN: this is listed in Kinsky/Halm as Anh.15, p. 728. This spurious waltz is mentioned in the Biamonti catalog on p. 1048, but not given a separate catalog number.]

Further editions of such pieces are reported by Marta Walter in her article "Zu den Beethovenfälschungen," in *Schweizerische Musikzeitung,* Vol. 95, February 1955, pp. 55-56. In it there are references – among others – to a waltz based on the scherzo of the Piano Sonata Op. 14, No. 1 and she also adds important information to the elaborations of Nottebohm and Kinsky/Halm. Otto Kinkeldey reports on waltz forgeries in America in his article, "Beginnings of Beethoven in America," which appeared in *Musical Quarterly,* Vol. XIII, No. 2, April 1927, beginning on p. 217, and on other waltzes, pp. 245-47. According to this author's explanation, from 1830, a whole flood of waltzes poured forth over North America that carried the name of Beethoven, and brought indiscriminate chaos to real and artificial arrangements and vocal settings. Also, what was particularly enjoyed were songs made over from Beethovenish instrumental melodies. However, the collecting of these curiosities, which are buried today and rest forgotten in libraries, doesn't belong here!

I still wish to point out that Kinsky/Halm lists the two Piano Sonatas in G and F (GA Series 16, Nos. 160 and 161) among the list of doubtful works and the eight variations on the song "Ich hab ein kleines Hüttchen nur" (GA Series 17, No. 182) are considered to be bogus works. We are referring to Anh. 5 (No. 1 and No. 2) and Anh. 10 as listed in the Kinsky/Halm appendix (pp. 719 and 724). In the new GA, the little "Ecossaise in G major" (GA Series 25, No. 306) [WoO 23], which is listed in the series of the original piano works, should be removed (compare the explanation in the listing with entry No. A 4), and should only possibly be included in an appendix to the piano works. This also refers to another work, which exists only in a piano version by someone else, the first setting of a string quintet in C major (listed as No. 41 in this catalog), whose score has been lost. [TN: this is listed in Kinsky/Halm as WoO 62, p. 508; it was most probably arranged by Anton Diabelli, who published the two- and four-hand piano versions in 1838.] Into this context should also be included our numbers 5 and 102, which are piano transcriptions whose author one suspects to be Beethoven, but cannot prove.

Vocal Works

A 38 Duet: "Auf der Liebe Rosenbetten" (On Love's Bed of Roses), with piano accompaniment, in G major. The author of the text is unknown. Thayer's No. 269. [TN: Thayer does give the incipit (the first three bars).] Under No. 95 at the end of Adler's catalog of the Artaria Collection (Vienna 1890), this song is listed as being by Beethoven's father. [TN: the comment by Adler actually reads: "Presumably written by Beethoven's father, Johann van Beethoven. Not clear (or neat). Unknown handwriting." What is very unclear is what led Adler to even presume that this song was written by Beethoven's father, especially since Thayer made no such assertion in his catalog from 1865, and he obviously also saw the work since he gives a three-bar incipit.] Where is the autograph to be found today?

A 39 "An Sie" or "Nachruf" ("To Her" or "Obituary"); song for one vocal part with piano accompaniment, in A-flat major. The author of the text is unknown. According to Nottebohm's listing, p. 192, the song appeared as a work of Beethoven before 1844 with Bachmann or with Nagel in Hanover; besides this one, there are still editions that name as composer either Carl Dames, or L. Dames (?) or Marianne Czegka, née Auernhammer. Kinsky/Halm lists all these editions under Anh. 18, p. 730, which should include another Danish edition under the title *Til Hende* (To Her), where it appeared in A major as the work of Beethoven in *Sang-Album for en mindre Stemme*, Journal 7, Verlag Hansen, Copenhagen 1902. This version deviates rather considerably from the German editions.

In his work that appeared in 1860 in *Beethoven. Eine Kunststudie*, Part 5, where Wilhelm [von] Lenz lists a group of songs with piano accompaniment, besides many known ones, we list only the following eight numbers:

A 40 "Aus dunklem Laub" (From Dark Foliage), three-part song, p. 353. [TN: adapted from Op. 26. See below.]

A 41 "An mein Liebchen" (To My Dearest), p. 349. [TN: adapted from Op. 8. See Dorfmüller, p. 295.]

A 42 "Liebe und Wein" (Love and Wine), p. 349. [TN: adapted from Op. 8. See Dorfmüller, p. 295.]

A 43 "Der Wunsch" (The Wish), p. 349. [TN: adapted from Op. 25. See below.]

A 44 "Der Verstoßene" (The Outcast), p. 349. [TN: adapted from Op. 25. See below.]

A 45 "Sehnsucht nach dem Rhein" (Longing for the Rhine), p. 349. [TN: adapted from Op. 75, No. 1. See below.]

A 46 "Lebensglück" (Life's Happiness), text by Tiedge, p. 348. [TN: adapted from Op. 88. See below.]

A 47 "Abschied" (The Parting), text by Tiedge, p. 348. [TN: adapted from WoO 124. See below.]

To the best of our knowledge, these eight songs are not original works; we must mention them here, however, because Lenz quotes them as such. A 40, an unaccompanied trio for men's voices (therefore not a piano song!), is based on the theme of the variations of the Sonata, Op. 26, and appeared in 1821 with Lischke in Berlin. A 41 and A 42 are listed as pieces 2 and 3 of the journal, *Drey Lieder / Abschiedslied, An mein Liebchen, Liebe und Wein*, and are transcriptions from Op. 8; (A 41 uses the theme of the variations of the finale; A 42 is from the trio of the minuet); the text is added by C. P. [TN: the author of the text is only identified by the initials on the title page and is not known.] Lenz did not mention the first piece; it is an "Abschiedslied," after the theme of Op. 35, and obviously cannot be identical with our number A 47, since Tiedge is named there as the songwriter. The journal appeared about 1825 from Cappi in Vienna. A 43 and A 44 correspond to Nos. 3 and 2 in the journal, "Drey Andante für das Klavier mit unterlegtem Texte. . .," Vienna 1814, by Ludwig Maisch. A 43 corresponds to the theme of the variations from Op. 25, [and] A 44 to the theme of the variations from Op. 26, but in G major. [TN: According to Dorfmüller, both A 43 and A44 are taken from themes from Op. 25. See Dorfmüller, p. 303.] Lenz has not mentioned the first piece of the collection, "Das Glück der Liebe," which is after the theme of the piano variations GA No. 176 = Series 17, No. 15 [WoO 77]. According to information from Fritz

Kaiser, A 45 is identical with Op. 75 No. 1, with a new text added to it by the Princess Luise zu Wied. It appeared in 1844 in Bonn by J. M. Dunst under the publisher's number 144. A 46 and A 47 have not yet been identified. [TN: the identity of A 46, "Lebensglück," and A 47, "Abschied," both with texts by Tiedge, may lie in an edition of these two songs published by Zulehner in Mainz, and after 1818 by Schott, under the title, "Zwei Lieder von Tiedge," PN: 105c. Entry A 46 is actually a song with piano accompaniment, "Das Glück der Freundschaft," Op. 88, under a new title as "Lebensglück," and A 47 is "La partenza," WoO 124 (originally with an Italian text by Metastasio), now with a German text under the title "Abschied." It appears that Hess knew of these two songs from the listing by Wilhelm von Lenz, but was not aware of their complete publication and translation history. See Kinsky-Halm pp. 245-6 and 586-7.]

The following nine a cappella songs on texts of [Pietro] Metastasio are listed as pieces 7-15 of No. 264 in Thayer's catalog:

A 48 *Nel mirarvi o boschi*, quartet, D major. [TN: written by Baron Carl Doblhof-Dier and copied by Beethoven. See below.]

A 49 The same piece, *Nel mirarvi o boschi* as a duet. [TN: written by Baron Carl Doblhof-Dier and copied by Beethoven. See below.]

A 50 *Quanto è bella la campagna*, trio, G major. [TN: written by Baron Carl Doblhof-Dier and copied by Beethoven. See below.]

A 51 *Venne contento*, duet, G major. [TN: written by Alexander Cornet and copied by Beethoven. See below.]

A 52 *Su questo collo erboso*, duet, A major. [TN: written by Alexander Cornet and copied by Beethoven. See below.]

A 53 *La pastorell' al prato*, quartet, C major. [TN: written by Baron Carl Doblhof-Dier and copied by Beethoven. See below.]

A 54 *0 care selve antique*, trio, E-flat major. [TN: written by Baron Carl Doblhof-Dier and copied by Beethoven. See below.]

A 55 *Se lontan ben mio*, trio, G major. [TN: written by Baron Carl Doblhof-Dier and copied by Beethoven. See below.]

A 56 *L'onda che mormora*, trio, D major. [TN: written by Baron Carl Doblhof-Dier and copied by Beethoven. See below.]

Concerning the autographs, the same pieces are mentioned under the Italian a cappella songs. Beethoven has copied these nine pieces himself to study, and Thayer inadvertently considered them as works of Beethoven, an error that, according to Hans Böttcher in *Beethoven als Liederkomponist,* Benno Filser Verlag, Augsburg 1928, no author of our day has ever bothered to correct. [TN: this is hardly a fair assessment, since even Hess was writing nearly 30 years after Böttcher's comment, and now the correct identification is somewhat widely known.] Thayer's pieces 7-9 and 12-15 (A 48 - A 50 and A 53 - A 56) come, according to Nottebohm's conclusions in *Beethovens Studien*, p. 232, from the Baron Carl Doblhof-Dier (1762-1836), and are located in his *Sei Divertimenti campestri at due, tre e quatro Voci*, while the two remaining pieces [A 51 - A 52] come from Alexander Cornet, a song teacher living in Vienna about 1796; Nottebohm finds them in Cornet's *Sei Duetti per 2 Soprani con Accompo di Cembalo. . .*, which appeared in 1793 by

Artaria in Vienna. Doblhof and Cornet were classmates of Beethoven with Salieri.

A 57 *Dona nobis pacem*, four-part vocal fugue in C major. Published in Seyfried's *Studien,* pp. 227-232, as *"Fuga at quatro voci."* Since this piece cannot be identified through any autograph, and also appears in no other presentation up to this time, it must therefore be viewed as possibly not coming from Beethoven. However, it must be remembered that Beethoven's known autographs were more complete in Seyfried's time than today. [TN: since Hess prepared this catalog, the autograph of the fugue in Beethoven's own hand was discovered in Stockholm, in the Stiftelsen musikkulturens frömjande, and should, therefore, now be considered genuine. In spite of his not being certain of its genuineness, and before the discovery of the autograph, it was published by Hess in the SBG, Vol. XIV, 1971, p. 142. For more information, see Alfred Orel's "Ein 'Donna nobis pacem' von der Hand Ludwig van Beethovens" in *Festschrift Karl Gustav Feller zum 60. Geburtstag*, G. Bosse, Regensburg 1962, pp. 402-6.]

A 58 "Bundeslied" (Fellowship Song), text by Goethe, for two solo male voices and men's chorus a cappella (by Engelbert Humperdinck), based on the theme of the variation movement from the Septet, Op. 20. It appeared in the essay by Max Friedländer, *Engelbert Humperdinck als Beethovenforscher*, in *Die Musik,* Vol. 18, No. 6, March 1926, p. 450. The piece was printed on p. 452. We would not have specifically mentioned Humperdinck's delightful joke here at all, if it would not have been taken as pure coin [face value] by Hans Böttcher in his *Beethoven als Liederkomponist*, where Böttcher actually lists this joke of Humperdinck in his Table IV as an original song of Beethoven!

A 59 Folksong treatment, "As I Was Wandring," in D major, for voice, piano, violin and cello. The autograph is unknown. It is listed as a work of Beethoven through Thomson, 1841, in the sixth volume of the Scottish songs; however, it was listed as a work of Haydn under the text, "No, Henry I must Not," in the years 1817 and 1822 (1817 under the Welsh songs). It may, therefore, very well be an arrangement by Haydn. The melody is given in Thayer as piece 289 of No. 176, p. 109. [TN: the Thomson edition is correctly, Volume Six of the "Melodies of Scotland" by Coventry & Hollier, London 1841, song 289. The pages are not numbered, but the songs are. The text is by Robert Burns.]

Besides those listed under entries No. 247 and 248 and printed by Seyfried as being by Beethoven in *Studienkanons*, there are still three more mentioned in the same book:

A 60 Four-part Canon, C major (No. 4, Seyfried, pp. 333-5). [TN: this was published by Hess in the SBG, Vol. V, 1962, p. 92.]

A 61 "Ähnliches Beispiel" (Similar Example), (No. 5, Seyfried, p. 335).

A 62 "Canon chromatique" (No. 6, Seyfried, p. 336).

A 60 is listed in Nottebohm I, pp. 194-97, in Beethoven's writings on fugal theories for the year 1809; we don't know if it deals with a composition of his own or a study copy. The latter is more likely, because A 61 and A 62 are transcriptions from Marpurg's *Abhandlung von der Fuge*, first published in Berlin in 1753-4 in German, and published in a French edition in 1756. Beethoven is known to have owned the French edition. [TN: Friedrich Wilhelm Marpurg (1718-1795) was a famous music theorist.]

A 63 "Ein anders ist's das erste Jahr" (It's Something Different, the First Year); four part canon, in F major. This entry is taken from Thayer, No. 80, where it is given as a work of Beethoven; actually, however, it is only a transcription by Beethoven from the *Leipziger Allgemeine Musikalische Zeitung*, from 1 January 1800. See also the reference in Nottebohm, *Zwei Skizzenbücher von Beethoven aus den Jahren 1801-1803*. [TN: these were originally published in 1865 and 1880 respectively, as two separate books.] A newer edition [bringing both books together] was published with a foreword by Paul Mies, Breitkopf & Härtel, Leipzig 1924, with the canon on pp. 20-21. The canon is found in Beethoven's transcription in the so-called "Kessler Sketchbook," now in the Gesellschaft der Musikfreunde, A 34, in Vienna.

A 64 "Schusterkanon" (Cobbler's Canon); a three-part canon in B-flat major, 18 bars; the text begins "Schau, wie das Weiberl geht." Printed for the first time in Schünemann's edition of *Beethoven Konversationshefte I*, Max Hesse, Berlin 1941, p. 386. Reprinted by MacArdle/Misch; see also the reference on p. 340, as No. 291. The canon would not likely be from Beethoven; its melodic and harmonic sequences rather remind [one] of a composer like Carl Gottlieb Herring. His "Caffee-Kanon," [Fritz] Jöde, p. 241, is something notably similar to this "Cobbler's Canon." The natural explanation probably is that Beethoven talked with [Josef Karl] Bernard about canons, and then wrote down this canon in the course of the conversation. [TN: the *Schustercanon* is given by Karl-Heinz Köhler and Grita Herre in *Ludwig van Beethovens Konversationshefte* Vol. 1, VEB Deutscher Verlag für Musik, Leipzig 1972, p. 392.]

A 65 "Karfreitagskantate" (Good Friday Cantata); for four voices, three clarinets, three horns and three trombones. The discovery of such a work is reported by H[ermann] Abert in the *Zeitschrift der Internationalen Musikgesellschaft,* Vol. 13, Issue 7, 1912, pp. 218-221. A copy of this piece was found in the estate of the musician and music dealer from Biberach, Joh. Maximilian Kick (born in 1749) and his son, the music director and organist Jak. Friedrich Kick, also from Biberach. [TN: Biberach is a city in Bavaria, southeast of Augsburg.] It was found by Abert, who printed it in its entirety in the appendix of the relevant number of the aforementioned magazine, which gave rise to much speculation. Dr. Edward J. Dent of Cambridge would, however, shortly after the publication had taken place, be on the right track when he pointed out that the *Karfreitagskantate* is a German transcription and orchestration by an unknown person of the chorus produced by Seyfried for men's choir after an arrangement, of the first and third of the "Equale for Four Trombones" which Beethoven had composed about 1812. It thus is an arrangement of an arrangement. Mr. Abert discusses it in the same year and in the same magazine, on pp. 311-2 (Journal 9). Since then there has been complete silence about this work, so these few hints will have to suffice.

A 66 Unknown Chorus with Three Solo Voices. Max Unger listed the Beethoven autographs: Ms 42 and W. 6, 7 of the Paris Conservatory [TN: now the BN] as "Fragmente eines unbekannten Werkes" (Fragments of an Unknown Work). However, they have turned out to be copies by Beethoven from the first finale of Mozart's *Don Giovanni*; the same piece is mentioned on pp. 100-1 and 114-5 of the *Neues Beethoven-Jahrbuches,* Vol. VI, Henry Litolff, Braunschweig1935. The same piece is mentioned by Wilhelm Virneisel in "Kleine Beethoveniana," from *Festschrift zum 60. Geburtstage von Joseph Schmidt-Görg,* Beethoven-Haus, Bonn 1957, p. 361 and the following pages, particularly p.

362. Since Virneisel's text returns to Unger's work in all points and he has named this as a work of Beethoven, so we must include it here with the "Doubtful and Falsely Attributed Works."

Appendix A

LOST WORKS

This Appendix lists works for which original autographs do not survive; however, based on other evidence, we have a reasonable expectation that they were finished, or almost finished. Many of Beethoven's original autographs are missing, but those works were published in his lifetime; and since they are known to be authentic, they are not listed here. Essentially, the entries listed here were described by some reliable authority who saw the finished work, or we have surviving sketches or drafts that indicate the works were actually finished. On occasion, we have a partially surviving autograph of the completed work; I have also listed these. In some cases, it is difficult to accurately separate unfinished works from lost ones, and some overlapping may occur in this list.

This list differs from Appendix B which lists works that may never have existed. Appendix B contains works that are essentially known only by descriptions of the works by others. No sketches, drafts or autographs survive for those and some doubt may exist whether Beethoven ever actually wrote them.

For reasons of economy, the entries given below are shortened, and the reader is encouraged to examine the full entry in the main body of this catalog.

Hess 4: It is almost certain that Beethoven did write an "Ecossaise in G major for Wind Band;" however, all trace of the original autograph has vanished. We know it only by Carl Czerny's transcription of it for piano based on the memory of Wenzel Krumpholz. Fortunately, the witness and transcriber are reliable individuals.

Hess 12: Oboe Concerto in F major. The autograph was sent to Bonn by Haydn. The autograph has completely vanished. There are incipits to all three movements and extensive sketches to the second movement.

Hess 40: String Quintet Movement, for two violins, two violas and cello, in D minor. Composed in 1817 as a prelude to a fugue (which Beethoven didn't complete). The autograph (Artaria 185a) used to be in Berlin, and has been missing since the Second World War.

Hess 41: This String Quintet in C major was the last work that occupied Beethoven before his death. The autograph passed to Anton Diabelli, who published arrangements that he did for piano two-hands and four-hands based on the original autograph, which is now lost. Some sketches do survive.

Hess 52: Piano Sonata in C major, which is listed in Thayer and in the Gräffer-Katalog as having been published by Mollo, where an incipit is given. No trace of the published edition or the autograph has ever been found.

Hess 116: Vocal components to the *Ritterballet*. There seems to be enough consensus that there was at least some sort of choral refrain for this work. An autograph auctioned in 1910 may have contained this missing vocal part, but that has vanished also.

Hess 139: A song, "Minnesold von Bürger," was given to Carl Amenda by Beethoven. It was last seen when Amenda's son sent it to Herman Härtel in Leipzig in 1852. There is no trace of the autograph now.

Hess 143: An early setting of Schiller's "An die Freude" does survive in a few brief sketches, but it is not completely certain whether Beethoven ever finished this early setting. In any event, no finished autograph has been found.

Hess 147: Earlier setting of *Der Kuss*, Op. 128. The presumption is because Nottebohm mentioned it and Unger suggested it based on a fragmentary setting in Paris, that there once existed an earlier setting of this song. The fragment could be a sketch for the published version and not a separate early setting. Rather than a "lost" work this could just as easily be a nonexistent work and be better placed in Appendix B.

Hess 226: A cappella quartet, "Silvio, amante disperato," WOO 99, No. 12. Thayer evidently saw this in the mid-19th century, because he cataloged and recorded the key signature, number of bars and its incipit. No trace has been found since.

Hess 245: Fragment of a String Quartet Fugue. This autograph is in the Beethoven-Haus. Because of the structure of the fugue form and because what is left is complete, this appears to be the last page of what was actually a finished work. Hess suggests that this might have been part (a movement) of a larger work, and suggests that entry 29 may have been a part. The missing pages have not been found.

Hess 255: Two Canons, "Sankt Petrus war ein Fels," and "Bernardus war ein Sankt," may be lost works. According to Kinsky/Halm, they were written in an undated letter to Carl Peters. Thayer copied the letter along with the two canons. However, Ludwig Misch says that Thayer only copied the incipits, not the whole canons. The letter along with the full musical text, if there ever was a fuller musical text, is now lost.

Hess 296: A small Cadenza written for Léon de Saint-Lubin. The autograph for this piece was in the Austrian National Library, but has been missing since 1948. Unfortunately, it was never photocopied or published before being lost. Its description by several scholars verifies that it was an authentic piece.

Hess 317: A cantata, "Europens Befreyungsstunde," on a text by Josef Karl Peters. Beethoven began to write this about 1814, and there are few sketch pages surviving. If he did finish it, this would be considered a lost work; however, it is doubtful he did finish, since if he had, discussions of it, offers to publishers or performance references would surely have survived also. There are none of those sorts of references.

Hess A 38: A duet, "Auf der Liebe Rosenbetten," in G major. This song was examined by Thayer, who cataloged it and noted a three-bar incipit. Adler who saw it 25 years later attributed it to Beethoven's father Johann. If it really was by Beethoven's father, it never should have been included in a catalog of works by Ludwig van Beethoven. In any event, it is lost, regardless of who wrote it.

Appendix B

NONEXISTENT WORKS

This appendix collects all those works listed by Hess that may not actually exist. It does not include those works for which there were known autographs that have been lost. Nor does it include works that are known to have been completed at one time, based on surviving sketches. Rather, this Appendix lists those works which are reported to have been done by others, and in one case by Beethoven himself, but which may never have actually been completed or even begun.

This list gives the Hess entry number first, with a very brief description of the nature of the work referenced. For fuller description or bibliographic references, the reader should consult the complete entry in the main body of this work.

Hess 14: The "first" version of Second Piano Concerto, Op. 19. Hess has assumed that this work has existed in two fundamentally different forms: a "first" and a "final" version. In all probability, this is a single work that simply underwent many revisions over a long period of time. The key to understanding Hess's reason for creating an entry for this work is to assume that Beethoven at some point reached a "finished first form," with which he was satisfied for a substantial period of time. Hess's premise also assumes that sometime latter he became dissatisfied with this "first" form and set about to thoroughly rewrite it in order to create the "final" form that we know as Op. 19 today. There is a period of nearly twenty years between the first drafts of this concerto and its final published form. The fact that Beethoven may have performed this work from some early draft copies isn't really convincing that a satisfactory "early" or "first" version existed.

Hess 20: Hugo Riemann, who found "transcription-like parts not in Beethoven's hand," presumed them to be by Beethoven, based on an assertion by Anton Schindler that Beethoven wrote a set of dances in Mödling fitting the general description of what Riemann found. We have only Schindler's assertion that they ever existed, and no Beethoven autograph is known.

Hess 25: This is another one of those "early version" entries by Hess. Hess assumed that there was an "early version" of Op. 3 because an autograph of a final movement survives in the Library of Congress. It is one of six movements written for this work. What is interesting to note is that there are very minor differences between the surviving autograph of the supposed "first version" and the final version, and that Hess presents no evidence that the missing movements ever existed. This may have been simply a very slightly variant draft of one movement, and not a true "early version" of Op. 3.

Hess 39: String Quintet in F major. This is unpublished and missing and is known only from posthumous writings. A copy of this youthful work of Beethoven was sent in 1826 to Prince Galitzin, but has not been seen since.

Hess 55: This entry was predicated on the belief that an early printing of the "Veni Amore Variations," WoO 65, were fundamentally different from the later 1802 edition. When a copy of the early edition was discovered in the Netherlands by Dr. Clemens von Gleich, it became apparent that the early edition was virtually identical to the later one, except for a few minor printing errors in the text. Basically Hess entry 55 doesn't exist; and there is no "early" version of this work.

Hess 116: Our knowledge of the existence of "vocal components" to the *Ritterballett* is based solely on 19th and
20th century speculation. Even though Hugo Riemann
reported the existence of an autograph that was auctioned in London in 1910, which "may" have been a
vocal component to this work, no confirmation can be
made, because now no trace of this can be found. No
sketches or drafts are known for any "vocal component" to the *Ritterballett*.

Hess 117: This entry is supposed to encompass all the incidental music that Beethoven wrote for Kufner's
Tarpaja. This would fall into three categories: the
surviving part, the *Triumphal March* (which was published in the GA and should, by definition, not have
been included in the Hess catalog); the *Introduction to
a Second Act* (which we now know was for an early
version of *Fidelio* and not for *Tarpaja*); and finally the
additional "lost" music based on Georg Schünemann's
speculation that such music existed. No evidence has
ever been found that Beethoven wrote any additional
music beyond the *Triumphal March*.

Hess 137: This lost song correctly titled, "Ich wiege dich in
meinem Arm" (I Cradle You in My Arms), if it ever
existed, was probably a lullaby. This otherwise unknown song is referred to in a price list of 1822 compiled by Beethoven in preparation for possible publication. Beethoven did occasionally offer works for sale
that he planned to write, or would write if a buyer
were interested, but had not yet actually written. No
autograph or sketches are known. This work may
never have existed.

Hess 190: Piano setting of WoO 155, No. 21. This two-stave
setting is in Anton Schindler's hand, and there is no
evidence that Schindler was copying an authentic, but
now lost, Beethoven transcription. Cooper refers to

this as a "ghost," and Hess later withdrew it from this catalog.

Hess 306: An alternate text for the canon, WoO 168, as "Wie Silber die Rede, doch zu rechter Zeitschweigenist lauteres Gold"as recalled by Fanny Del Rio. This alternate text is probably the result of her faulty memory and does not constitute a revision of the well known one.

Hess 307: A canon, "Ewig Dein" for Toni von Arneth. Max Unger reported the existence of a canon under this title for Toni von Arneth, while WoO 161, a canon with the same title, was written for Antonia Adamberger. This is either the same canon with the names of the recipients confused, or the same canon was presented to both women. "Toni" is a nickname for Antonia.

Hess 308/9: Two canons for Friedrich Kuhlau. Mentioned to exist in 1837, and repeated by Wilhelm von Lenz in 1860. These two canons have never been found, nor is there any supporting evidence that they ever existed. They are probably confused with the known one which is WoO 191, or perhaps they were two drafts for WoO 191 which have not survived.

Hess 313: Vocal piece for Soliva. First reported by Thayer in 1865; all later scholars, including Hess himself, regarded this as a duplication of "Te solo adoro," WoO 186.

Hess 314: "A Mourning Cantata for Cressener" was also reported by Thayer as having been composed in 1781. Not likely, since Beethoven would have been only ten years old for most of that year and this choral work would have been an ambitious project for so young a child who had not yet published a single piece. No trace has ever been found.

Hess 315: This fugue, for which we have no description, was sent by Franz Josef Haydn to Bonn in 1793. It is considered a lost work by Hess, but is probably a known work that has never been properly identified.

Hess 316: This Quintet, like entry 315 above, was sent to Bonn by Franz Josef Haydn in 1793. Proper identification would probably reveal this to be some known work and not a lost one.

Hess 318: Unfinished String Quintet mentioned by Cobbett, but without any supporting data. This entry may just as well be the same as 316 above or 319 below.

Hess 319: String Quintet mentioned in 1805 by Beethoven. This may also be the same one that is mentioned as entry 316 or a part of 318, or possibly entry 39. These are all acknowledged by Hess as possibly being the same piece.

Hess 320: An Andante in G for a string quartet. This entry is also based on uncorroborated information from Cobbett, and may be either a quintet or quartet. It too may be identical to all, or a part of entries 39, 316, 318 or 319.

Hess 328: Two-part canon taken by Hess from a reference from Nottebohm that is identical to entry 275, which Hess took directly from the original source. They are the same piece. One entry can, therefore, be considered real and the other nonexistent. It doesn't matter which.

Appendix C

CORRECTLY IDENTIFIED WORKS

The works listed in this appendix fall into three types. Listed among the first type are works that were once thought to be written by Beethoven, but now can be shown to have been written by another composer or arranger. The second type consists of works that were thought to be lost works that have now been found. While the third type also identifies duplicate entries. Hess occasionally took information from two separate sources or references, thus creating two entries without realizing that those references were in fact referring to the same work. It is hoped that this appendix will provide to the reader a quick reference to locate these corrections in this new edition of the Hess catalog.

Most of the corrected identifications are taken from Hess's "Anhang" or "A" list. As new information comes to light, that list should dwindle over time. It is hoped that as new catalogs of Beethoven's works are created, future editors will drop those entries that are now thoroughly discredited. I would like to remind the reader that this is only intended to be a synopsis of the usually larger entries in this book and that each entry here is truncated for reasons of economy. For a more thorough description, the reader is urged to consult the main entry number.

Hess 2: This set of dances found in an autograph by A. von Perger may not be by Beethoven. They are now generally believed to be by Beethoven's brother Karl and no sketches or autograph in Beethoven's hand exist.

Hess 49/50: Two Piano Trios in E-flat major and B-flat major. Hess took these primarily from references by Wilhelm von Lenz and W. W. Cobbett, without ever comparing the actual works. He presumed them to be lost works. They have been identified as WoO 38 and WoO 39, and were actually printed in the 19th century Gesamtausgabe.

Hess 80: This cadenza for the Piano Concerto, Op. 37, was first discovered by Max Unger who told Hess about it. Hess never examined the original autograph before including it in this catalog. Hess later learned that it was actually written by Sigismund Thalberg.

Hess 102: There are piano transcriptions of nine of the Twelve Contretänze, WoO 14. Hess believed that all nine were transcriptions by Beethoven. The numbering of the set of transcriptions does not follow the numbering of the orchestral version. Shin A. Kojima says that Nos. 1 and 9 of Hess 102 (Nos. 8 and 12 from WoO 14) were probably arranged by Karl van Beethoven, Ludwig's brother, based on Ludwig's sketches.

Hess 107: Incidental music to Christoph Kuffner's *Tarpeja*. There are two parts to this entry, a *Triumphal March* and an *Introduction to the Second Act*. The March has been widely acknowledged to be for *Tarpeja*; however, it is this *Introduction* that was assumed to be part of it as well, by 19th century and early 20th century scholars. The *Introduction* is now believed to have been written for the second act of the 1805 version of *Fidelio*, which was in three acts at that time. It was discarded and never used.

Hess 138: A song, *Adorato – o Nice*. The title of this work was taken from a price list compiled by Beethoven in 1822. Since Hess could find no song published under this title he assumed it to be a lost work. It is actually, however, *No, non turbarti*, WoO 92a, a well known work that was published under a different title.

Hess 205: Hess has correctly identified this "fragment of an unknown movement for piano trio in B-flat major" as the ending of an "unknown setting of the folksong" WoO 155, No. 14. It continues to be occasionally listed or mentioned by others as an unknown piano trio, rather than an unknown setting for the folksong.

Hess 229: Duet, "Languisco e moro per te, mio ben, ch'adoro," which is found written out by Beethoven in the Wielhorski Sketchbook in St. Petersburg. While it is entirely in Beethoven's handwriting, Richard Kramer has identified it as a piece that Beethoven copied out of Friedrich von Matthisson's *Der Volkommene Capellmeister*.

Hess 252: A four-part Canon, "Glück fehl' dir vor allem!," originally thought to have been written in 1817 for Anna Giannatasio Del Rio. It was first published as a work of Beethoven by Frimmel in 1888. It is now known to have been written by Michael Haydn in 1795, and published as a work of his in 1800. Beethoven may have been aware of the work and may have copied it for Miss Del Rio, but the autograph is now lost.

Hess 274: This is found in the Weilhorski Sketchbook, like entry 229 above. Richard Kramer suspects that it is also a copy of a canon by Friedrich von Matthisson.

Hess 275 and 328: Hess lists these as two separate canons, based on information from different sources. They are, however, the very same piece.

Hess 310: Hess entered this as an unknown "Prelude for organ, C major." He even incorrectly cited the source, but never looked at it. It turns out that this is a very slightly adapted version of the ending of the first of the *Two Preludes in All Major Keys*, Op. 39.

Hess 311: Hess presented this song, "Grasmücke," as a song by Beethoven; however, he didn't look at the music until several years later, when he discovered that it is musically identical to a well known song, "Blümchen Wunderhold," Op. 52, No. 8, with a different text. This new text was presumably done by the publisher, Carl Reinecke, in 1890.

Hess 312: This song, "Sigen ist des Lebens Freude" was created by adding a text to one of Beethoven's instrumental canons, WoO 160, No. 2, which is also listed in this catalog as entry 248. The text was apparently added by J. H. Fischer, when he published the song in 1844.

Hess A 1: This Symphony was discovered by Fritz Stein about 1908, who put it forward as a lost work by Beethoven. It has been identified as the work of Friedrich Witt for over half a century. All connection with Beethoven has been thoroughly discredited.

Hess A 3: An unknown arrangement for the "Marsch zur großen Wachtparade," which is found in a manuscript in the SBB. Clemens Brenneis has identified the arranger as Baron Eduard von Lannoy for a special charity concert given in Vienna in April 1844.

Hess A 6: A Piano Concerto movement in D major was included in the old 19th century Gesamtausgabe by Guido Adler as a work by Beethoven. In 1925, Hans Engel identified it as the first movement of Piano Concerto, Op. 15, by Johann Joseph Rösler.

Hess A 9: *Sonata a tre* in six movements. This is a pastiche of movements taken by A. Pochon from several sources, and published through Fischer in New York in 1926. Movements I and III are taken from Georg Friedrich Handel's oratorio *Esther* and Movements II and IV are from a sonata by Ph. E. Bach. The last two movements are actually by Beethoven, and are musically identical to entry 29 of this catalog.

Hess A 10: *Andante favori*, WoO 57, as a string quartet. This was published by F. A. Hoffmeister about 1806. Hess suggests that the arrangement is by either Hoffmeister or F. Ries. However, he describes it as primitively crafted, so it could hardly be by Ries. It is almost certainly the work of Hoffmeister.

Hess A 12: Serenade Op. 41 is generally believed to by Ferdinand Ries, but corrected by Beethoven, so it may not properly belong to this list. Contrary to Hess, Peter Clive suggests Franz Xavier Kleinheinz as the arranger, see the reference to his statement in entries A 12 and A 13 above.

Hess A 13: Notturno Op. 42 is also thought to have been transcribed by Ferdinand Ries, but looked over by Beethoven prior to publication, and would therefore not properly belong to this list. Contrary to Hess, Peter Clive suggests Franz Xavier Kleinheinz as the arranger, see the reference to his statement in entries A 12 and A 13 above.

Hess A 14: Trio for Piano, Violin and Cello, E-flat major, Op. 63. This transcription has long been thought to have nothing to do with Beethoven, however Kinsky/Halm suggests that it was prepared by Franz Xavier Kleinheinz. This view is supported by Peter Clive, see reference to his statements in entries A 12 and A 13 above.

Hess A 16: Trio for Piano, Violin and Cello in D major, from a manuscript in the British Library. Until the early 20th century, this was attributed to Mozart and actually given a Köchel number. Then it was attributed to Beethoven by Georges de Saint-Foix, until Otto Erich

Deutsch established that the handwriting is that of Leopold A. Kozeluch.

Hess A 17: Two pieces for Violin and Piano, also for String Quartet for *Prometheus*. These pieces were included in a publication of *Prometheus* prepared by Charles Zulehner for Simrock in 1831. No connection has ever been established between these insertions and Beethoven, and they are almost certainly by Zulehner.

Hess A 18: Three Pieces for Piano Four-Hands have all been identified by Otto Erich Deutsch as the work of Leopold A. Kozeluch, and are derived from his ballet, *La ritrovata figlia Ottone II*.

Hess A 20: Rondo in B-flat major for Piano Two-Hands is in the same handwriting as A 16 and A 18, and is also by Leopold A. Kozeluch.

Hess A 22: *Trauermarsch* in C minor is found in the album of Mozart's student, Babette Ployer. It has variously been attributed to either Beethoven or Mozart; however, because of its source, it is almost certainly by Mozart.

Hess A 24: *Alexandermarsch* was used in a ballet, "Der blöde Ritter," by Louis Antoine Duport, which is a pastiche of musical pieces from several composers. Hess says it is probably by Louis Luc Loiseau de Persius (1769-1839). It was later put into the music for Georg Friedrich Treitschke's "Ehrenpforten," and together with Beethoven's closing chorus (WoO 97), performed in 1815. This is its first public association with Beethoven. It circulated widely during the Congress of Vienna in a version for piano by Friedrich Starke as "Alexander's Favorite March" and the march appeared as the work of Beethoven in a piano setting in 1829. Because this march achieved fame in piano versions by others, doubt has been cast on its authenticity; however there are sketches in Berlin for an orchestral version and those sketches are marked "Duport Marsch" in Beethoven's own hand. There can be no doubt that the original orchestral version is by Beethoven. Persius may have only completed Beethoven's sketches, or more likely; he adapted Beethoven's orchestral version for the Duport ballet.

Hess A 25: *Pariser Einzugsmarsch* which first appeared about 1818-9 was not attributed to Beethoven until Schuberth published it in 1859. The *Musikalischem Conversations-Lexikon* in 1879 identified the composer as Johann Heinrich Walch.

Hess A 26: Another *Trauermarsch* in F minor appeared about 1830 as the work of Beethoven. Nottebohm has identified it as the work of Johann Heinrich Walch. This same march was published by Pietro Mechetti in a two-hand piano version transposed to B-flat minor, and arranged by Ph. Röth. Jean Witold also suggests that Walch was the composer of this and entry A 25 above.

Hess A 27: *Sehnsuchtswalzer* in A-flat major is a pastiche of two works not by Beethoven. The first part of this waltz is by Franz Schubert and the second part is taken from a waltz by Fr. H. Himmel. While the sources are now known, the name of the arranger who put the two waltzes together as a work of Beethoven is still not known.

Hess A 39: *An Sie,* or *Nachruf* in A-flat major, a song for voice and piano, appeared as a work of Beethoven before 1844, according to Nottebohm. There are, however, published 19th century editions of the work that appear with either Carl Dames or L. Dames as composer, and still another which lists Marianne Czegka, née Auernhammer, as composer.

236

Hess A 45: A song, *Sehnsucht nach dem Rhein*, has been identified by Fritz Kaiser as Op. 75, No. 1, with a different text by Pricess Luise zu Wied.

Hess A 46 and A 47: Both of these songs appeared as "Zwei Leieder von Tiedge." Actually, A 46 is the song "Das Glück der Freundschaft," Op. 88, under a new title as "Lebensglück," and A 47 is "La partenza," WoO 124, with a German text instead of the original Italian, under the title "Abschied."

Hess A 48-50 and A 53-56: These are a series of a cappella songs on texts of Pietro Metastasio by Baron Carl Doblhof-Dier that were copied for study by Beethoven. Because they were in Beethoven's handwriting, Thayer mistook them for authentic works of Beethoven.

Hess A 51 an A 52: These are also a cappella studies by Alexander Cornet which were copied by Beethoven and mistaken by Thayer as authentic.

Hess A 57: This four-part fugue in C major, *Dona Nobis Pacem,* was first published by the unreliable Seyfried in 1832. For over a century, no trace of the original autograph could be found, and its authenticity was doubted. The original autograph in Beethoven's own hand was discovered in Sweden. This is now considered to be an absolutely authentic work.

Hess A 58: An a cappella song, *Bundeslied*, on a text by Goethe, is by Engelbert Humperdinck and is based on a theme from Beethoven's Septet, Op. 20.

Hess A 59: Folksong arrangement, *As I was Wandering,* was listed as a work of Beethoven in Vol. 6 of Thomson's edition of the *Scottish Songs* in 1841. It is actually an arrangement by Haydn, not Beethoven. Whether this was deliberate or accidental on Thomson's part is not known.

Hess A 61 and A 62: These canon studies are in Beethoven's handwriting, but are transcriptions taken from Friedrich Wilhelm Marpurg's *Abhandlung von der Fuge* for study purposes.

Hess A 63: A canon, *Ein anders ist's das erste Jahr*, was copied out of the *Leipziger Allgemeine Musikalische Zeitung* from January 1800. The original composer has not been identified, and evidently Beethoven liked it well enough to make a copy.

Hess A 64: This *Schusterkanon* is found written out by Beethoven in one of his conversation books. It bears a striking resemblance to Carl Gottleib Herring's *Caffee-Kanon*. Beethoven had a discussion with Josef Karl Bernard, and probably wrote it out in the course of this conversation.

Hess A 66: This *Unknown Chorus with Three Solo Voices* was found in Paris by Max Unger. It turns out that Beethoven copied parts of the first finale of Mozart's *Don Giovanni*.

Appendix D

FOLKSONG ARRANGEMENTS

From the end of the eighteenth and into the early nine-teenth centuries, there was intense interest in "folk poetry" and "folk songs" – an interest which led such famous contemporaries of Beethoven as Johann Gottfried Herder, Johann Wolfgang von Goethe and Clemens Brentano, as well as the Edinburgh collector and publisher, George Thomson (1757-1851), to become active in researching, editing and publishing this previously neglected genre. Thomson was not the first to enter this field in the British Isles, but spurred on by the success of others, he began publishing in 1793. He first contacted Beethoven on 5 October 1803, and they actively collaborated until sometime in the summer of 1820.

Before approaching Beethoven, Thomson had already published several collections containing folksong settings by Leopold Kozeluch and Ignace Pleyel, a pupil of Haydn, as well as Haydn himself. Beethoven was expected to set the melodies for either one or two voices, with piano, violin and cello. Thomson sent Beethoven the unadorned "airs" without words, and Beethoven was unaware that in many cases words were being supplied independently of the music, and he frequently complained about their absence. This partly explains why some of the Beethoven settings are marked by Hess as "without text;" however, most of these, if not all, have now been identified. Thomson, on the other hand, frequently complained about Beethoven's settings being too difficult and asked him to make alterations, which, surprisingly, Beethoven did. It is these first versions and in some cases the altered second versions that resulted in many of the entries in this catalog. What started out as a pot-boiler project for Beethoven soon became one that interested him greatly. On his own motivation, he even began setting many continental folksongs, which he offered to Thomson, who declined to publish them. Many of these are listed in this catalog as well.

As Thomson published the folksong settings, he numbered them 1-308; however, not all of the 308 are by Beethoven. Some are by Haydn, Kozeluch, Pleyel and others, so his numbering doesn't work very well as a catalog of Beethoven's settings. Because Hess only listed settings not in the old Gesamtausgabe, only two numbers in his list are also in the Thompson list. They are entries 178 and A 59. In 1940, a new catalog of the Beethoven and Haydn settings as published by Thomson was prepared by Cecil Hopkinson and C. B. Oldman as "Thomson's Collections of National Song," and published in *Transactions of the Edinburgh Bibliographic Society*, Vol. 3, pt. 1, Edinburgh. In this catalog, the Beethoven settings are renumbered 1-126; however since they only include what Thomson published, this list contains only the same two settings from the Thomson numbering and are now listed as 19 and 124 by Hopkinson and Oldman. These numbers could be used as a catalog system of the Beethoven settings if it were not for the fact that they do not include the discarded first or second versions of several settings, and they do not include any of Beethoven's continental folksong settings because Thomson never published any of those.

The most important work done on Beethoven's folksong arrangements in recent years has been by Barry Cooper. Not only did his work in this area result in a new and comprehensible understanding of the process of producing over 180 works, but many unresolved questions were answered. His work resulted in a new classification of the Beethoven folksong arrangements, which at first glance seems complex, this is only because it is a new approach to cataloging. After some examination, it is in reality a very comprehensible and straightforward approach to this very complex portion of Beethoven's creative endeavors. Cooper has arranged the settings into "Groups," some eighteen of them, based on when Beetho-

240

ven worked on them. He has used Roman numerals to designate the groups, with the individual settings within those groups or clusters designated by Arabic numbers. Once one gets used to the groups, this is a very well reasoned and comprehensible system. Cooper published his new numbering system, along with a great deal of analysis and commentary, in *Beethoven's Folksong Settings: Chronology, Sources, Style*, Clarendon Press, Oxford 1994. Cooper makes the comment that, "the settings listed in Hess, *Verzeichnis*, are of three types, indiscriminately intermingled: independent settings with no WoO number (Hess 133-4, 168, 192, 194-8, 203, 206); settings listed under WoO 158 in Kinsky/Halm (Hess 152-67, 169-77, 179-89); and variant or abandoned versions of the whole or part of settings already listed (Hess 178, 190-1, 193, 199-202, 204-5, 207)."

Another new cataloging system for numbering the Beethoven folksong settings has been developed by Petra Weber-Bockholdt. Weber-Bockholdt both uses, and overhauls, the WoO system used by Kinsky/Halm. The result is confusion. The Irish songs are now in three broad groups, followed by a Scottish group and then a group of Welsh songs. WoO 156, which had been twelve Scottish songs is now reduced to only four English ones. The Continental folksong settings faired even worse, and in one extraordinary move, she did not used the Hess catalog entry numbers for her identification, but rather Weber-Bockholdt used the publication order numbers, which function like chapter numbers employed by Hess in Vol. 14 of the *Supplemente zur Beethoven Gesamtausgabe*. It is presented in this Appendix only because Petra Weber-Bockholdt is the editor of the Scottish and Welsh folksong volume in the new collected edition, *Ludwig van Beethoven: Werke: Neue Ausgabe sämtlicher Werke*, G. Henle, Munich 1999. She is also preparing the volume on the Irish folksongs for this series. She has employed the following abbreviations shown below: Kont for Continental folksongs; Ir for Irish; Sch for Scottish; Eng for English; and Wal for Welsh.

The principal reason for adding this separate Appendix, rather than incorporating it into the primary concordance, is that the Cooper numbers and the Weber-Bockholdt numbers apply only to the folksong settings and to no other entries in the Hess catalog. Two items have been added to the entries shown in this Appendix at the end of the list, because they are of interest to understanding the folksongs and because the were added to the SBG by Hess after the publication of this catalog.

Hess number	Cooper number	Weber-Bockholdt number	Kinsky/Halm number
133	XVIII/1	29 Kont 28	-
134	XVIII/2	29 Kont 29	-
152	V/6	Ir III 61	WoO 158/2/1
153	V/18	Ir III 62	WoO 158/2/2
154	XII/4	22 Sch 5	WoO 158/2/3
155	XII/7	22 Sch 6	WoO 158/2/4
156	XII/12	29 Kont 1	WoO 158/1/1
157	VI/5	22 Sch 2	WoO 158/2/5
158	IX/9	29 Kont 11	WoO 158/1/11
159	IX/10	29 Kont 12	WoO 158/1/12
160	IX/1	29 Kont 13	WoO 158/1/13
161	IX/2	29 Kont 14	WoO 158/1/14
162	IX/3	29 Kont 15	WoO 158/1/15
163	IX/5	29 Kont 19	WoO 158/1/19
164	IX/6	29 Kont 20	WoO 158/1/20
165	IX/7	29 Kont 21	WoO 158/1/21
166	X/1	4 Eng 1	WoO 158/3/1
167	X/4	29 Kont 24	WoO 158/3/2
168	X/5	29 Kont 25	-
169	XVII/2	22 Sch 21	WoO 158/3/3
170	VI/7	22 Sch 3	WoO 158/2/6
171	IX/13	29 Kont 18	WoO 158/1/18
172	IX/11	29 Kont 2	WoO 158/1/2
173	IX/12	29 Kont 3	WoO 158/1/3
174	IX/4	29 Kont 4	WoO 158/1/4
175	XVII/3	22 Sch 22	WoO 158/3/4
176	XIV/7	22 Sch 14	WoO 158/3/5
177	VIII/6	29 Kont 16	WoO 158/1/16
178	VII/1	20 Ir 13	original duet version
179	I/24	22 Sch 1	WoO 158/3/6
180	II/5	Ir III 60	WoO 158/2/7
181	IX/14	29 Kont 23	WoO 158/2/23
182	IX/15	29 Kont 5	WoO 158/1/5

Hess number	Cooper number	Weber-Bockholdt number	Kinsky/Halm number
183	IX/16	29 Kont 6	WoO 158/1/6
184	IX/17	29 Kont 9	WoO 158/1/9
185	IX/18	29 Kont 10	WoO 158/1/10
186	XI/1	29 Kont 17	WoO 158/1/17
187	XI/2	29 Kont 7	WoO 158/1/7
188	XI/3	29 Kont 22	WoO 158/1/22
189	XI/4	29 Kont 8	WoO 158/1/8
190	(I/20)	-	A ghost? Hess refers to a two-stave setting of the melody of WoO 155/21 in Schindler's hand. See C/F, p. 228.
191	(I/18)	-	Abandoned setting of the melody of WoO 155/19 in Schindler's hand. See C/F, p. 228.
192	IV/2	Ir I 5 (2nd ver.)	-
193	(II/6)	-	Abandoned coda for WoO 152/20 found in Artaria 187. See C/F, p. 229.
194	II/9	Ir II 30 (1st ver.)	-
195	V/20	Ir II 40 (alt. ver.)	-
196	I/37	Ir II 41 (1st ver.)	-
197	II/1	Ir II 49 (1st ver.)	-
198	III/8	Ir II 48 (1st ver.)	-
199	(V/8)	-	Autograph version of WoO 154/11. Hess chose to give this a separate number, although it is essentially the same as published. See C/F, p.229.
200	(XII/1 alternate str. parts)	-	(Op. 108/4)
201	(VI/12 alternate str. parts)	-	(Op. 108/7)
202	VII/3	-	Autograph version of Op. 108/11, essentially the same as published, with key transposed from F to E-flat. See C/F, p. 229.
203	I/43	-	Op. 108/20, 1st setting.
204	(I/3)	-	Abandoned coda for WoO 155/7. See C/F, p.229.
205	(I/6)	Wal 14 (alt. ver.)	Abandoned coda for WoO 155/14. See C/F, p. 229.
206	I/4	Wal 20 (1st ver.)	First version of WoO 155/20.
207	(IX/6)	-	Rough draft for WoO 158/1/20 (SBH 591).

| SBG 38 | I/3 | Wal 7 (alt. ver.) | Authentic version of WoO 155/7. The version published by Thomson and in the GA omits nine bars and adds one. See C/F, p.229. |
| SBG 52 | (IX/5) | 29 Kont 19 (1st ver.) | This is a rough draft of WoO 158/1/19. See C/F, p. 229. |

THE
SEVENTH SYMPHONY
IN A MAJOR
OPUS 92

a fragment of the beginning
in a transcription for piano
Hess 96

by

Ludwig van Beethoven

prepared from the manuscript by
Mark S. Zimmer

published by
Vance Brook Publishing
West Newbury, Vermont
2003

Symphony Nr. 7 op. 92 for Piano

Hess 96 (fragment)

L. van Beethoven

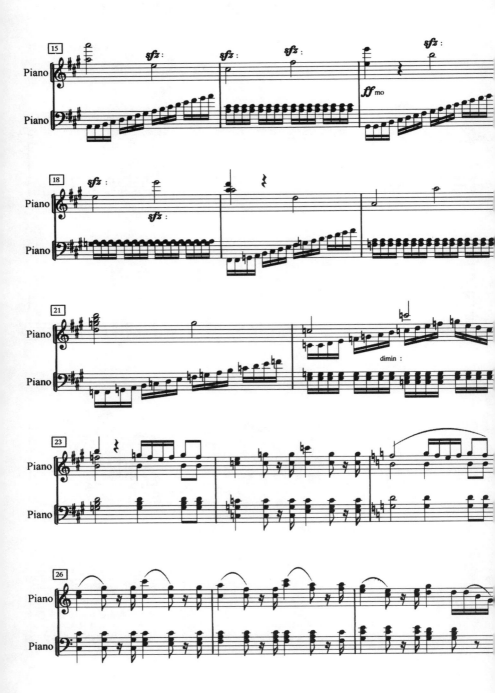

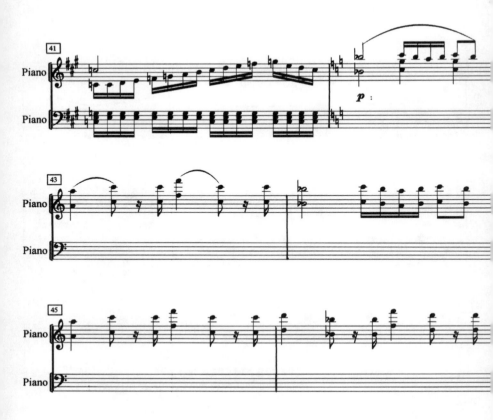

CONCORDANCE

For the purpose of easier identification, it is advantageous to be able to compare the numbers given to the works in both this catalog and the large Kinsky/Halm catalog. Because Kinsky/Halm always lists the numbers for Hess 2 and Hess 3, we then give that number here if it is identical in both catalogs; alternatively, if two numbers are given, then the left applies to Hess 2 and the right indicates Hess 3. Numbers without further identification listed under the Kinsky/Halm heading are always understood to be WoO numbers (Work without Opus number). A number shown in parentheses means that the relevant work is in fact mentioned under this number, but not listed with its own number. [TN: in addition to the Hess 2 and Hess 3 numbers and the Kinsky/Halm numbers, I have added the relevant Bruers, Nottebohm, Grove, Thayer, Marx and Biamonti numbers. For the most part, Hess listed all the relevant Thayer numbers and Nottebohm numbers in the body of this catalog; however, they are listed again here for the sake of clarity and completeness. The publication of this catalog in 1957 really rendered the Hess 2 and 3 numbers obsolete, and they are seldom cited anymore.]

This Catalog	Hess 2 or 3	Kinsky/Halm	Bruers	Nottebohm	Grove	Thayer	Marx	Biamonti
1	2	-	(Op.93)	(Op.93)	(Op.93)	(170)	(174)	547
2	3	12	344	-	-	290	291	182
3	4	-	-	-	-	(136)	-	II-A53
4	-	23	346	-	-	294	163a	532
5	5	13	350	p.140	-	291	292	218
6	6	18	145	-	-	147	151	501
7	7	18	340a & 340c	p.198	-	283a	(151)	780
8	8	19	-	p.140	-	157	166	517
9	9	19	340b & 340c	-	-	283b	166	781
10	10	5	148	-	148	296	299	33
11	-	-	-	-	-	-	-	665
12	248	-	338	-	-	281	-	49
13	11	(37)	315	-	-	-	-	54
14	12	(Op.19)	(Op.19)	(Op.19)	(Op.19)	(58)	(37)	75
15	12a	-	-	-	-	-	209	641
16	-	(Op.80)	(Op.80)	(Op.80)	(Op.80)	(142)	(147)	(486)
17	14	26	294	-	-	17	27	32
18	19	28	308	-	-	285	288	137
19	30	-	302 & 339	-	-	282	286	129
20	31	17	309	-	-	-	-	710

This Catalog	Hess 2 or 3	Kinsky/Halm	Bruers	Nottebohm	Grove	Thayer	Marx	Biamonti
21	-	(Op.20)	(Op.20)	(Op.20)	(Op.20)	(69)	(80)	205
22	13	32	298	-	-	-	-	161
23	-	32	298	-	-	-	-	161
24	-	(32)	298	-	-	-	-	161
25	-	(Op.3)	(Op.3)	(Op.3)	(Op.3)	(18)	(30)	42
26	15	9	345	-	-	293	-	101
27	18	11	(168)	(150)	(168)	(95)	(63)	163
28	17	(Op.9)	(Op.9)	(Op.9)	(Op.9)	(53)	(69)	219
29	- 275	-	318	-	-	46	-	80c
30	- 278	-	318	-	-	46	-	80d
31	- 279	-	318	-	-	46	-	80e
32	20	(Op.18)	(Op.18)	(Op.18)	(Op.18)	(75)	(82)	178
33	21	-	-	(14 p.16)	-	-	-	64
34	22	(Op.14/1)	301	-	(Op.14/1)	(68)	(78)	315
35	- 31a	-	-	-	-	-	-	685
36	-	-	-	-	-	-	-	680
37	-	-	-	-	-	-	-	I-A7
38	- 31b	-	-	-	-	-	-	338
39	27	-	-	-	-	-	-	II-A45
40	29	-	-	-	-	-	-	684

This Catalog	Hess 2 or 3	Kinsky/Halm	Bruers	Nottebohm	Grove	Thayer	Marx	Biamonti
41	28	(62)	174	(p.152)	174	-	277	846
42	45	34	-	-	-	-	-	740
43	36	44a	293	-	-	-	-	124
44	- 36a	43b	150	-	150	-	47b	122 & 123
45	- 36b	44b	-	-	-	-	-	125
46	35	-	-	-	-	-	-	3
47	37	(Op.3)	(Op.3)	(Op.3)	(Op.3)	(18)	(30)	668
48	-	-	-	-	-	-	-	8
49	- 276	38	153	p.143	153	13	11	31 & II-A63/1
50	- 277	39	154 & 348	p.144	154	173 & 297	177	542 & II-A67 & II-A63/2
51	39	48	313	-	-	Supp. 6	4	4
52	246	-	342	-	-	-	-	II-A58
53	44	50	305 & 314	-	-	-	-	21
54	257	-	-	-	-	-	-	II-A71
55	-	65	177	p.154	177	11	21	24 & 299
56	- 269	61a	-	-	-	-	-	825
57	- 55b	-	-	-	-	-	-	784
58	- 55c	-	-	-	-	-	-	47a
59	- 55c	-	-	-	-	-	-	47b
60	- 55d	-	-	-	-	-	-	267

This Catalog	Hess 2 or 3	Kinsky/Halm	Bruers	Nottebohm	Grove	Thayer	Marx	Biamonti
61	- 55e	-	-	-	-	-	-	285
62	46	61	-	-	-	-	-	736
63	- 46a	-	289	-	-	-	-	20
64	-	-	-	-	-	-	-	67
65	47	(Op.37)	(Op.37)	(Op.37)	(Op.37)	(73)	(85)	730
66	49	(53)	-	-	-	-	-	159
67	50	-	-	-	-	-	-	551
68	- 50a	-	-	-	-	-	-	354
69	51	-	-	-	-	-	-	152
70	- 281	-	-	-	-	-	-	385
71	- 282	-	-	-	-	-	-	387
72	- 286	-	-	-	-	-	-	398
73	-	-	-	-	-	-	-	251
74	-	-	-	-	-	-	-	253
75	228	200	198	-	198	216	224	688
76	-	(Op.15)	(Op.15)	(Op.15)	(Op.15)	(33)	(64)	168
77	-	(Op.15)	(Op.15)	(Op.15)	(Op.15)	(33)	(64)	(167)
78	-	(Op.15)	(Op.15)	(Op.15)	(Op.15)	(33)	(64)	(167)
79	-	(Op.19)	(Op.19)	(Op.19)	(Op.19)	(58)	(37)	76
80	-	-	-	-	-	-	-	353

This Catalog	Hess 2 or 3	Kinsky/Halm	Bruers	Nottebohm	Grove	Thayer	Marx	Biamonti
81	52	(Op.58)	(Op.58)	(Op.58)	(Op.58)	(131)	(137)	510/1
82	53	(Op.58)	(Op.58)	(Op.58)	(Op.58)	(131)	(137)	510/2
83	54	(Op.58)	(Op.58)	(Op.58)	(Op.58)	(131)	(137)	510/3
84	55	(Op.61)	(Op.61)	(Op.61)	(Op.61)	(130)	(134)	512/1
85	246 55a	(Op.61)	(Op.61)	(Op.61)	(Op.61)	(130)	(134)	512/2
86	56	Op.134	Op.134	Op.134	Op.134	256	270	841
87	57	(29)	(278)	-	-	-	(297)	(440)
88	58	-	-	-	-	-	-	65
89	59	(1)	(149)	-	(149)	(12)	(24)	30
90	60	(Op.43)	(Op.43)	(Op.43)	(Op.43)	79	91	289
91	69	(Op.121b)	(Op.121b)	(Op.121b)	(Op.121b)	(231)	(248)	290
92	68	(Op.122)	(Op.122)	(Op.122)	(Op.122)	(232)	(256)	767
93	67	(Op.84)	(Op.84)	(Op.84)	(Op.84)	(154)	(163)	529
94	-	(Op.84)	(Op.84)	(Op.84)	(Op.84)	(154)	(163)	529
95	-	(Op.84)	(Op.84)	(Op.84)	(Op.84)	(154)	(163)	529
96	-	(Op.92)	(Op.92)	(Op.92)	(Op.92)	(169)	(173)	662
97	-	(Op.91)	(Op.91)	(Op.91)	(Op.91)	180	(184)	584
98	261 69a	(Op.1/2)	(Op.1)	(Op.1)	(Op.1)	(16/1)	(36)	183
99	64	(18)	(145 & 273)	-	-	-	(151)	504
100	61	(8)	(140)	p.137	(140)	36	42	93

This Catalog	Hess 2 or 3	Kinsky/Halm	Bruers	Nottebohm	Grove	Thayer	Marx	Biamonti
101	62	(7)	(139)	p.136	(139)	37	43	92
102	63	(14)	(141)	(p.138)	(141)	(93)	(103)	314
103	70	33/1	284	-	-	-	-	197
104	71	33/2	-	-	-	-	-	198
105	72	33/3	-	-	-	-	-	199
106	73	33/4&5	317	-	-	29	-	200
107	74	(29)	(278)	-	-	-	(297)	714
108	75	(Op.91)	(Op.91)	(Op.91)	(Op.91)	180	184	557
109	76	(Op.72)	(Op.72a)	(Op.72)	(Op.72)	125	130a	423
110	77	(Op.72)	(Op.72)	(Op.72)	(Op.72)	125	130b	427
111	- 85b	(Op.72)	(Op.72)	(Op.72)	(Op.72)	(125)	(130a)	413
112	- 85a	(Op.72)	(Op.72)	(Op.72)	(Op.72)	(125)	(130b)	-
113	85	(Op.72)	(Op.72)	(Op.72)	(Op.72)	(125)	(187)	569
114	-	(Op.72)	(Op.72)	(Op.72)	(Op.72)	(125)	(187)	782
115	78	-	333	-	-	266	116	379
116	- 78a	(1)	(149)	-	(149)	(12)	(24)	(29)
117	79	2b	337	-	-	279	284	-
118	- 78b	(113) & 114 & 124 & 257	(113) & 114 & 257	-	-	166 & 235	245 & 171	742
119	80	92a	332/23	-	-	264/23	-	304 & 681
120	81	93	332/25	-	-	264/25	-	352

This Catalog	Hess 2 or 3	Kinsky/Halm	Bruers	Nottebohm	Grove	Thayer	Marx	Biamonti
121	83	(Op.72)	(Op.72)	(Op.72)	(Op.72)	(125)	(130b)	414
122	84	(Op.72)	(Op.72)	(Op.72)	(Op.72)	(125)	(130b)	415
123	- 268	-	-	-	-	-	-	571
124	-	105	288	-	-	(219)	(230)	696
125	87	105	(288)	-	-	219	230	696
126	88	111	292	-	-	26	-	22
127	97	103	321	-	-	185	190	574
128	89	112	-	-	-	-	-	27
129	90	116	286/1	-	-	-	-	44
130	91	116	(286/1)	-	-	-	-	44
131	92	128	286/2	-	-	-	-	201
132	93	151	-	-	-	239	249	768
133	94	(158/1)	-	-	-	-	237/1	725/1
134	95	(158/1)	-	-	-	-	237/2	725/2
135	98	125	-	-	-	-	-	174
136	99	127	-	-	-	-	-	186
137	108	-	-	-	-	-	-	682
138	109	92a	332/23	-	-	264/23	-	681 & 304
139	115	-	-	-	-	-	-	185
140	- 115b	(Op.82/1)	(Op.82/1)	(Op.82/1)	(Op.82/1)	(163)	(158)	513/1

This Catalog	Hess 2 or 3	Kinsky/Halm	Bruers	Nottebohm	Grove	Thayer	Marx	Biamonti
141	-	(Op.48/6)	(Op.48/6)	(Op.48/6)	(Op.48/6)	(109)	(122)	(367/6)
142	-	(Op.83/1)	(Op.83/1)	(Op.83/1)	(Op.83/1)	(155)	(165)	350
143	-	(Op.52)	(Op.52)	(Op.52)	(Op.52)	(28)	(31a)	II-A7 & (189)
144	253 115d	(Op.52/2)	(Op.52/2)	(Op.52/2)	(Op.52/2)	(28)	(31a)	(34)
145	115e	(126)	-	-	-	-	-	117
146	-	(117)	(233)	(p. 177)	(233)	(23)	(22)	77
147	-	(Op.128)	(Op.128)	(Op.128)	(Op.128)	(237)	(247)	169
148	254 115a	131	287/1	-	-	267	279	526
149	- 267	-	287/2	-	-	267	-	527
150	-	-	-	-	-	-	-	707 & 731 & 760
151	-	-	-	-	-	-	-	51
152	116	158/2/1	-	-	-	177/1	-	667/1
153	117	158/2/2	-	-	-	177/2	-	667/2
154	118	158/2/3	-	-	-	177/4	-	667/3
155	119	158/2/4	-	-	-	177/5	-	667/4
156	120	158/1/1	-	-	-	177/6	-	692/1
157	121	158/2/5	-	-	-	177/7	-	667/5
158	122	158/1/11	-	-	-	177/8	-	663/1
159	123	158/1/12	-	-	-	177/9	-	663/2
160	124	158/1/13	-	-	-	177/10	-	663/3

This Catalog	Hess 2 or 3	Kinsky/Halm	Bruers	Nottebohm	Grove	Thayer	Marx	Biamonti
161	125	158/1/14	-	-	-	177/11	-	663/4
162	126	158/1/15	-	-	-	177/12	-	663/5
163	127	158/1/19	285	-	-	177/13	-	663/6
164	128	158/1/20	-	-	-	177/14	-	663/7
165	129	158/1/21	-	-	-	177/15	-	663/8
166	130	158/3/1	-	-	-	177/16	-	667/6
167	131	158/3/2	-	-	-	177/17	-	667/7
168	132	(158/1)	-	-	-	177/18	-	667/8
169	133	158/3/3	-	-	-	177/19	-	667/9
170	134	158/2/6	-	-	-	177/20	-	667/10
171	135	158/1/18	-	-	-	177/22	-	663/9
172	136	158/1/2	-	-	-	177/23	-	663/10
173	137	158/1/3	-	-	-	177/24	-	663/11
174	138	158/1/4	-	-	-	177/26	-	663/12
175	139	158/3/4	-	-	-	177/27	-	667/11
176	140	158/3/5	-	-	-	177/28	-	667/12
177	141	158/1/16	-	-	-	177/29	-	692/2
178	142	(153/13)	(224/13)	(p. 168)	-	177/30	(178)	615
179	143	158/3/6	-	-	-	177/31	-	667/13
180	144	158/2/7	-	-	-	177/32	-	667/14

This Catalog	Hess 2 or 3	Kinsky/Halm	Bruers	Nottebohm	Grove	Thayer	Marx	Biamonti
181	145	158/1/23	-	-	-	-	-	663/13
182	146	158/1/5	-	-	-	-	-	663/14
183	147	158/1/6	-	-	-	-	-	663/15
184	148	158/1/9	-	-	-	-	-	663/16
185	149	158/1/10	-	-	-	-	-	663/17
186	150	158/1/17	-	-	-	-	-	692/3
187	151	158/1/7	-	-	-	-	-	692/4
188	152	158/1/22	-	-	-	-	-	692/5
189	153	158/1/8	-	-	-	-	-	692/6
190	250	(155/21)	-	-	-	-	-	667/15
191	-	(155/19)	(226/19)	(p. 172)	(226/19)	(178/82)	(179)	591 & 667/16
192	154	(152/5)	(223/5)	(p. 163)	(223/5)	(174/5)	(178)	562
193	165	(152/20)	(223/20)	(p. 165)	(223/20)	(174/20)	(178)	562
194	155	(153/5)	(224/5)	(p. 167)	(224/5)	(174/31)	(178)	564
195	156	(153/11)	(224/11)	(p. 167)	(224/11)	(174/41)	(178)	564
196	157	(153/12)	(224/12)	(p. 167)	(224/12)	(174/42)	(178)	564
197	158	(153/15)	(224/15)	(p. 168)	(224/15)	(174/50)	(178)	564
198	159	(154/9)	(225/9)	(p. 169)	(225/9)	(174/49)	(178)	566
199	166	(154/11)	(225/11)	(p. 170)	(225/11)	(174/56)	(178)	565
200	163	(Op.108/4)	(Op.108/4)	(Op.108/4)	(Op.108/4)	(176/209)	(180)	661/1

This Catalog	Hess 2 or 3	Kinsky/Halm	Bruers	Nottebohm	Grove	Thayer	Marx	Biamonti
201	164	(Op.108/7)	(Op.108/7)	(Op.108/7)	(Op.108/7)	(176/207)	(180)	661/2
202	162	(Op.108/11)	(Op.108/11)	(Op.108/11)	(Op.108/11)	(176/203)	(180)	661/3
203	161	(Op.108/20)	(Op.108/20)	(Op.108/20)	(Op.108/20)	(176/222)	(180)	661/4
204	167	(155/7)	(226/7)	(p. 171)	(226/7)	(175/68)	(179)	534
205	-	(155/14)	(226/14)	(p. 172)	(226/14)	(175/77)	(179)	286 & 534
206	160	(155/20)	(226/20)	(p. 172)	(226/20)	(175/83)	(179)	534
207	(128)	(158/1/20)	-	-	-	(177/14)	(179)	(663)
208	170	99/3a	332/1	-	-	264/1	199	143
209	171	99/3b	332/2	-	-	264/2	199	144
210	172	99/3c	332/3	-	-	264/3	199	146
211	173	99/1	332/4	-	-	264/4	199	58
212	174	99/6	332/5	-	-	264/5	199	60
213	175	99/10a	332/6	-	-	264/6	199	149
214	176	99/2	332/16	-	-	264/16	199	202
215	177	99/11	332/17	-	-	264/17	199	128
216	178	99/9	332/18	-	-	264/18	199	127
217	179	99/7a	332/19	-	-	264/19	199	109
218	180	99/10b	332/20	-	-	264/20	199	148
219	181	99/10c	332/21	-	-	264/21	199	150
220	182	99/7b	332/22	-	-	264/22	199	110

This Catalog	Hess 2 or 3	Kinsky/Halm	Bruers	Nottebohm	Grove	Thayer	Marx	Biamonti
221	183	99/5a	332/26	-	-	264/26	199	336
222	184	99/4a	332/27	-	-	264/27	199	341
223	185	99/4b	332/28	-	-	264/28	199	342
224	186	99/3c	332/29	-	-	264/29	199	147
225	187	99/3b	332/30	-	-	264/30	199	144
226	188	99/12	332/31	-	-	264/31	199	335
227	189	99/5b	-	-	-	-	-	59
228	190	-	-	-	-	-	-	141
229	193	-	-	-	-	-	-	350
230	-	-	-	-	-	-	-	215
231	191	-	-	-	-	-	-	216
232	192	-	-	-	-	-	-	217
233	-	-	-	-	-	-	-	56
234	-	-	-	-	-	-	-	80a
235	-	-	-	-	-	-	-	80b
236	-	-	318	-	-	46	-	80f/1
237	-	-	318	-	-	46	-	80f/2
238	-	-	318	-	-	46	-	80f/3
239	-	-	318	-	-	46	-	80g
240	-	-	-	-	-	-	-	80h

This Catalog	Hess 2 or 3	Kinsky/Halm	Bruers	Nottebohm	Grove	Thayer	Marx	Biamonti
241	-	-	-	-	-	-	-	80i
242	-	-	-	-	-	-	-	80L
243	-	-	318	-	-	46	-	80m
244	-	-	318	-	-	46	-	80n
245	-	-	-	-	-	-	-	82 & 100
246	-	-	-	-	-	-	-	81
247	210 168	160a	-	-	-	263/1	-	85
248	209	160b	-	-	-	263/1	-	86
249	219	167	-	-	-	Anh. 263	280	610
250	196	169	322	-	-	201	211	647
251	197	170	-	-	-	-	212	651
252	206	171	-	-	-	-	-	683
253	211	173	323	-	-	220	231	711
254	-	(173)	-	-	-	-	-	301
255	203	175	324	-	-	225	241	715
256	226	(175)	(324)	-	-	(225)	(241)	721
257	229	177	-	-	-	-	-	734
258	212	181b	-	-	-	-	-	750
259	213	181c	-	-	-	-	-	751
260	216	(181)	-	-	-	-	-	785

This Catalog	Hess 2 or 3	Kinsky/Halm	Bruers	Nottebohm	Grove	Thayer	Marx	Biamonti
261	199	183	327	-	-	248	272	769
262	194	184	203	-	203	-	-	773
263	230	(186)	(272/1 & 326)	-	-	(243)	(249a & 258)	786a
264	231	(186)	(272/1 & 326)	-	-	(243)	(249a & 258)	786b
265	205	188	-	-	-	-	-	802
266	201	189	329	-	-	251	264	805
267	214	190	-	-	-	-	-	807
268	198	192	330	-	-	254	268	824
269	-	193	-	-	-	-	-	833
270	208	196	331	-	-	261	-	834
271	227	197	-	-	-	-	274	842
272	202	203	328	-	-	249	262	804
273	200	35	222	-	222	-	264	809
274	218	-	-	-	-	-	265	351
275	221	-	-	-	-	-	-	388
276	- 244e	-	-	-	-	-	-	151
277	-	-	-	-	-	-	-	305
278	195	100	320	-	-	91	-	303
279	222	101	200	-	200	98	96	331
280	204	198	336	-	-	277	111	848

This Catalog	Hess 2 or 3	Kinsky/Halm	Bruers	Nottebohm	Grove	Thayer	Marx	Biamonti
281	207	199	-	-	-	-	278	585
282	225	201	349	-	-	298	200	689
283	223	202	325	-	-	242	293	778
284	235	204	-	-	-	-	252	826
285	233	-	-	-	-	-	-	794
286	234	205a	-	-	-	-	-	171
287	241	205b	-	-	-	-	-	580
288	244	205c	-	-	-	-	-	671
289	242	205d	-	-	-	-	-	674
290	-	205e	-	-	-	-	-	709
291	243	205f	-	-	-	-	-	765
292	240	205g	-	-	-	-	-	791
293	236	205h	-	-	-	-	-	806
294	239	205i	-	-	-	-	-	843
295	224	205k	-	-	-	-	-	844
296	-	-	-	-	-	-	-	743
297	-	-	-	-	-	-	-	643
298	-	-	-	-	-	-	-	11
299	-	-	-	-	-	-	-	735
300	-	-	-	-	-	-	-	718

This Catalog	Hess 2 or 3	Kinsky/Halm	Bruers	Nottebohm	Grove	Thayer	Marx	Biamonti
301	-	-	-	-	-	-	-	719
302	215	(181)	-	-	-	-	-	836
303	220	-	-	-	-	-	-	777
304	- 244d	(181)	-	-	-	-	-	I-A9
305	232	-	-	-	-	-	-	556
306	217	(168)	-	-	-	-	-	II-A72
307	-	-	-	-	-	-	283	-
308	- (244f)	-	-	-	-	-	-	-
309	- (244f)	-	-	-	-	-	-	-
310	-	(Op.39/1)	(Op.39/1)	(Op.39/1)	(Op.39/1)	(9)	(17)	375 & I-A10
311	-	(Op.52/8)	(Op.52/8)	(Op.52/8)	(Op.52/8)	28/8	31a/8	I-A8
312	-	(160b)	-	-	-	-	-	I-A11
313	96	186	272/1 & 326	-	-	243	249a & 258	789
314	247	-	-	-	-	-	-	II-A16
315	249	-	-	-	-	-	-	-
316	-	-	-	-	-	-	-	-
317	-	-	-	-	-	-	-	572
318	- 272	-	-	-	-	-	-	II-A46a
319	- 273	-	-	-	-	-	-	II-A46b
320	- 274	-	-	-	-	-	-	-

This Catalog	Hess 2 or 3	Kinsky/Halm	Bruers	Nottebohm	Grove	Thayer	Marx	Biamonti
321	- 266	-	-	-	-	-	-	262
322	237	-	-	-	-	-	-	705
323	238	-	-	-	-	-	-	706
324	258	-	-	-	-	-	-	-
325	259	-	-	-	-	-	-	-
326	260	-	-	-	-	-	-	-
327	- 280	-	-	-	-	-	-	384
328	- 283	-	-	-	-	-	-	388
329	- 284	-	-	-	-	-	-	390
330	- 285	-	-	-	-	-	-	396
331	-	-	-	-	-	-	-	306
332	-	-	-	-	-	-	-	307
333	-	-	-	-	-	-	-	308
334	-	-	-	-	-	-	-	309
335	-	(130)	(256)	(p. 186)	(256)	(273)	(238a)	728
A1	1	A1	299	-	-	-	-	II-A57
A2	(6) (9)	(18)	145	p. 140	-	-	151	II-A38
A3	-	-	-	-	-	-	-	II-A39
A4	263	-	341	-	-	284	287	II-A35
A5	-	16	-	-	-	136	-	II-A52 & 54

This Catalog	Hess 2 or 3	Kinsky/Halm	Bruers	Nottebohm	Grove	Thayer	Marx	Biamonti
A6	-	A7	297	-	-	-	18	II-A18
A7	23 to 26b	A2	300	-	-	-	-	II-A44
A8	256	(Op.30/3)	(Op.30/3)	(Op.30/3)	(Op.30/3)	(96)	(106)	II-A47
A9	(275)	-	-	-	-	-	-	-
A10		(57)	(170)	-	(p. 151)	112	(126)	II-A6
A11	32	A4	304	-	-	21	-	II-A59
A12	33	Op.41	41	41	41	(92)	98	371
A13	34	Op.42	42	42	42	(50)	31e	372
A14	-	Op.63	63	63	63	(25)	46	II-A65
A15	-	Op.64	64	64	64	(18)	30	II-A60
A16	38	A3	307	-	-	-	-	II-A66
A17	-	(Op.43)	(Op.43)	p. 192	(Op.43)	(79)	(91)	II-A43
A18	41 to 43	A8	296	-	-	-	-	II-A42
A19	- 55f	A9	-	-	-	-	-	II-A20
A20	40	A6	303	-	-	-	-	II-A48
A21	245	(Op.119)	119/12	Op.119/12	(Op.119)	233	(242)	II-A13
A22	255	-	-	-	-	-	-	II-A36
A23	-	A17	-	-	-	-	-	II-A30
A24	-	A11	-	p. 189	-	-	-	II-A5
A25	-	A12	-	p. 189	-	-	-	II-A41

This Catalog	Hess 2 or 3	Kinsky/Halm	Bruers	Nottebohm	Grove	Thayer	Marx	Biamonti
A26	-	A13	-	p. 189	-	-	-	II-A37
A27	-	A14/1	-	p. 190/1	-	-	-	II-A56
A28	-	A14/2	-	p. 190/2	-	-	-	II-A50
A29	-	A14/3	-	p. 190/3	-	-	-	II-A29
A30	-	A14/4	-	p. 190/4	-	-	-	II-A26
A31	-	A14/5	-	p.190/5	-	-	-	II-A68
A32	-	A14/6	-	p. 190/6	-	-	-	II-A69
A33	-	A16/1	-	p. 190/7	-	-	-	II-A31
A34	-	A16/2	-	p. 190/8	-	-	-	II-A27
A35	-	A16/3	-	p. 190/9	-	-	-	II-A62
A36	-	A16/4	-	p. 191/10	-	-	-	II-A40
A37	-	A15	347	p. 191	-	295	-	II-A28
A38	86	-	334	-	-	269	281/1	II-A11
A39	114	A18	-	p. 192	-	-	-	II-A9
A40	100	(Op.26)	(Op.26)	(Op.26)	(Op.26)	(88)	(92)	II-A12
A41	103	(Op.8)	(Op.8)	(Op.8)	(Op.8)	(50)	(31e)	II-A8
A42	104	(Op.8)	(Op.8)	(Op.8)	(Op.8)	(50)	(31e)	II-A34
A43	106	(Op.25)	(Op.25)	(Op.25)	(Op.25)	(92)	(98)	II-A23
A44	107	(Op.26)	(Op.26)	(Op.26)	(Op.26)	(88)	(92)	II-A22
A45	105	(Op.75/1)	(Op.75/1)	(Op.75/1)	(Op.75/1)	(158/1)	(168/1)	II-A55

This Catalog	Hess 2 or 3	Kinsky/Halm	Bruers	Nottebohm	Grove	Thayer	Marx	Biamonti
A46	101	-	-	-	-	-	-	II-A33
A47	102	-	-	-	-	-	-	II-A1
A48	-	-	332/7	-	-	-	264/7	-	II-A17/1
A49	-	-	332/8	-	-	264/8	-	II-A17/2
A50	-	-	332/9	-	-	264/9	-	II-A17/3
A51	-	-	332/10	-	-	264/10	-	II-A17/8
A52	-	-	332/11	-	-	264/11	-	II-A17/9
A53	-	-	332/12	-	-	264/12	-	II-A17/4
A54	-	-	332/13	-	-	264/13	-	II-A17/5
A55	-	-	332/14	-	-	264/14	-	II-A17/6
A56	-	-	332/15	-	-	264/15	-	II-A17/7
A57	-	-	-	-	-	-	-	II-A24
A58	-	(Op.20)	(Op.20)	(Op.20)	(Op.20)	(69)	(80)	II-A14
A59	-	(158c)	-	-	-	176/289	-	II-A10
A60	- 244a	-	-	-	-	-	-	II-A15/1
A61	- 244b	-	-	-	-	-	-	II-A15/2
A62	- 244c	-	-	-	-	-	-	II-A15/3
A63	-	-	319	-	-	80	-	II-A25
A64	-	-	-	-	-	-	-	II-A51
A65	-	-	-	-	-	-	-	II-A32
A66	252	-	-	-	-	-	-	II-A19A & II-A19B

Index

275